THE COUNTERFEIT LADY UNVEILED

SPIRO PETERSON was born in New Haven, Connecticut, and educated at Trinity College and Harvard University. He is associate professor of English at Miami University in Oxford, Ohio, where he teaches seventeenth-century literature. His interest in criminal fiction evolved from a story of the social backgrounds of Daniel Defoe's novels. He has written the Introduction to Elkanah Settle's *The Notorious Impostor* (*1692*) *and Diego Redivivus* (*1692*), published in 1958 by The Augustan Reprint Society, and articles on Defoe for *Publications of the Modern Language Association, The Huntington Library Quarterly,* and *Philological Quarter-ter.*

THE COUNTERFEIT LADY UNVEILED

and

OTHER CRIMINAL FICTION OF SEVENTEENTH-CENTURY ENGLAND

A Selection
Edited with Forewords and Notes

by

SPIRO PETERSON

Anchor Books
Doubleday & Company, Inc.
Garden City, New York
1961

COVER DESIGN BY ROBIN JACQUES
TYPOGRAPHY BY SUSAN SIEN

CONTENTS

"I thought [*it*] *good to erect this monument of their shame and wickedness, which may serve instead of a continual Sessions, an everlasting Tyburn, to fright these vile miscreants from their enormous practices."*

Francis Kirkman, "The Preface," *The English Rogue,* Pt. III (1674)

"'But, alas, should I set myself to collect these dreadful stories, it would be easy in little time to present you with hundreds of them.'"

John Bunyan, *The Life and Death of Mr. Badman* (1680)

FOREWORD

"Crime, like disease, is not interesting," writes George Bernard Shaw in the preface to *Saint Joan*. "It is something to be done away with by general consent, and that is all about it." Yet crime in literature—the savagery of Medea, the villainy of Iago, the depravity of Moll Flanders—has always exercised a strange fascination upon readers. In presenting this selection of criminal fiction written in the period 1660–1700, I have tried, first, to choose stories that have some of the same fascination. Each criminal narrative had to be rich in incidents delivered with all the gusto of popular storytelling. Happily, although quite accidentally, I was drawn to at least one story of this kind for each decade in the period. The book as a whole provides a variety of criminal motifs: bigamy and thievery in *The Counterfeit Lady Unveiled* (1673), burglary in *The Triumph of Truth* (1664), highway robbery in *Jackson's Recantation* (1674), counterfeiting in *Don Tomazo* (1680), and imposture in *The Complete Memoirs of the Life of that Notorious Impostor Will. Morrell* (1694).

The term "criminal" I define loosely to mean the fairly professional violator of the law who practices his art regularly and who has certain skills and attitudes toward his work. For a knowledge of the law, I am especially indebted to Leon Radzinowicz's *History of English Criminal Law* (Macmillan, 1948). The terms "criminal fiction" and "criminal biography," used interchangeably here, are both misleading. For although the main character of each story is a real criminal, some of whose exploits can be verified by historical record, he is also a creature of the writer's imagination, and some of his other exploits are demonstrably fictions. Criminal biography (or fiction) focuses upon a single rogue of reality, but crudely and persistently it introduces narrative techniques that we now associate with the novel.

One of the main pleasures for the reader is that he recognizes the familiar world of this criminal fiction. The settings of the stories range from solid middle class to a grim underworld. Their styles are intentionally "natural." Their characters, although biased in favor of predatory motives, display at times a striking ordinariness. Thus the criminal fiction forms part of a new realism that was practiced also by John Bunyan, Aphra Behn, and other writers discussed by Ernest A. Baker in *The History of the English Novel*, Volume III (Barnes & Noble, 1950)—a realism that achieved brilliance in Restoration comedy and culminated in the great novels of the next century. Indeed, *The Counterfeit Lady Unveiled* has been recognized since 1914 as the important link in the chain of realistic novels from Thomas Nash to Daniel Defoe. Congreve's famous pronouncement in the preface to his novelette *Incognita* (1692) sums up a growing opposition to the unreality of the romances: "Novels are of a more familiar nature; come near us, and represent to us intrigues in practice, delight us with accidents and odd events, but not such as are wholly unusual or unprecedented, such which not being so distant from our belief bring also the pleasure nearer us." In preparing the book, I was also guided by a second purpose; namely, the selection of crime fiction that reflects this realism. As a result, the collection has a definite sociological emphasis.

Four of our criminal biographies were published during the reign of Charles II, the Merry Monarch, and the fifth made its appearance in the soberer reign of William III. Together the five make available firsthand sociological materials for the further study of a period that historians regard as an important transition to the modern era. As a result of the Civil War (1642–51) and the Glorious Revolution (1688), the political power was being shifted from the Court to the City, from the Crown to Parliament. A parallel development was the rise of the middle class, and the assertion of its political strength in the Whig Party and of its literary values in the drama and prose fiction. In 1690, Locke stressed the individual's natural right to own property "in peace and safety," but slighted the duty of the citizen to society as a whole. In social structure, England was becoming, especially in the eighteenth century, a commercial nation. With the accumulation of wealth in homes and shops, crimes against property were increasing. Accordingly, the laws continued to exact capital punishment for relatively minor offenses. The criminal fiction of the period 1660–1700 has to be read against this social background. All our criminals—Colonel James Turner, Mary Carleton, Francis Jackson, Thomas Dangerfield, and William Morrell—lived constantly in the shadow of the hangman's noose. Criminal behavior during the seventeenth and eighteenth centuries assumes an even broader significance in the light of a statement by the modern criminologist Edwin H. Sutherland that "criminality often is merely an alternative reflection of the general values of a social system in which great emphasis is placed upon the success goal—attainment of individual wealth—and relatively slight emphasis is placed upon the proper means and devices for achieving this goal" (*Principles of Criminology*, rev. Donald R. Cressey; Lippincott, 1955, p. 87).

The crimes described in this selection are somewhat similar to the "cony-catching" of late-sixteenth- and early-seventeenth-century rogue literature. No attempt is made in the subsequent forewords to discuss these similarities either as plagiarism or as recurrent criminal patterns. The curious reader may wish to consult Frank Aydelotte's *Elizabethan Rogues and Vagabonds,* Chapter 4 (Clarendon Press, 1913), or examine the rogue pamphlets reprinted in A. V. Judges' *The Elizabethan Underworld* (Dutton, 1930). Perhaps an even closer resemblance exists between late-seventeenth-century crimes and early-twentieth-century "rackets," as they are frankly revealed in the "autobiography" of Chic Conwell (Edwin H. Sutherland's *The Professional Thief,* University of Chicago Press, 1937). In the criminal literature of the past, the reader will find striking parallels to the modern criminal's "system," code, argot, and even "confidence game." For instance, Mary Carleton's swindle of the young lawyer in *The Counterfeit Lady Unveiled* is really the "crossbiting" of Robert Greene's *The Black Book's Messenger* (1592) and also the "badger game" of the modern professional thief's repertoire.

All five criminal biographies are reprinted complete from first editions. In preparing the text, I have tried to make the book as readable as possible without sacrificing the flavor of the original. Certain modernizations, however, were necessary to carry out this purpose. The spelling, in general, has been modernized to agree with *Webster's New International Dictionary.* Names of places and streets are spelled in their modern forms. Archaic words and slang are given as they appear in the *Oxford English Dictionary* or Eric Partridge's *A Dictionary of Slang.* Difficult words and phrases are explained in the notes at the end of the anthology. My general practice has been to alter the punctuation and the wording infrequently and only where necessary, in order to bring out as clearly as possible the author's intended meaning. Paragraph and chapter divisions have been made, in places, to facilitate the reading. Year dates are given according to the current practice of beginning the year on January 1, and not (as in the seventeenth century) on March 25.

It is a privilege to acknowledge my gratitude to the owners of the rare originals edited and reprinted in this collection: The Henry E. Huntington Library (San Marino, California) for *The Counterfeit Lady Unveiled,* the Harvard College Library for *The Triumph of Truth* and *Jackson's Recantation,* and the Yale University Library for *Don Tomazo* and *The Complete Memoirs.* To Miami University, I express my appreciation for its encouragement of research by various grants. To my wife, Yerevan, I am deeply thankful for invaluable assistance.

SPIRO PETERSON

Miami University
Oxford, Ohio

For
George Sherburn

THE
COUNTERFEIT LADY
UNVEILED
(1673)

Francis Kirkman

FOREWORD

Like the true Restoration man that he was, Francis Kirkman emphatically approved of the new freedom that Charles II brought with him. Especially important to him were the signs of revival in literature. In 1661, as he launched one of his first publications, *The Thracian Wonder*, Kirkman the bookseller bemoaned the sad effects of the recent tyranny. As long as readers would buy books, he promised to print them, "since ingenuity is so likely to be encouraged by reason of the happy restoration of our liberties." He never lost his confidence that ingenuity would bring its own rewards. In a long career (1652–?80) as translator, author, and publisher, he aimed to please. Certain pieces he addressed to the "gentle reader," and others that came later he wrote for "the meridian of the City." The two dominant interests in his life were first the romances and then, with increasing strength, the rogue biographies. In his taste, as well as in his occasional lack of it, Kirkman was like many Englishmen of the period.

Books were Kirkman's whole life. In his autobiography, *The Unlucky Citizen* (1673), he describes himself as a Don Quixote, a man always spellbound by romances. Like the young heroine of *The Counterfeit Lady Unveiled,* he delighted in such favorites as *Parismus, Don Bellianis, Amadis de Gaul, Cassandra,* and *Cleopatra.* As a youth, having read "that famous book of the *Friar and the Boy*" and the *Seven Wise Masters of Rome,* the young Kirkman laid out his only sixpence on *Fortunatus,* that Lady Fortune might thereby smile benignly upon him. Now the die was cast, and he must thereafter see himself as a gallant knight-errant. He hesitated to pick a profession. Since Amadis and the other knights eventually found nobility in their obscure parentage, Kirkman believed (again like his young "Counterfeit"), "I had such a fond and idle opinion that I might in time prove to be some great person." He first chose to be a surgeon because that profession was most often mentioned in the romances. Next he would be a bookseller, but following the wishes of his father ("profit it was he aimed at"), he had to compromise by serving two apprenticeships to scriveners. He especially liked to tell of the trick he used for reading romances *sub rosa,* by enclosing them inside lawbooks. And bookseller he did become, around 1661.

Kirkman's discovery of rogue biography was probably a happy accident. Overly ambitious as a bookseller, he had got into legal troubles in a plot to pirate "the best plays then extant." On two occasions he had been cheated by Henry Marsh, one of his partners in the pirating venture. After the Plague, burdened with debts and poor relations, Kirkman was trying to recoup his fortunes. He took over the estate of Marsh, who had died, and here, among many liabilities, he found some assets. Chief among these were the rights to the first part of Richard Head's *The English Rogue,* a book so obscene that it had to be expurgated before it could be licensed for publication by Marsh in 1665. Kirkman's name and fortune were to be linked with this book and its sequels up to 1680, the probable year of his death. Perhaps it is not too fanciful to suggest that he also made his discovery of another rogue book among Henry Marsh's effects. This was *The Case of Madam Mary Carleton, Lately Styled the German Princess,* printed in 1663 "for Sam. Speed at the Rainbow in Fleet-street, and Hen. Marsh at the Princes Arms in Chancery-Lane." Large sections of this highly dramatic autobiography were to be incorporated verbatim into Kirkman's *The Counterfeit Lady Unveiled*.

Of the five books which Kirkman produced as an author, three were picaresque or criminal narratives. He wrote a second part (1668) of *The English Rogue* and with the original author, Richard Head, "clubbed" harmoniously to produce a third and fourth parts (1671). Two years later, at a period when he was harassed by debt and fear of imprisonment, he published *The Counterfeit Lady Unveiled* in February and *The Unlucky Citizen* in November.

All three books were middle class in their tone and appeal. The remarkable thing about Kirkman's later preoccupation with the rogue and the criminal was that it brought with it a change in style. When he translated romances, he fell into the outmoded fashion of highly decorative conceits and freshly coined English words. His important advance in the new realism of the Restoration was his intuition that "City readers" would like his rogue books and that he must, as he says in his prefaces, write with all the naturalness and unrhetorical simplicity at his command. He created a world of ordinary people—apprentices, innkeepers, weavers, watchmakers, apothecaries—and he had to give these characters suitable language and speech rhythms. The blend of realism and an appropriate style was the supreme achievement of *The Counterfeit Lady Unveiled*.

The main character of Kirkman's novel was the most notorious criminal of those flamboyant times. Most Londoners knew about Mary Carleton, alias the German Princess. As many as twenty-four books, published between 1663 and 1673, sensationalized her adventures. Samuel Pepys saw the German Princess on display at the Gatehouse Prison, and at the end of her trial for bigamy he stoutly cheered her victory. News of the Lady reached the royal court. In ballads, newspapers, and pamphlets, writers made comparisons with "the German Princess." To whet the appetite of readers, a criminal biographer claimed, in 1692, that his subject was "a rarity beyond . . . a Clancie, a Morrell, a German Princess, or any of our most famous impostors." In the next century Daniel Defoe made the heroine of his *Roxana* (1724) reflect, "I might as well have been the German Princess." Not very long after her death on the gallows, the German Princess had become a legend for the most ingenious kind of imposture.

In *The Counterfeit Lady Unveiled*, Kirkman presents the tragic story of her moral degeneration. His heroine starts out innocent or self-deceived, and gradually engages in deliberate crime. In a remarkably modern way, Kirkman is definitely curious about the effects of a hardening conscience. His effort at psychological realism, in the year 1673, is indeed significant in the history of the English novel. For he has strongly grasped the idea of character motivation. In the preface, he challenges the reader to discover "what her inside was" by reading the book. He tries to give reasons for the lady's "decline." All her crimes he sees as being derived from a central compulsion to act a role, to pretend, or to assume a disguise. On one occasion, in a perfectly conventional way, he condemns Mary Carleton's tricks as "so innate and natural with her that they were part of herself." Then, right after this, he provides an explanation that was far ahead of the times. He tells of knowing highborn kleptomaniacs who "could never be pleased with anything that could be bought unless they stole it, and they have been so often guilty that at last the shopkeepers, who knew them, would let them steal and take no notice of it, for soon after some friend who watched them would come and pay for it."

In addition to keen observations of people, the book has a strong sociological element. One of the most rewarding approaches to the John Carleton affair, for instance, is to examine his actions in the light of seventeenth-century law. On the one hand, the fortune-hunting John had to tread carefully in order not to violate the law that made it a capital crime without benefit of clergy, if a misdoer should take and marry by force or fraud a woman of estate "against her will." The hunted Mary, on the other hand, had to manage shrewdly to circumvent the law that made bigamy a felony. Elsewhere there are other sociological implications—the old *soldado* who assaults in love as in war, the young lawyer who can't refuse money, or (best of all) the "witty baggage" who makes a "speech" in Newgate— "these crimes, which men would slip through and make nothing of, were accounted highly criminal with women." Finally, so far as sociology is concerned, the German Princess is Kirkman's *pièce de résistance*. Her triumphs are increasingly anti-social. Like Moll Flanders a half century later, Mary Carleton undergoes the frustration of a talented woman seeking success in a free-enterprise society, which cannot provide her with the institutionally controlled means of achieving success. In a sense, she is a victim of the "cultural chaos" that sociologists today call "anomie."

The Counterfeit Lady Unveiled may serve, according to its preface, "as a looking glass wherein we may see the vices of this age epitomized." Besides its sociological value, the book should interest readers today for its realistic techniques. Of the criminal biographers who disguise their fiction as fact, Kirkman is the most talented. Instinctively he knows when to hasten the story and when to expand an incident into a brilliantly detailed scene. In his technique he glimpses—sketchily, to be sure—the modern idea of point of view, as, for example, when he interrupts his account of Mary's affair with the two young lovers "that I may not seem to romance by telling you all their private discourses, which would be impossible." *The Counterfeit Lady Unveiled* will, above all, attract readers today for what Kirkman called its "divertissement."

ABOUT KIRKMAN: R. C. Bald, "Francis Kirkman, Bookseller and Author," *Modern Philology*, XLI (1943), 17–32; Strickland Gibson, *A Bibliography of Francis Kirkman*, Oxford Bibliographical Society, 1949; *The Wits, or, Sport upon Sport,* ed. John James Elson, Cornell University Press, 1932. ABOUT THE BOOK: Ernest Bernbaum, *The Mary Carleton Narratives 1663–1673,* Harvard University Press, 1914; C. F. Main, "The German Princess; or, Mary Carleton in Fact and Fiction," *Harvard Library Bulletin,* X (1956), 166–85; *The Complete Newgate Calendar,* ed. J. L. Rayner and G. T. Crook, The Navarre Society, Ltd., 1926, Vol. I; Captain Alexander Smith, *A Complete History of the Lives and Robberies of the Most Notorious Highwaymen, Footpads, Shoplifts, Cheats of Both Sexes,* ed. Arthur L. Hayward, Brentano's, 1926.

THE COUNTERFEIT LADY UNVEILED. *Being a Full Account of the Birth, Life, Most Remarkable Actions, and Untimely Death of Mary Carleton, Known by the Name of the German Princess*

TO THE READER

Before you proceed in reading this book, I would have you begin here, and then you are likely to know what you shall find in it. I intend for you a particular account of the birth, life, most remarkable actions, and death of a famous woman called Mary Carleton, but better known by the name of the German Princess. You have had some account of her by books already printed,[1] but I think, as this is the last, so it is the best. I am sure here is most in this, and most pains have been taken about this. I have gathered my intelligence from several that knew her and from all that hath been written of her; and in having this book you will have all that is, or I think can, or will be said of her. Had she given any account herself of her actions she could best have done it, but as she acted them with all privacy, so she desired to conceal them, and she would never answer any particular question, nor would she own any particular action. If any told her they had heard she had twenty husbands and desired to know the truth, she would answer that she had been told she had fifty, but would not answer punctually to any question. You will find her temper by reading the passages of her life, which I in this manner describe to you.

I first give you the best and truest account of her birth, the place where, and time when, and who were her parents. I acquaint you with the manner of her education and first marriage with one Stedman, her supposed second marriage with one Day, then some of her rambles and her traveling to her pretended country Cologne, where by a mistake she gets the name and title of Lady Maria Wolway, and how by the continuation of that mistake she gets a quantity of jewels, and cheating her landlady who had been her assistant, she leaves that place and comes for England. Upon her arrival here, she chances into the house of Mr. King, her husband Carleton's brother-in-law, who supposing her to be a princess at best, and a lady at least, contrives how to get her married to his wife's brother John Carleton. I give you a full account of all passages in the wooing, wedding, and pretended discovering of this lady. Her indictment for having two husbands, and her being acquitted, and the circumstances how. You then have an account of her acting at the theatre, and her leaving that employ at the entreaty of two young novices who she cheats and abuses. Next how a country gentleman entertains her as his wife, or mistress rather, till she finding her opportunity cheats him of money and jewels and leaves him. She then cheats a young man of a round sum of money by a counterfeit letter which induces him to entertain her in his lodgings, where she robs him and leaves him. After that she pretends to bury a friend, and getting a pall of velvet and several pieces of plate for the solemnity, she runs away with all, leaving a coffin with hay and brickbats. She then cheats a mercer, and after him a weaver and laceman of several rich commodities; and causing a tailor to make her clothes, she not only gets off without payment for them, but also robs him of plate, &c. She likewise gets gloves, ribbons, hoods, scarfs, &c. from an Exchange shop without payment. She draws in and trepans a young lawyer out of a £100. She often changes her lodging and steals silver tankards, and as often visits alehouses and gets silver bowls and other drinking cups. For some of these facts she is caught, indicted, found guilty, and sent to Jamaica.

I then relate to you the manner of her voyage thither, entertainment there, and her return to London, where she presently falls to her old trade of pilfering and cheating of several, till she meets with an apothecary, to whom she pretending to be a rich citizen's niece, thereby cheats him of a £100. Lastly her cheating a watchmaker of a round sum of money and several watches. After all this, she is taken in Southwark; I give you a clear account of the manner how, and how she behaved herself in the prison of the Marshalsea, and afterwards in Newgate. The manner of her trial and condemnation at the sessions in the Old Bailey, and her deportment in prison from the time of her condemnation till her execution, her penitence before and at her execution, and lastly her last speech, death and burial. This is the sum of what you shall read in this ensuing treatise, before which I have placed her true original picture as it was taken by her own order and appointment in the year 1663 when she was tried about her marriage with her husband Carleton, and being acquitted, she was so confident as to write, print, and publish a book, calling it *The Case of Mary Carleton*,[2] and under her picture she caused these lines to be placed:

> *Behold my innocence, after this disgrace,*
> *Dares show an honest and a noble face;*
> *Henceforth there needs no mark of me be known,*
> *For the true counterfeit is hereby shown.*

And underneath [were] added these words:

"Ætatis meæ proximo 22 Januar. stilo novo vicessimo primo 1663. M. C."[3]

So that she began with a lie, for her age was, as I have said, seven or eight years more. Only the day was true as she alleged to the last. If you behold her picture, and did know her or ever see her, you will conclude it very like. Only she was somewhat thinner faced, nine years time had made that alteration; and you will find that the dressing of her head is different from the present fashion and from what she now wore, which was à la mode, a large parcel of frizzled hair, which is called a tower;[4] and her habit now at her trial was an Indian striped gown, silk petticoat, white shoes with slaps, laced with green; and in these she was hanged, and I think buried. This was her outside. What her inside was, by reading this book, you will be sufficiently acquainted, for I have related at large all these several passages which you have here read in epitome. And she may very well serve as a looking glass wherein we may see the vices of this age epitomized. And to the end that we may see her vices and thereby amend our own wicked lives is the intent of

Your Friend,
F. K.

THE COUNTERFEIT LADY UNVEILED

Let nature be never so liberal to us in the complete forming of our bodies after the most exact copies of proportion, and let us be never so well accomplished in all our outward qualities so that we may imagine ourselves to be complete, yet if grace be not implanted in our hearts whereby to guide us in our actions, we are like a fair vessel at sea which is sufficiently furnished with all her sails and tackling, but yet wants the only thing to guide and steer her by, her rudder, without which it is very difficult to guide her to any safe harbour. The truth hereof we may every day experiment in ourselves, and we need look no further than into our own actions when we are only led by our natural inclinations, but in regard we either cannot or will not so soon see mistakes and crimes in ourselves as in others, therefore we have plentiful examples; and of all that this age [has] produced, none does so clearly demonstrate the truth of our frailness and imbecility, when governed by our own wild desires, than this ensuing narrative.

The intent of my discourse is to give you an account of the most considerable actions of a woman whose infamous carriage hath made her famous through the whole kingdom, but more especially in and about this city of London, where for the most part she hath played her pranks, and which hath been the scene of her most considerable actions, and where at last she made her untimely exit. If I should promise to give you a true account of her whole life I should deceive you, for how can truth be discovered of her who was wholly composed of falsehood? But that I might not err from the truth in what I shall relate to you, I have took some pains to gain intelligence; some I had from herself, some from those who were considerably concerned with her, and some from Mr. John Carleton, her unfortunate husband; and what I could not gather from these informations, I have supplied by books which have been formerly written of her, both in her defence and against her; and I have carried so even a hand in my belief of what I read that I hope I shall do her no wrong in misrepresenting anything of her.

That I may orderly begin my discourse, it will be convenient in the first place to let you know the time and place of her birth, and from what parentage she was descended, but here now I am but just begun, if I should credit what fame relates of her and how various people are in their reports of her in these particulars, I should be at a stand, but although I shall contradict the opinion of many and what she always declared of herself, yet I tell you that according to my best intelligence, which I think is sufficiently authentic, she was no German, but an absolute (I will not say true) Englishwoman; and although London hath been dishonoured, or she hath rather dishonoured London with her lewd practices, yet the city of Canterbury in the county of Kent was the place of her birth. Her parents were of honest and good report, her father being a musician and belonging as a chorister to that cathedral. His name was Moders, he died long since, and her mother married with an honest innkeeper of the same place where she now lives, or lately did so. I know in this my relation I differ from her own,[5] who denied that she was of this county or of so mean parentage. For if you will believe her, she thus reported that she was born in Cologne in Germany, and that she had lived there or thereabouts the most part of her life, and that her father, named Henry van Wolway, was a licentiate and doctor of the civil law and lord of Holstein, that he was esteemed for his services done to that city in mediating their peace and security, and neutrality in the Swedish and German War,[6] and for other effects of his counsels and endeavours to the ecclesiastical Prince Elector and the House of Lorraine in all those turmoils of that country in the first rupture of the Spanish and French War. This is the character she gives of her father, but I am sufficiently assured of the contrary, and that this was but a romance, and that she had told this lie so often that she at last believed it herself to be true. I have known many more of her temper in this particular, especially when they relate anything that is honourable or glorious of themselves; we have had in England pretended princes in the time of King Henry the VII. A Perkin Warbeck, one who was of an outlandish and mean extraction, yet he gave out himself to be heir of the crown of England, as son to Edward the Fourth, and he did so well personate the Prince himself and was so well backed on by others that he without any difficulty persuaded several kings and princes of the truth of his assertion, and was had in so particular an esteem of the King of Scotland that he not only treated him as the Prince he represented, but he also gave him a fair and virtuous lady to wife, who was very near a kin to himself; and this counterfeit so well behaved himself in everything that he won the affections of many Englishmen to be of his side, and although he and his whole party were routed, and himself taken prisoner, yet he could not be persuaded in the least to acknowledge himself to be other than the true Prince, and in that opinion or resolution he died, being executed for that treasonable practice. Such was the humour of that man, and his example hath our German Lady imitated. For as a German she would be esteemed, a lady she gave herself out to be, and the vulgar who are inclined to multiply and magnify every novelty gave her out to be a princess, and for such a one did she pass in the common report of all, but I suppose that humour is over, and that now they do or will believe what I write, that she was daughter to a musician at Canterbury. And it is to be doubted that she who denied her earthly parents, and particularly her father in her words, and in her actions denied or practiced against the laws of God, her Heavenly Father (if He was not the more merciful to her) might have disowned her and denied her a place in his Heavenly Kingdom.

Having now given you the best and truest account of her birth and extraction, the place where and the persons who, I should proceed to tell you the time when, but in that I can give you less certainty than the other. For I altogether believe her own report to be false, but as she related I must give it you, not knowing how to disprove her: she was, as she said, born on the 22 of January 1642. Although I do not believe this to be true, yet I find it to be very ominous, for according to this account she was executed on her birthday and lived in all just thirty years. Now that she was much elder by at least seven or eight years is not only my opinion, but also that of her husband and several of her intimate acquaintance.

And now I have told you all I know of her birth and age, I can say little of her education, only, those that knew her when young relate that she was very much addicted to her pleasure, loved fine clothes and gallantry, and endeavoured to exceed her betters in the bravery of her habit; that she took much pleasure in reading, especially love books and those that treated of knight-errantry; she was well read in *Parismus and Parismenos, Don Bellianis of Greece,* and all those other books that related to love and arms; she proceeded to *Amadis de Gaul,* and reading of his fair lady, the Princess Otiana, she oftentimes fancied herself to be some such princess or at leastwise a lady of honour that did belong to her; after this she read *Cassandra, Cleopatra,* and the rest of those romances,[7] and could and often did give a very perfect account of their adventures; and from her frequent and often reading, she believing all she read to be true, was much in love with the actions of those great and renowned heroes, and supposed herself to be no less than a *heroina,* or that in time she should be dignified with some illustrious title. But all these high imaginations and fancies of herself proved to be only so, and no reality. The meanness of her quality did not suit with her spirit, and although she intended for herself no less a fortune than a knight or some great man to be her husband, yet she failed in her expectation and was glad to accept of a shoemaker. I suppose she might have read the story of *The Gentle Craft* and was satisfied with that assertion so often used here, that "A shoemaker's son is a prince born,"[8] and that although she herself were not a princess or lady, yet that she might be the mother of princes. Whatever she conceited I know not, but married she was to one Stedman, a gentleman of the gentle craft, and that about eighteen years ago, that she lived four years with him and had two children by him which soon died, and her husband's quality being mean, and he not being able to maintain her at that height which she always aimed at, she was discontented and was resolved to seek her fortune, and falling acquainted with the master's mate of a ship that was bound for Barbados, she purposed to run away from her husband and go with him; but although she went on board the ship, yet her husband understanding her intent and finding that the best of his moveables were gone, he to recover them stopt her and by a warrant took her out of the ship, and carried her to Dover Castle.

This breach between her and her husband was not so

well made up, but that it was soon after broken, for she still continuing her resolve of trying her fortune, slipt away from him and shipped herself for another voyage, but whether it was to Barbados or what other place I cannot learn, neither is it much material to the story. In this voyage she spent about two years, and then it was that she first put in practice some of her good qualities. At her return, although Canterbury was not far off and her husband Stedman lived there, yet she was married to one Day, a chirurgeon of Dover. What means she used to manage this affair I know not, only that she was indicted for having two husbands, but so carried the matter that she was acquitted, and this emboldened her to proceed and undertake a third marriage, which was to the aforesaid John Carleton and which was the first occasion of her being publicly taken notice of in London, where she hath since acted so many several projects, to the recital of which I would hasten because it is the most material and most expected and desired of all the world, to whom I hope I shall give a sufficient satisfaction in this my undertaking. But before I come to those particulars in order to my orderly management of my story, I must not only acquaint you with the management of her marriage with the said Carleton, but with some particular passages of her life which preceded it and which are as yet unknown to most people.

She having been indicted for having two husbands, Stedman and Day, and being acquitted, she thought it not convenient to stay longer in that county of Kent or indeed in the kingdom of England, and therefore once again shipped herself for foreign parts. Whether it was France or Holland where she first landed, I know not, but she saw both before she returned, and from those parts she traveled to the so-much-by-her-talked-of city of Cologne, and in this voyage and journey she attained to some perfection in the languages of those several countries, a smattering knowledge she had before, for she was always well pleased to converse with strangers and to read books of those languages, and by these means she gained the knowledge of those languages which she so much boasted of, but I have heard her husband Carleton and several others say that she was not so well skilled in any language except English, no, not in her own pretended native language, High Dutch,[9] as to hold any considerable discourse, but would always wave and decline it, and as for Latin or Greek, she knew no more of it than Jack Adams, the town fool.[10] But were she minded, she could discourse very well in English; her tongue was well hung, and she knew it, and loved to hear herself talk.

But to proceed, she after some rambles about the countries, fixt at Cologne. When she arrived there, she, being mistress of a considerable sum of money, took up her lodging at a house of entertainment there and lived in the greatest splendor she had ever done, and as it is usual in England for ladies and persons of quality to go in the summertime to Epsom or Tunbridge Wells, so it is as customary to go to the Spa, a place well known in those parts; her designs without all question were to advantage herself, and she intended to use her best artifices upon that occasion. But Fortune was so favourable to put such an adventure upon her, as the like hath seldom been heard of, and thus it was. As she was one evening walking in one of those pleasant walks that were adjoining to those medicinal waters, she was met and accosted by a gentleman, whom she thus described.[11] He was an old gentleman that had fair demesnes about Liége or Lüttich, not many miles distant from Cologne, a man of serious gravity and venerable aspect for his gray hairs, but disfigured with some scars his youthful luxury had given him, which were repaired and supplemented by art, but so that he plainly spoke his infirmity through the ruined arches of his voice. This man, whom she herself hath thus described, accosted her in the rude military way, for he had been a *soldado* and had caught, as he said, that rotten, hoarse cold and snuffling in the trenches of Breda in the brigade of Count Henry of Nassau in Spinola's army, and had afterwards served Monsieur Tilly against the king of Sweden, whom he had seen fall

at Lützen.[12] This gentleman, meeting and accosting her as
if she had been long known to him, raised some wonder,
for she could not believe herself to be known at that place,
but she soon found he was mistaken in her, for in his applications and discourse he gave her the title Madam
Maria and sometimes of Wolway. She could not tell what to
imagine when he called her by the right name of Maria,
but when he added the other of Wolway she was sensible
of his mistake, but she finding him civil enough in his de-
portments and actions, and withal that his pretenses were
amorous, she permitted him to proceed in his discourse,
which he did in such manner that he would not be denied
his suit, since as he said he had never known what a repulse
meant in his life. Our new-made Madam, not finding any
prejudice likely to accrue by her admitting him, gave him
such answers as were indifferent and only complemental,
and desired for that time to retire home to her lodging. He,
understanding her mind, readily attended her, and at their
arrival there, after some few words of course they parted.
She was glad she was rid of him, that she might consider
of the adventure, but she could not gather any profitable
or advantageous meaning of herself without the help of her
landlady, to whom she having discovered what had happened, and she [the landlady], having seen this inamorato,
told her his quality, for he was very well known there;
and she, being now acquainted with this, desired to know,
if she might, the reason of his mistake in her name. To this
she received a satisfactory answer, for her landlady also
told her that there was such a lady living at Cologne or
else in the nunnery of the Barefooted Clares, who was of
that name of Maria van Wolway, and whom she had seen
and who indeed did very much resemble her.

This discourse of the landlady did not only satisfy but
please our new Madam, and she who was always ready-
witted on such occasion did purpose to make some advantage of his adventure, and therefore presently applied herself to her landlady, desiring her advice in this mistake.
"Truly," said the landlady, "I cannot think it will be any

disadvantage to you to continue the mistake, for although the gentleman is old, yet he is of great estate, and if he will deceive himself, let him; you cannot but reap some advantage thereby, for he can do no less than make you some presents which I advise you to accept of, and so you may continue your acquaintance with him so long as it shall stand with your benefits." Our lady was not deaf to this discourse, but listened very attentively and resolved to follow her landlady's directions and not questioning but by her assistance to reap some profit, and her landlady was well enough pleased to engage in this affair for her own interest, because she expected some profit in the visits which she expected he would make there. And as they projected it, so it fell out, for our *Soldado* the next day met his mistress and, waiting on her home, was there indifferently received by her, and that I may come to the main point of my story, I in short tell you that she used such artifice in the manage of this affair, being withal assisted by her landlady, that he presented her several fair jewels, some whereof were of real worth, and others that appeared to be so but since proved to be otherwise, as her husband Carleton, to whose hands they afterwards came, doth affirm.

This was the adventure of our *Soldado* and our new dignified lady. She by this means did get a name which she always held and which indeed was very fortunate to her, not only in her present transactions with her suitors, but afterwards in her husband Carleton; but that I may quite finish this adventure and come to that, I will proceed. She was doubtful that it would not always be such fair weather, and therefore she was resolved to make hay while the sun did shine. She had many resplendent jewels that gave a great lustre, but she was willing to have more and some money to boot; therefore her suitor still continuing his courtship, and that importunately, and pressing to marriage, she knew then that all would come out, that she should be discovered, and that she having always delayed it till her return to Cologne, and her lover intending to go thither with her, could no longer be deluded, and that then the true Maria van Wolway would be known. Wherefore she devised how to manage her affairs, and thus she accomplished them.

She at length consented to go to Cologne, but first her lover was to go home and fetch such habit and other necessaries as were convenient for his intended match. His habitation was not far off, and he had made several trips thither & never returned empty-handed, but still brought some jewel or another, such as his ancestors had left or he had otherwise come to by the fortune of the Wars, and when she had them together they were a very fair parcel; but now at his going home he promised to bring her more variety, but she resolved not to expect him in his return. However, he having a chain of gold and a medal which was given him for some remarkable good service in the War and which he always wore next his shirt, she with small entreaties prevailed with him to leave that also behind him. He, knowing that if he had her, as he did not question, then he should have all again, was very free with her, and so he parted. She, knowing that it was then full time to be gone, acquainted her landlady with her design, who had had a pretty share in the spoils of our captain; but our lady was resolved she should not carry it off, she would have all herself and admit of no sharers, in order whereunto she persuaded the landlady to get her a conveniency[13] to be gone, not to the intended Cologne, but to another place where she should not be suspected and therefore not followed by her lover. The landlady was willing to accommodate her and therefore went out, leaving her at home, but she did not intend to stay there. For this ungrateful woman, so soon as her landlady was gone out, did break open a chest wherein she put all her treasure, and there she found not only what had been given her by the captain, but also a considerable sum of money, all which she took, and packing it up with her own parcel, away she went; and having privately provided herself of a passage to Utrecht, there she made a stop for a while, thence passed to Amsterdam, where she sold the gold chain and some other jewels. From thence she passed to Rotterdam, and so, coming to The Brill, took shipping for England.

These were the adventures of our lady, and now being possessed of so much wealth, she did believe herself to be one, and she having had such good success by this name of Maria van Wolway, she resolved to continue it. She cared not for either her old lover or her landlady, nor how they would resent her departure; she believed she had done well in chousing the old fool of his jewels, and that she had done very well in so cheating her landlady, who had assisted her. She had now been absent some years and was somewhat altered in her face and garb, but much more in her tongue, for she now either spoke all Dutch or else a mixture of that and English. However, she would no more go to Dover or Canterbury to look after her old husbands, but to London she would go to get a new one, and such a one as she hoped as should exceed her late good fortune, and then it was that she contrived all her story of her birth, parents, travels, love, and other adventures, which not only cheated her husband John Carleton and his friends, but also many other people in this city of London.

Being now landed at Billingsgate towards the end of March, *Anno Dom.* 1663, it being early in the morning, and coming with other company, among the rest a parson was most officious in attending on her. They walked together without designing whither, but to the next convenient house they should find open, and the first that they came to was the Exchange Tavern in the Poultry near the Royal Exchange. Thus have I given you the truest account that I can get of her life, from her birth to her arrival at this tavern, where the greatest and most politic of her actions were managed, where she first had the title of Princess, and where the management of her marriage with John Carleton was begun, carried on, and finished. The world hath formerly had an account of it, for in the year 1663, aforesaid, after her trial for having two husbands was over, and she was cleared and quit, she in a confident bravery did write her own *Case*, caused it to be printed, and had the boldness to dedicate it to an illustrious person. The aforesaid book I examined and, comparing it with her husband Carleton's report, cannot find it or her guilty of any considerable untruth; therefore I shall, in the continuation of her story, give it you as she hath related it, according as it is now corrected, and thus as I shall proceed.[14]

We came, said she, to the Exchange Tavern right against the Stocks, betwixt the Poultry and Cornhill, the house of one Mr. King, not having any knowledge of the master or his acquaintance, and free God knows from any design, for I would have entered any other house if I had found the doors open or could have raised the folks nearer to my landing, for I was distempered with the night's passage; but it was so early in the morning, five o'clock, that there was nobody stirring elsewhere. Only, here by mishap Mr. King himself was up and standing at the bar, telling of brass farthings, whom my companion desired to fill a pint of wine, which he readily performed and brought to a room behind the bar. While the wine was a-drinking (which was Rhenish wine, the compliment being put upon me, as the fruit of my own happy country), he very rudely began to accost me and to offer some incivilities to me, which I found no other way to avoid than by pretending want of rest to the master of the house, and acquainted him with my charge of jewels, and that I was (as I do justify myself to be) a person of quality. Hereupon, a room was provided for me to repose myself in, and my gallant took his leave with a troublesome promise of waiting upon me another day to give me a visit, which I was forced to admit and to tell him I would leave word wherever I went; but he considering, as I suppose, of the unfeasibleness of his desires and the publicness of the place, neglected his promise and troubled me no more.

He being gone, Mr. King began to question me what countrywoman I was, and of what religion. I frankly told him and acquainted him withal what charge I had about me, which to secure from the danger of the town that was full of cozenage and villainy, he advised me to stay with him till I could better provide for myself.

I rested myself here till eleven o'clock at noon, when I arose and was very civilly treated by Mr. King who, well knowing I was a stranger and well furnished with money, omitted no manner of respect to me. Nor did I spend parsimoniously and at an ordinary rate, but answerable to the quality and account, at their fetching and itching questions, I gave of myself.

This invited him earnestly with all submiss address to request my staying with them till I had dispatched and had provided all things for my public appearance, for the better furnishing and equipping whereof I acquainted him I would send by post to my steward for the return of some moneys to defray the expenses thereof, which letters he viewed and conceived such imaginations in his head thereupon that it never left working till it had wrought the effect of his finely begun and hopefully continued enterprise.

These letters he himself delivered, at my desire to have them carefully put into the mail, to the posthouse, and thereafter observed me with most manifest respects. In the interim of the return of these moneys, I was slightly and, as it were by the by, upon discourse of my country (wherein they took occasion to be liberally copious) engaged into some discovery of myself, my estate and quality, and the nature of both, the causes of my coming hither, &c. but I did it so unconcernedly and negligently, as a matter of no moment or disturbance to me, though I had hinted at the discontent of my match, that this did assure them that all was real and therefore it was time to secure my estate to them by a speedy and secret marriage.

Let the world now judge whether, being prompted by such plain and public signs of a design upon me, to counterplot them I have done any more than what the rule and a received principle of justice directs: "to deceive the deceiver is no deceit."

I knew not, nevertheless, which way their artifices tended, till Master King brought into my acquaintance old

Mr. Carleton, his father-in-law, and soon after Mr. John Carleton, his son. It seems it had been consulted to have preferred George, the elder brother. He, troubled with a simple modesty, and a mind no way competent to so much greatness, was laid aside, and the younger flushed and encouraged to set upon me. By this time they had obtained my name from me, viz., Maria de Wolway.

To the addresses of Mr. John Carleton, I carried myself with so much indifference, not superciliously refusing his visits or readily admitting his suit, not disheartening him with a severe retiredness or challenges of his imparity, nor encouraging him with a freedom or openness of heart or arrogance of my own condition, that he and his friends were upon the spur to consummate the match, which yet I delayed and dissembled with convenient pretenses, but herein I will be more particular in the ensuing pages.

In the meanwhile, to prevent all notice of me and the disturbance of their proceedings that might be occasioned thereby, they kept me close in the nature of a prisoner, which though I perceived, yet I made no semblance thereof at all, but colluded with them in their own arts and pretended some averseness to all company, but only my enamorate, Mr. Carleton. Nor was anybody else suffered to come near me or to speak with me insomuch, as I have been informed, that they promised £200 to one whom for his advice they had too forwardly, as they thought, imparted the business, the sum of £200 to be silent, lest that it should be heard at Court, and so the estate and honour which they had already swallowed would be lost from their son and seized by some courtier who should next come to hear of this great lady.

After many visits passed betwixt Mr. Carleton and myself, old Mr. Carleton and Mr. King came to me and very earnestly pressed the dispatch of the marriage, and that I would be pleased to give my assent, setting forthwith all the qualities and great sufficiencies of that noble person, as they pleased to style him. I knew what made them so urgent, for they had now seen the answers I had received by the post, by which I was certified of the receipt of mine and that accordingly some thousands of crowns should be remitted instantly to London, and coach and horses sent by the next shipping, with other things I had sent for; and to reinforce this their *commendamus* the more effectually, they acquainted me that if I did not presently grant the suit and their request, Mr. Carleton was so far in love with me that he would make away with himself or presently travel beyond sea and see England no more.

I cannot deny but that I could hardly forbear smiling to see how serious these elders and brokers were in this love-killing story, but keeping to my business, after some demurs and demands, I seemed not to consent, and then they began passionately urging me with other stories, some of which long repetition I will now insert.

Wednesday, the first of April, Mrs. King made a great feast where were divers persons of quality, as she said—amongst the rest, her brother Mr. John Carleton. At which entertainment Mrs. King did advise me to call her cousin, the which I did. Thursday, the second of April, Mr. John Carleton came in his coach with two footmen attending on him, calling him my Lord, and Mrs. King did also call him my Lord. With that I asked Mrs. King if it was not the same person that dined with us yesterday. She said, "True, it was so, but he was in a disguise then, and withal that in a humour he would often do so. But," saith she, "I do assure you he is a lord." Upon that I replied, "Then his father must be an earl, if living." She affirmed that he was a person of great honour. The same time my Lord presented me with a rich box of sweetmeats. I could do no less than thankfully accept thereof.

My Lord came every day to Mr. King's, and by his importunity would carry me abroad in a coach to Holloway and Islington. Mrs. King would often ask me what my Lord did say to me. I told her, "Nothing that I observed, but his Lordship abounded in civility mixt with compliments." "How," said she, "Madam, he loves you." "Loves me, for what, Mistress King?" I replied. She said, "For your great parts and endowments." I asked her how my Lord could tell that I had either. She said my Lord must have very good eyes if he could see within me, or else I must be very transparent.

After which, I did order the matter so, that his access to me was not so easy. Mistress King importuneth me to admit my Lord to visit me. I told her plainly that I did not understand his Lordship's meaning. He provided me a great banquet, at which his Lordship's mother was very fine drest, who questioned what I was. I told my Lord that I had received civilities from him, and he had the like from me, and that I had no necessity to give any account to any person what I was, for anything that I intended, and that if any design or affair of his required any such thing out of convenience or otherwise, he might forbear it. His Lordship excused his mother's inquisition by saying she was his mother, and that parents did think themselves concerned in looking after the good of their children. "But" (said he) "Madam, wave all this; however I will marry you tomorrow."

"What?" (said I) "My Lord, without my consent? My Lord, I desire your Lordship not to come near me any more. I will not lie under such questioning and scrutiny. Your Lordship will be safe in following my advice, in not coming at me any more." Upon this his Lordship wept bitterly. I withdrew myself from his presence. He writ a letter of high compliments to me (the which letter was lost in that violent surprise of me and my things by the force of Mr. George Carleton, my husband's father). At the same time I had a gown making upon my own account by Mrs. King's tailor in the Strand. I took a coach and went thither. All this while the young Lord, not knowing where I was, remained impatient until my return, where I found him standing at the bar (in a very pensive and melancholy manner, as if he had been arraigned for not paying his reckoning) at the Exchange Tavern, and suddenly claspt about my middle and violently carried me to my chamber. I asked his meaning. He answered that I had forbid him my presence, that it had almost made him mad, that he desired nothing more of me than but to let him look upon me. Upon that he did, with a very strange gesture, fix his eyes upon me. In compassion to him, I asked him what his Lordship meant and intended; he replied in a kind of discomposed manner, "I would have you to be my wife." I answered him, "My Lord, I rather think you have courted me for a mistress than for a wife. I assure you that I will never be a mistress to the greatest of princes, I will rather choose to be a wife to the meanest of men."

Upon which, he uttered divers asseverations in confirmation of the realty of his intentions, and earnest desire of the honour in making me his wife without any respect to what I had.

After my Lord had insinuated his affections so far that I began to understand him and did mix and scatter some such like acceptable words, which put him into some confidence of obtaining me, he began like other lovers to set forth the amplitude of his fortunes and those brave things he would do if I would finish his suit. Among many other finenesses and grandeurs he would bestow on me, I well remember he told me that he had given order for a great glass coach of the new fashion to be presently made, against our wedding was over, where eleven or twelve might conveniently sit, and that he would suit it with a set of lackeys and pages, the neatest and handsomest of the town for their liveries and persons, that I might see I had married a person that not only dearly loved me, but would also highly honour me with the most splendid accommodations that England yielded.

At the very same time, he had changed, as he told me (and part of it I saw), £200 of silver into 200 pieces of gold for the better portableness thereof, that his Princess might see nothing of meanness belonging to him and that as soon as the coach was made and all things fitted to it, he would presently go to Court, and carry me with him, and introduce me to the King and Queen: his further intention being, which as yet he concealed to me, to get a knighthood and have something of honour to oppose the envy of men that so great an estate was conferred on a private person.

And now my Lord spoke nothing but rodomontades of the greatness of his family, of the delights and stateliness of his lands and houses, the game of his parks, the largeness of his stables, and convenience of fish and foul, for furnishing his liberal and open housekeeping, that I should see England afforded more pleasure than any place in the world, but they were (without the host) reckoned and charged beforehand to my account and to be purchased with my estate, which was his, by a figure of anticipation, when we two should be all one, and therefore he lied not, but only equivocated a little.

But he did not in the least mention any such thing to me, nor made any offer of inquiry what I was, no, not the least semblance or shadow of it. He seemed to take no notice of my fortunes; it was my person he only courted, which having so happily and accidentally seen, he could not live if I cherished not his affections. Nor did I think it then convenient or civil to question the credit of his words and the report given me of him. His demeanour I confess was light, but I imputed that to his youth and the vanity of a gallant, as necessary a quality and as much admired as wit in a woman.

The last day of my virgin state, Easter eve, the tailor brought me my gown to my lodging. I being drest and adorned with my jewels, he again renewed his suit to me, with all importunity imaginable. His courteous mother was also now most forward, pressing me to consent by telling me that she should lose her son and his wits, he being already impatient with denials and delays, adding withal that he was a person hopeful and might deserve my condescension. I withstood all their solicitation, although they continued it until twelve of the clock that night. The young Lord, at his taking his leave of me, told me he would attend me betimes the next morning and carry me to St. Paul's Church to hear the organs, saying that there would be very excellent anthems performed by rare voices, the morrow being Sunday, the 19 of April last. In the morning betimes, the young Lord cometh to my chamber-door, desiring admittance, which I refused, in regard I was not ready. Yet so soon as my head was dressed, I let him have access. He hastened me and told me his coach was ready at the door, in which he carried me to his mother's in the Greyfriars, London, where I was assaulted by the young Lord's tears and others' to give my consent to marry him, telling me that they had a parson and a license ready, which was a mere falsehood and temporary fallacy to secure the match.

So on Easter morning, with three coaches, in which with the bride and bridegroom were all the kindred that were privy to the business and pretended a license, they carried me to Cloth Fair by Smithfield and in the church of great St. Bartholomew's married me by one Mr. Smith, who was well paid for his pains. And now they thought themselves possessed of their hopes, but because they would prevent the noise and fame of their good fortune from public discourse, that no sinister accident might intervene before Mr. Carleton had bedded me, offense being likely to be taken at Court (as they whispered to themselves) that a private subject had married a foreign princess, they had before determined to go to Barnet, and thither immediately after the celebration of the marriage we were driven in the coaches, where we had a handsome treatment, and there we stayed Sunday and Monday, both which nights Mr. Carleton lay with me, and on Tuesday morning we were married again, a license being then obtained to make the match more fast and sure, at their instance with me to consent to it.

This being done and their fears over, they resolved to put me in a garb befitting the estate and dignity they fancied I had, and they were so far possessed with a belief of it that they gave out I was worth no less than 80,000 *livres per an.*, and my husband, as I must now style him, published so much in a coffeehouse, adding withal to the extolling of his good hap that there was a further estate, but that it was my modesty or design to conceal it, and that he could not attribute his great fortune to anything but the Fates, for he had not anything to balance with the least of my estate and merits. So do conceited heights of sudden prosperity and greatness dazzle the eyes and judgment of the most, nor could this young man be much blamed for his vainglorious mistake.

My clothes being made at the charge of my father-in-law, and other fineries of the mode and fashion sent me by some of his kindred and friends (who prided themselves in this happy affinity and who had an eye upon some advantages also, and therefore gave me this early bribe, as testimonies of their early respect), and as for jewels I had of mine own of all sorts, for necklaces, pendants, and bracelets of admirable splendor & brightness. I was in a prince-like attire, and a splendid equipage and retinue, accoutred for public view among all the great ladies of the Court and the town on May Day ensuing. At which time in a lady's coach, which the same friends procured for my greater accommodation, and accompanied with the same lady with footmen and pages, I rode to Hyde Park in open view of that celebrious[15] cavalcade and assembly, much gazed upon by them all, the eximiousness of my fortune drawing their eyes upon me; particularly that noble lady gave me precedence, and the right hand, and a neat treatment after our *divertissement* of turning up and down the park.

I was altogether ignorant of what estate my husband was and therefore made no nicety to take those places his friends gave me, and if I be taxed for incivility herein, it was his fault that he instructed me no better in my quality, for I conceited still that he was some landed, honourable and wealthy man.

Things yet went fairly on, the same observances and distances continued, and lodgings befitting a person of quality taken for me in Durham Yard, where my husband and I enjoyed one another with mutual complacency, till the re-

turn of the moneys out of Germany failing the day and
their rich hopes, old Mr. Carleton began to suspect he was
deceived in his expectation, and that all was not gold that
glistered. But to remove such a prejudice from himself, as
if he were the author of those scandals that were now prepared against my innocence, a letter is produced and sent
from some then-unknown hand, which reflected much upon
my honour and reputation; and thereupon on the fifth or
sixth of May ensuing, I was by a warrant dragged forth of
my new lodgings with all the disgrace and contumely that
could be cast upon the vilest offender in the world, at the
instigation of old Mr. Carleton who was the prosecutor, and
by him and his agents divested and stript of all my clothes,
and plundered of all my jewels and my money, my very
bodies, and a pair of silk stockings being also pulled from
me, and in a strange array carried before a justice.

But because this story hath not yet been fully discovered,
I will more manifestly here declare it. That letter, above
said, came from one in Lombard Street. The contents of this
letter were near to this purpose:

SIR,

I am unknown to you, but hearing that your son
Mr. John Carleton hath married a woman of a pretended great fortune and high birth, I thought fit to
give you timely notice of what I know and have heard
concerning her, that she is an absolute cheat, hath
married several men in our county of Kent, and then
run away from them, with what they had; if it be the
same woman I mean, she speaks several languages
fluently and hath very high breasts, &c.

I was at the Exchange Tavern, as it was designed, when
this letter was brought, and thereupon their countenances
were set to a most melancholy look and pale hue, which
showed a mixture of fear and anger. Presently I was brought
before the inquisition of the family and examined concerning the said letter which I constantly, innocently, and dis-

dainly denied, so that they seemed something satisfied to
the contrary, and so my husband and I went home in a
coach, but that very same night all the gang came to my
lodging, where after most vile language, as "Cheating
Whore," and the like, they pulled me up and down, and
kept me stript upon a bed, not suffering my husband to
come near me, though I cried out for him to take my part
and do like a man to save me from that violence, who at a
distance excused it by putting all this barbarity upon his
father. In fine they left me not a rag, rinsing every wet
cloth out of the water and carrying them away. The whole
was a most unwomanly and rude action at the best of it, if
I had been such as they pretended me to be, and not to
be paralleled.

See the fickleness and vanity of human things, today em-
bellished and adorned with all the female arts of bravery
& gallantry, and courted and attended on by the best rank
of my sex, who are jealous observers what honour and respect they give among themselves, to a very punctilio; and
now disrobed and disfigured in misshapen garments, and
almost left naked, and haled and pulled by beadles and
such like rude and boisterous fellows before a tribunal, like
a lewd criminal.

The justice, by whose mittimus, upon an accusation
managed by old Mr. Carleton that I had married two husbands, both of them in being, I was committed to the Gatehouse. Being interrogated by the justice whether or no I
had not two husbands, as was alleged, I answered, if I had,
he was one of them, which I believe incensed him something the more against me, but I did not know the authority
and dignity of his place, so much am I a stranger to this
kingdom.

There were other things and crimes of a high nature ob-
jected against me, besides, that I cheated a vintner of £60
and was for that committed to Newgate, but that lie
quickly vanished, for it was made appear that I was never
a prisoner there, nor was my name ever recorded in their

books; and that I picked a Kentish lord's pocket and cheated a French merchant of rings, jewels and other commodities; that I made an escape when sold and shipped for the Barbados. But these were urged only as surmises, and old Carleton bound over to prosecute only for bigamy, for my having two husbands.

Thus the world may see how industrious mischief is to ruin a poor helpless and destitute woman, who had neither money, friends, nor acquaintance left me. Yet I cannot deny that my husband lovingly came to me at the Gatehouse the same day I was committed, and did very passionately complain of his father's usage of me merely upon the disappointment, as he said, of their expectations, and that he could be contented to love me as well as ever, to live with me and own me as a wife, and used several other expressions of tenderness to me.

Nor have I less affection and kind sentiments for him, whom I own and will own till death dissolve the union, and did acquaint him with so much there, and protested my innocence to him. Nor do I doubt, could he have prevailed with his father, but that these things had never happened. If now after my vindication he prove faithless and renege me, his fault will be doubly greater in that he neither assisted my innocence when endangered, nor cherished it when vindicated by the law.

In this prison of the Gatehouse I continued six weeks in a far better condition than I promised myself, but the greater civilities I owe to the keeper, as I am infinitely beholding to several persons of quality who came at first, I suppose, out of curiosity to see me, and did thereafter nobly compassionate my calamitous and injurious restraint.

All that troubled me was an abusive pamphlet[16] which went under my husband's name, wherein most pitifully he pleaded his frailty and misfortune, and intituled it to no lesser precedent than Adam, which I suppose was had out of the new ballad of your humble servant, a hint whereof please the reader to take in this abridgement:

Reader,

I shall not give myself the trouble to recollect and declare the several motives and inducements that deceitful, but wise enough, woman used to deceive me with, &c. Her wit did more and more engage and charm me. Her qualities deprived me of my own: her courteous behaviour, her majestic humility to all persons, her emphatical speeches, her kind and loving expressions, and amongst other things, her high detestation of all manner of vice, as lying, &c. Her great pretense to zeal in her religion, her modest confidence and grace in all companies, fearing the knowledge of none, her demeanour were such that she left no room for suspicion, not only in my opinion, but also in others both grave and wise.

And all this is real and not feigned, and more convincingly and apparently true, by this foil of his own setting. As for his undertaking to tell the story of the management of the business betwixt us, he is so far from doing me justice herein that he wrongeth me and his own soul by lying.

For confutation of which, I refer the reader to the ensuing trial. Only there is one passage that I am unwilling to let slip, that is, he saith there that my father was in town upon my commitment and did acknowledge me to be his daughter, and that I had played many such tricks. It's strange this father of mine could not be produced at the trial, if that had been true.

And yet a little before this, upon his visiting me in the Gatehouse, where I was destitute of money and subsistence, at my first coming in he seemed very tender of me and charged the keeper I should want nothing, for as far as 40 shillings went, he would see him paid, which I believe he must ere long, and after that sent me a letter, which is the only paper I have by me of his, the other amorous and loving scribblings being lost and taken from me the same time that they plundered me of my jewels. I do not know what I may do for them, but I hope I shall never cry for those epistles. This done in these words, so that my love and my dear could be hot and cold almost in an instant:

My Dearest Heart,

Although the manner of your usage may very well call the sincerity of my affection and expressions to you in question, yet when I consider that thou art not ignorant of the compulsion of my father and the animosity of my whole relations, both against you and myself for your sake, I am very confident your goodness will pardon and pass by those things which at present I am no way able to help; and be you confident that, notwithstanding my friends' aversion, there shall be nothing within the reach of my power shall be wanting that may conduce both to your liberty, maintenance, and vindication. I shall very speedily be in a condition to furnish you with money to supply you according to your desire. I hope Mr. Bailey will be very civil to you, and let him be assured he shall in a most exact measure be satisfied and have a requital for his obligation. My dearest, always praying for our happy meeting,

I rest, your most affectionate husband,
John Carleton

May the 11th
1663.

Other of my husband's friends came to visit me in the Gatehouse (of the many hundreds of others I shall say nothing). One of them said, "Madam, I am one of your husband's friends and acquaintance. I had a desire to see you because I have heard of your breeding." "Alas," said I, "I have left that in the City amongst my kindred, because they want it."

Another in his discourse delivered as an aphorism "that marriage and hanging went by Destiny." I told him, "I had received from the Destinies marriage, and he in probability might hanging." To wave many others of the like nature.

My innocence furnished me with several of those answers

and repartees to the mixt sort of visitants, who either for
novelty or design came to trouble me. I was advised indeed
to seclude myself from such company, but because there
might be no disadvantage pretended by reason I kept
close, and evidence might be puzzled, not having seen me
in so long a time, as afterwards at my trial might have been
suggested, I gave all persons the freedom of my chamber.
But for the nobler sort, I may in some measure thank my
stars that out of this misfortune extracted so much bliss,
as the honour of their acquaintance, which otherwise at
large I had been in no capacity to attain.

The time of the sessions of the peace for London and
Middlesex being arrived, I was conveyed from the Gatehouse to Newgate, where by the civility of the master of
the prison I had lodgings assigned me in his own house,
which adjoins to the Sessions House yard; and there I was
publicly seen by all comers, that my enemies might want
no advantage of informing their witnesses of my person,
age and condition, and so square their evidence. But my
innocence and my good angels preserved me from the
worst of their malice.

From thence, on Wednesday, June the third, in the evening, the first day of the court's sitting in the Old Bailey,
I was brought down to the bar, and there an indictment
upon my arraignment was read against me, to which I
pleaded not guilty; and, as instructed by my friends & a
good conscience (being altogether ignorant of the laws and
customs of this kingdom), put myself for my trial upon God
and the country, without making any exception or ever so
much as examining what my jury were.

And because they approved themselves men of honesty,
judgment, and integrity, and did me so much justice, I can
do no less than take occasion here to return them my
humble thanks that they would regard the oppressed condition of a helpless prisoner and not give credit to the
wicked asseverations of a wretch, who only swore to the
purpose against me; and to let the world know my particular gratitude, I will transcribe into this my *Case*, as one of

the happiest and fairest remarks therein, the names of those upright jurors, viz., William Rutland, Arthur Vigers, Arthur Capel, Tho. Smith, Fran. Chaplin, Robert Harvey, Simon Driver, Robert Kerkham, Hugh Masson, Tho. Westley, Richard Clutterbuck, and Randolph Tooke.

The indictment was *in haec verba.*

> That she the said Mary Moders, late of London spinster, otherwise Mary Stedman, the wife of Tho. Stedman late of the city of Canterbury in the county of Kent, shoemaker, 12 May, in the reign of his now Majesty the first, at the parish of St. Mildred's in the city of Cant. in the county aforesaid, did take to husband the aforesaid Tho. Stedman and him the said Thomas Stedman then and there had to husband. And that she the said Mary Moders, alias Stedman, 21 April, in the fifteenth year of his said Majesty's reign, at London, in the parish of great St. Bartholomew's, in the ward of Farringdon without, feloniously did take to husband one John Carleton and to him was married, the said Tho. Stedman her former husband then being alive and in full life, against the form of the statute in that case provided and against the peace of our said Sovereign Lord the King, his Crown and Dignity, &c.

Thus have you read her *Case,* as she herself relates it, and by this you may see how this cheat was managed on both sides. Carleton and his friends were as covetous as she was cunning. How she contrived to have answer of her letters from the foreign post, which coming to their hands blinded them and caused them to imagine her no less than a princess. I know not but these letters were her masterpiece; it was this that was the best card in the whole pack. They had seen her jewels before, as her landlady told her brother Carleton:

> *Jewels she hath as sanguine ruby,*
> *Onyx and sapphire with a blue dye,*

Diamond and topaz with the opal,
Emerald and agate, turquoise: take all.
What shall I say? She hath gems in plenty.
Pray enter on her, Rome is empty.[17]

The sight of these jewels were enough to persuade an
easy soul to great matters, but when the letters come that
mentioned thousands of crowns, and a coach and horses,
they were all then cock-a-hoop,[18] and stark nothing then but
clapping up of a marriage was discoursed of; but her landlord was mistaken in his opinion of this German Princess,
for no less did he take her to be, and therefore being very
desirous to advance his brother John Carleton, the father,
mother, and all the friends sat in close consultation.

Their daddy, mammy, friend and knight
In judgment one did all unite
And did agree without long tarry
That knight should Lady Princess marry.
But as the council was adjourning,
The lady sister entered mourning,
Acquainting them that foreign knight,
With coal black hair and eyes like spright,
Had at the house inquiry made
For German Princess, and like blade
Or gallant, à la mode did swear
That heart from body he would tear
Of him that durst crack princess nut
Or dare with her to go to rut,
And wherefore he found the man
Should dare to usher Princess hand,
Withal he'd give two hundred pound
Princess to see on English ground,
That he might carry her to Cologne
With greater joy than Anne from Boleyn.

This message, if it were true, must needs amaze and ter-
rify them all much more when it was seconded by another
alarum: letters sent to inquire of her.

They finding fresh pursuit by letters
To find out Princess though in fetters,
With promise fresh to give more money
To him should tell where lay dear honey.

All these passages how contrived I know not, but it put them all upon the spur to finish the marriage which, as you have read, was celebrated at great St. Bartholomew's, and then

They drove away to place called Barnet
And with them took a friend called Garnet,
Where being come they fell a-eating,
And hungry, all threw wine and meat in
Like misers at a city feast
That eat ten meals, nine at least.
At length their guts being stuffed with food
And all being set on merry mood,
They did begin to dance and caper,
Like poppet made up with brown paper.
Princess began a German dance,
And friend to buff like Mars did prance.
The Lord did dance in order meet,
And elder brother on's bare feet,
An ancient custom where young cit,
Before his elder—doth hit.
At length the couple went to bed,
And cap was put on young Lord's head,
The posset, too, of sack was eaten,
And stockin' thrown, too (all besweeten),
Which ceremonies being ended,
And that day's work by all commended,
The elder brother and his friend
Bid him ride soft to's journey's end.
Wishing them sport at very heart,
They left the Lord at Princess' mart.

Our young Lord, being thus assured of his princely bride, was very well pleased, but so was not his father who, like a grave politician, thought fit first to secure her person better by a second marriage, for the first being done on haste was without a license, and secondly he intended to secure her estate by a writing drawn to that purpose which was offered her to seal, as thus you have it:

> When house was cleared of all but friends,
> On Princess there was further ends
> Intended to be done in instance,
> Married to be again with license
> For to prevent the lawyers' bawl
> In court ecclesiastical,
> The which was done, and then old sir,
> With instrument well drawn sans blur,
> Reciting Princess' earth in hand
> And personal goods about to land,
> Desiring the sum might be made over
> To Lord his son and her great lover,
> To this he hoped she'd not be shy
> Being to prevent mortality.
> "Sir," quoth the Princess, "I'll consult
> My pillow and give you result,
> But till I die, I think not fit
> To part with 'state or wealth one bit.
> Besides, your son's to me but light wood
> And hasn't received honour of knighthood,
> Though in regard of my high birth
> He's called lord with cap to the earth.
> And judge, pray, sir, when friends arrive
> And see their Princess scrivener's wife,
> Will 't not disparage high descent,
> As Garters in Rump Parliament?"
> Like child rebuked crying for knife,
> Stood father without soul or life,
> Or without fodder cow in pound,
> Or ape in chain with whip scourged round,
> At length he spake to Princess' face
> With homespun language cobbler's grace:

"May it please your highness, daughter, I
No harm did think most verily."
Quoth she, "Pray, sir, no more of this.
We do forgive what is amiss,
And for to satisfy your will,
Time and his love shall it fulfil."

Ah, witty baggage, she had her answer as ready as they
their question, and still she carried herself in all actions
with such bravery that they had not the least suspicion.
For the old man, being fully satisfied, let loose some of his
old angels, furnished her with clothes, as she herself hath
related, and her husband Carleton told me within these
few days that the whole expense upon this account did
cost £160 and this was all spent in one month's time, for
no longer did they live together. The occasion she hath already told you was by a letter, and so saith her husband,
and I believe it so to be, but some say it was by a shoemaker that coming to make her shoes knew her when she
had lived with her husband Stedman, that she knew him
and took no notice but sent him away angry, wherefore he

Contrived in his horny pate,
Malice against the Lord's bedmate.

And hereupon one day waiting for our Lord and his
Princess' return from Hyde Park, where they were gone to
air themselves,

At coming home unto their court,
St. Hugh to Lord did straight resort,
Told him he could relate sad story
Would make him weep in all his glory
And curse the time that ever he
His hawk at hobby did set flee,
Enough to put him into lax,
Not to be stayed by cobbler's wax.
The knight did wonder what he meant,
And prayed him to declare intent
Of his address, for he did make

> *His teeth to chatter, knees to shake.*
> *"Why, then," quoth he, "your Lady gay*
> *Is Kentish breed and crowder's spray,*
> *And married is to a shoemaker*
> *That is no cobbler nor translator,*
> *And hath to boot (take 't not in dudgeon)*
> *Another husband called a surgeon,*
> *And you in order make the third,*
> *And Princess is not worth a —"*

This must needs be heavy news to our young Lord, but whether the discovery was made by this shoemaker or the aforesaid letter matters not much, but her husband tells me that she herself attempted it several times to him, for she would be melancholy and say she neither desired nor deserved that attendance and great expense, and that she was undone unless he would pity her, and many broken speeches out of which he might, but at present did not, pick out her meaning. For although he did not believe her to be a princess, yet he was very confident that she was a lady of that name and quality which she had named herself to be; as for her estate, he never inquired what and where it was, but did not question but some she had, and that considerable; but however he does protest to me that he loved her not so much out of respect of that, as her good parts, with which she was plentifully stored, and knowing how in all companies to demean herself so, that it was clearly her person and parts that he esteemed her for. Neither could it be expected he should look for much, for he was very young, not full nineteen years old. He followed his own inclinations as to her person, and the advice of his friends as to her estate. They had examined that as much as they durst or indeed could. But in conclusion, thus they found themselves outwitted, she not what they expected, and then their anger and revenge caused their carriage to her to be very coarse and indeed scurvy, as she hath already and I shall once again relate it:

The lackey-boy was sent away
To father and to mother; nay,
His sister, too, the good matchmaker,
Of story true must be partaker:
Who being come, the Lord did tell
His sad mischance, which made 'em yell
And to exclaim 'gainst German Lady
That had abused poor little baby.
At last they went into bedchamber,
Where Princess lay like dog in manger,
Till aged sir did her importune
The truth to tell, if such a fortune,
Or where she was a German Princess,
Or who had taken her by th' inches
'Fore son did enter lower quarters,
Or who wore senior cobbler's garters
When he did marry her in church,
And who she lamed and brought to crutch,
And who it was besides did scrub her,
And what the surgeon was did probe her.
This fierce assault did make the lady
To stand as mute as jointed baby,
And was surprised to hear the gabble
Of this connext and joined rabble,
By which the women thought her guilty,
With hand and knee they hilty tilty
Most shamefully did her assault,
Which made her royal back to halt,
Whilst antedated lord stood by
And like boy whipt did snob and cry.
At last old man, as fierce as Hector,
Having more of henbane than of nectar,
Laid hands upon the lady's garments,
Jewels and rings, and her attirements;
And gouty shank was held aloft,
And new silk stocking plucked off.
In fine, they stript her to her smock
So fine you might have seen her nock,

Then much despised by bawling litter,
Which made before their chops to twitter.
When all indignities were over,
In German vest they did her cover,
With justicore and a night-rail,[19]
And petticoat all black to th' tail,
The same reserved by ship's master
When she escaped from foreign cloister,
Thence brought 'fore Godfrey not of Bouillon,
For this did use her like a scullion;
And so by beadle fell and hostile,
He sent her to the Gatehouse bastille
Where, being come, the gates flew open
For to receive Dutch Froe van Slopen,
As great companion come to dwell
In prison close much like to hell.
The noise of princess' close restraint
Sent persons great to hear her plaint,
But when they heard her to discourse,
They nettled were like pampered horse
And did applaud her high-bred parts,
Not to be equalized at marts.
Or ladies, some with face like maple,
That spend their time in tittle-tattle,
With great respect they did her treat
And sent in money, wine and meat,
And bribes to keeper to be civil,
As he that candle holds to Devil:
Where I will leave her to her Fate,
Still great, though in confined estate.
And for her high-conceited Lord,
When reputation he had scored
On tick and borrow, then he went
To chamber where he body pent,
Believing German knight would call
His Lordship to account for all
His base abusing princely dame
And using her with so much shame.

And parents, full with shame and ire,
Did mope and dote like cats by fire.

And now I have again brought her to the Gatehouse,
and from thence she was conveyed to the Sessions House
in the Old Bailey to take her trial. Great was the confluence
of people to behold her; the presence of a real princess
could not have drawn more company together than this
counterfeit one did. Her indictment being read, and she,
set to the bar in order to her trial, prayed time till the next
day, her witnesses not being ready. This was granted, and
she, conferring with several friends who came to advise her,
was again the next day brought to her trial. The most material and considerable witness that came against her was
one James Knot who gave in evidence that he gave the
prisoner at the bar in marriage to one Thomas Stedman,
a shoemaker, who was then alive in Dover, that they were
married in Canterbury in St. Mildred's Church by one
Parson Man that was then dead, that the marriage was
about nine years before, that they lived together about four
years and had two children. This was the sum of what he
said to prove the marriage, but being asked by the court
several cross-questions, he could not fully and clearly answer, for he acknowledged that there was no other company but himself, the parties, her sister, the parson who
was dead, and the sexton who he knew not where to find.
Neither could he tell after what manner they were married; neither was their marriage registered. Thus was his
evidence but slender, not being seconded by any other, for
all else spake by report. The second marriage to Carleton
was not only proved, but acknowledged by the prisoner
who made a very pathetic speech, alleging that all this was
the malice of her husband's father, and how her husband
had courted her as he pretended, only for her virtues, ami-
able person, and noble deportment, that she had often desired him to desist, but that he or his friends having in-
tercepted some of her letters, whereby they understood how
considerable her means were, they therefore hurried her to

church to be married; that her husband's father, afterwards considering she had a considerable fortune, pressed her that in respect she had no relations here, to make over her estate to his son, that it would be much for her honour, satisfaction of the world, and for which she would be chronicled for a rare woman; that she having refused it, they had robbed her of her jewels and clothes of great value, and declared that she had formerly been married to one at Canterbury, which place she said she knew not, and that this was grounded on a letter of their own framing; that thereupon they had violently carried her from her lodging before a justice of peace, only to affright her to make her estate over; that they charging her with this fact, she was bound over and committed.

That since then they had been up and down the country, and finding none there fit for their purpose, they had gotten an unknown fellow to swear against her. She alleged that if any such marriage had been, there might be a certificate from the minister or register, but nothing of that nature was to be found, and that that only witness could not say whether she was lawfully married, or how. She did aver that she was never yet married to any but John Carleton, whom she called pretended Lord, but that those persons had sought always to take away her life, hiring people to swear against her, & had laid several scandals against her, and had framed this of themselves. That she was a stranger and foreigner and, being informed that there was matter of law in the trial, her innocence should be her counselor, and their lordships her judges, to whom she did refer her cause. That since she had been in prison, several from Canterbury had been with her, but as the keeper could justify, they all declared that they did not know her.

This was her plea, which she uttered with such a becoming confidence as pleased all her auditors. And the court having heard some witnesses that she produced on her side to take off the allegations of those that had witnessed against her, and finding such slender proof of the indictment, they therefore gave this charge to the jury:

That there was an indictment against Mary Moders, alias Stedman, for having two husbands at one time alive, Stedman and Carleton; that they had heard the proof of the first marriage which depend upon one witness, Knot; that all the evidence given on that side to prove her guilty of the indictment depended upon his single testimony; that he said she was married at Canterbury, but the particulars or manner of the marriage he did not remember. If she were born there, married there, and as he said had two children there, and lived there so long, it were easy to have brought somebody to prove this, that that was all that was material for the first marriage; for the second there was little proof necessary, she confessing it. The question was whether she were married to Stedman or not. They had heard what defence she had made. Now if they did believe that Knot, the single witness, had spoke the truth, they saw what the circumstances were: it were penal if guilty, she must die, a woman hath no clergy, she was to die by the law if guilty. This was the whole of the directions of the court, leaving it to the verdict of the jury who, going forth after some short consultation, returned and gave in their verdict of Not Guilty, to the great joy of the prisoner and the great satisfaction of the auditors, who expressed their content in clapping their hands and loud noise.

But many of those that were now so glad had little cause for it afterwards; for I know some that were then there present and were, as they expressed themselves to me, mighty well pleased that the German Princess had come off so well. These very persons were not long after cheated by her of a considerable quantity of plate, and then they cursed her as much as now they magnified her for a great wit and brave woman. But I shall very suddenly come to the relation of some of those stories, but first I will finish this of her marriage, husband, and his relations, who indeed were very severe in their prosecution, and there was much of malice in their actions, for they not only indicted her for this marriage with Stedman of Canterbury, but alleged her other marriage with the chirurgeon at Dover, but they could make nothing of it, and much less of another marriage which was pretended with an old doting bricklayer who also indicted her, but the bill was not found, and when he came to Newgate to see his pretended wife the German Princess, he did not know her, but mistook another for her, with whom he held large discourse to little purpose, and therefore I shall omit it. I have been informed that he had been choused by some such piece as our Princess, but whether it was she herself, the Devil in her likeness, or somebody else that was endued with some of her good qualities I know not, but she for her part always denied it, styling him ridiculous dotard and one that could be no younger than brother to Mother Shipton.[20] But let this suffice concerning this fellow.

She, being acquitted by the jury, desired of the court that her jewels and clothes might be restored; the court acquainted her that they were her husband's and that if any detained them from her, he might have his remedy. She then charging old Carleton with them, he declared they were in the custody of his son, her husband.

And now being cleared by the law, she was discharged of her imprisonment on Saturday the 6th day of June, and she did confess and declare that she had been very civilly used by the masters and keepers of both the prisons, and great reason they had for so doing, for great was the gain they received by this Diana. She was so famous and so generally beloved and visited by all that she fared the better, and so did those who had her in custody. So great novelty had not been known or seen in our age, nor in any other age as I can read of. I never heard of her parallel in everything, and I believe, had she been exposed to public show for profit, she might have raised £500 of those that would have given 6d. and 12d. apiece to see her. It was the only talk for all the coffeehouses in and near London.

Before she left her old lodging in Newgate she was offered twenty several other lodgings in other places in and about London, so many friends she had who all courted her company in hopes of great profit by her presence. But

I believe some of them may have by this time repented it, if ever she came into any of their houses, for it is well known that she rarely missed of playing some such project in any of her lodgings as should occasion them to court her to be again their tenant. She was not often sought after by any of her landlords to continue or return to their houses, but she was frequently hunted out to clap her up in a stronger, at her old lodging in Newgate, whither in time she returned. But before that she had many pranks to play, and the first was to see what further advantage she might make of her husband Carleton, and if she could not get, she endeavoured not to lose by him. Her clothes and jewels she wanted, and therefore knowing that he was in Gray's Inn, she takes lodging in Fuller's Rents, which was not far from it, and not long after, according to her expectation, her husband Carleton comes. His business was to desire her not to prosecute his father for the detaining of the jewels, and hers was to get them and, in order thereto, to allure her husband to stay with her, but he being in the company, custody and tuition of his master, she missed of her ends, and so they abruptly broke off. She, having thus missed, sent a letter to him, but receiving no answer, she went boldly to old Carleton, and boldly knocking at his door, he asked who was there. She answered, "Your daughter when a princess, but now your son's wife." He demanded her business. She told him she came to demand her jewels and other things, and also her husband's person. He replied, in short, that for the jewels her husband had them, and for himself he was gone. She then, threatening him to take her course, departed.

Thus you see what applications she made for her jewels and husband. As for him, he tells me that she was very desirous to cohabit with him and did several times afterwards woo him to it, but he, knowing her inclination and temper, declined and wholly refused. And as for the jewels, he tells me they were counterfeit, but she alleges that they being offered in Cheapside to a goldsmith, he valued them at £1,500. This I believe is a lie and a loud one. Neither do

I believe they were of so little value as her husband Carleton reporteth.

She, having acted as far as she could with her husband, sent him this Farewell,

> There was a time when Skinker Perkin
> Leaped into prince from a frieze jerkin.
> Time also was, as 't has been said,
> When Friar Bacon's brazen head
> Spoke monstrous things, but we do tell
> Of stranger things that have befell,
> How pretty monkey in disguise
> Held Peascod in her mouth as prize.
> Oh fatal time! how couldst thou be
> So cruel in thy managery?
> More fierce than erst thou wast to fellow
> Who, though in rage with drink more mellow,
> Did all his forepast fancies deem
> Of drunken brain the passing steam.
> Oh, my sweet Peascod, prithee think
> Like him that all thy hopes was drink.

And having spent some time in being treated by that numerous company that resorted to her and coveted her acquaintance, and in this manner spent all the money she had, [she] was now to consider of some course to raise more. Diet and lodging must be paid for, and clothes must be had, too, though some flushed young gallants that kept her company, pitying her condition, would either lend or give her a piece or two sometimes; and she had a very good faculty of begging or borrowing, for she was very well gifted in the art of high-drinking, and when she saw her cullies were maudlin drunk and kindhearted, she would pretend some present occasion and borrow what they had about them.

Nay, she had so rare a faculty in this art that when she was a prisoner in the Gatehouse, she prevailed with one of her fellow prisoners to lend her £5. This was much for a prisoner to do, and such a one, too, as I very well knew was not worth £5 more in the world, and without any estate or calling, no employment, but a pretended artist and one who gave himself out to be a right Rosicrucian and secretary to God and nature, a fellow that if he had any knowledge, knew not of it himself, for he could not utter and had only a parcel of hard words, with which persons being affected and expecting some great matters from him, he lived upon them and particularly one person of honour from whom he had lately gained that money and then, having given him some abuse and being in disgrace, was clapt up from this fellow. She borrowed, but I believe never returned, who I am sure was often since in want of sixpence. If she had the art of wheedling this fellow, sure she might do more upon others; but that course failing and she being now generally acquainted and resorted to, the players, in hopes of gaining by her, entertained her as an actress.

She who had acted on the large theatre of the world in public now came to act in a small theatre, I cannot say in private, for it was public enough at all times, but much more when she presented her part thereon, for it was a play of her own self that she acted in; it was styled by her glorious name of "The German Princess." As for my own part, although I have been a great frequenter of those *divertissements*, yet I never went to see her, but those who did, tell me that although there was a great confluence of people to behold her, yet she did not perform so well as was expected; many have exceeded her in that particular; and that she acted much better, and more to the life, in the wide world than in that epitome. I do not remember that ever I saw the play, but I think the Epilogue spoken by herself at last was thus,

> *I have past one trial, but it is my fear*
> *I shall receive a rigid sentence here.*
> *You think me a bold cheat. Put case 'twere so.*
> *Which of you are not, now you'd swear, I know.*
> *But do not, lest that you deserve to be*
> *Censured worse than you can censure me.*

The world's a cheat, and we that move in it
In our degrees do exercise our wit;
And better 'tis to get a glorious name,
However got, than live by common fame.[21]

I question not but she had clapping and general applause, but every new thing being, as they say, but nine
days' wonder; hers was not to last many years, although
it is now just nine years from her thus first acting on the
stage to her last acting at the gallows. There was a report,
indeed, when she was first discharged from Newgate, that
she intended to turn actress at one of the theatres and that
she would set up a coffeehouse. I suppose this was only
the opinion of people who thought those employments fit
for her, but however she was mighty angry at it and said
that it was a flam given out to sully her name and reputation, but it had been better for her to have applied her
mind to, and continued at, her acting at the theatre, or else
have taken a coffeehouse, at which employment she might
have done well enough, and which trade her husband
Carleton was afterwards necessitated to take up, but she
had other fish to fry. She had a running brain, and the
whole city of London was too little for her to act in. Indeed,
a bad Fate pursued her, and she was to run on for a while,
the squib was to run to the end of the rope, and then
bounce, flash, and make its exit. It was her Fate to do some
more worthy actions, such as would bring her again before her twelve godfathers, who would not be outwitted
when her crimes were mischievous, as for the future you
shall find them, and as numerous as ever were committed
by any in so short a time, which was indeed too long to
the cost of those with whom she had acquaintance.

Before she left the theatre, she had a large parcel of
young cullies that, having heard of her fame and seen her
person, were very desirous of a nearer acquaintance, and
she who mightily loved company and gallantry was free
enough of access and treated them all with a gallant in-

differency. Among the rest of her admirers, there were a couple of young fellows that had more money than wit, and so doted on hers, and for that cause kept her company; they had other designs than barely her converse, for they desired a nearer association with her body. She knew their meaning by their whining and accordingly was resolved to make her advantages. They sought out opportunities of being private with her, and she used such artifice that she would not entertain them but in company. Only sometimes in a large room at a tavern, she would step to an odd corner with one of them, who pretending some private business would then desire to know when he might wait on her at her lodging. She would commonly answer them that she was seldom there, but when she slept, being forced to spend all the day at the theatre, and the evening she dedicated to the service of him and such other worthy company as were desirous of hers, so that she had no time to spare for attending on her employ, which she began to be weary of. Her cully then desires her to leave it off, and tells her that she might live better and more at ease in her private lodgings, telling her that if she will do so, he will not be wanting to contribute handsomely to her maintenance. She thanks him, and tells him she will consider and suddenly resolve of it; he then gives her some further knowledge of his affection to her, which she answers very obligingly, and withal takes occasion to tell him that she wants such a point lace or some such other thing to act in, or to commend his watch or a ring, and so get it from him.

Thus did she handle these two blades for some time, without letting one know of the other's pretenses. Their importunity at last prevails with her to leave the playhouse and her lodging, for which and her diet they both severally pay; and now she was to play a private game, and finding that these young fools had money, she intends to have her share of it. They both court her for the happy time, as they call it, of enjoyment. She tells one of them that she is in hopes of being reconciled to her husband, which she desires above all things, telling him that she knew then she might have opportunities enough without scandal, for she knows him to be of so easy a nature that she can overrule him, and that until that time she must carry herself with all wariness and circumspection, and withal tells him that she doubts the other is so conversant with her, as being only set on by her husband to look into her actions.

This tale pleases her lover and clears him of one doubt, for he till then believed that the other was both his enemy and his rival, but now he looks on him only as his enemy. She tells the other much such another story, but that I may not seem to romance by telling you all their private discourses, which would be impossible, she manages her affairs so, she gets money out of one to buy her a new gown and other ornaments; and pretending an old debt which she owed to a mercer who would sue her husband, she, that she might keep it from the knowledge of her husband, which would spoil all her design upon him, persuades the other to lend her money to pay this debt; and thus they having done all that she can desire of them, and finding their moneys to be well shrunk and being desirous to be rid of them, she at their earnest importunity appoints one to go out of town two or three miles, where they were to continue and have their frolic for a day or two; and when she comes to a tavern, the place where they were to take coach, the other meets as if by chance, though it was by her own appointment, and so affrightens her and him that was first come. She, as pretending to be surprised, rails at them both, and they at one another, fall to fighting in the tavern, in which engagement she leaves them, taking coach, and returning to her lodging, telling her landlord and landlady that her husband had endeavoured to trepan her and had made use of these two persons, naming them, who had some design upon her, what she knew not, but that she was so sensible that their company would be such a stain to her honour that she would never see them more, and therefore desires them both not to admit either of them into their house.

By this stratagem is she rid of her two importunate lovers,

and passes in the opinion of her landlord and landlady for
a woman of great virtue; and not to belie her, she was not
much guilty of that crime of incontinency. Her husband
Carleton told me that he did not at all believe her to be a
common prostitute, not to be enjoyed by every one that
courted her, that she had no great inclination that way,
and if she did, it was not with any that brought their half
crown, crown, or half a piece; it must be greater kindnesses than these, and some considerable acquaintance and
knowledge of the party. I know several idle fellows that
would pretend they had been very inward with the German
Princess and could command her company at all times, and
it may be so, at some considerable treat at their charge,
for she much delighted in high treatments and would drink
as high as most men, and still made her greatest advantages
when she had outdrunk them; but when they came to the
other thing, let them be never so confident or debauched,
she knew how to frustrate their expectations, so that this
crime she was not so guilty of, as the world supposes. No,
it was her other tricks of cheating and its attendants, lying
and wheedling; at these she was her arts mistress, and these
were so innate and natural with her that they were part of
herself. You might as well expect to have a fish live out of
the water as to expect her to be without acting some of
these falsities, and in all these things she was as false as Hell.
I have heard of some persons of quality who were of that
base temper of stealing, that if they had occasion for any
laces, hoods, scarfs, or any such things to be bought at the
Exchange, they could never be pleased with anything that
could be bought unless they stole it, and they have been
so often guilty that at last the shopkeepers, who knew them,
would let them steal and take no notice of it, for soon after
some friend who watched them would come and pay for it.
Our princess was much of this thieving quality, her fingers
were birdlime; but withal she was too cunning to be
caught, or else it was very rare. She had the right art of
legerdemain, as you shall presently hear, but before I come
to that, I will have one relation more to show that she was

not easy to be courted to incontinence and that they who did win her to it paid full dear for their lechery.

You have already heard how she was rid of her two young lovers. It was not long after, before she had an old one, a gentleman of about fifty. He lodged in the same house with her and was so deeply in love with her that he would willingly have been at the charge of a constant maintenance, if she would have lived with him. Only, he not only distrusted, but knew her tricks and told her of them, and that he did believe the story of foreign birth was romantic, but however, if she would answer his love and live soberly with him, he would maintain her in as splendid a garb as she would desire, for he had £400 *per an.* and no charge but himself and a manservant. This was his discourse to her, to which she gave him various answers, but at last presenting her with some rings and such toys, he won her to consent.

Now in regard this their purpose could not be handsomely executed in the house where they were, and they designing to live in all freedom as man and wife, they therefore left that lodging and went to another at a convenient distance. He had promised her a jewel worth £50 which he would give her the first night she would lie with him, as an engagement of his truth to her, and he performed his word accordingly. Some time they lived thus together and complied with one another very reciprocally. Yet he, like an old fox knowing that he had a serpent in his bosom, would not trust her with any money nor himself neither. For all the time they lived together he did not keep above £10 in the house at a time, but still as he received his quarterly or half-yearly payments of rent, he carried the money to a goldsmith's and fetched it as he had occasion; and the goldsmith's bill he was very curious of, not leaving it in any box, chest, or trunk, that might be broken open, but still carrying it about him in his pocket. She minded all this well enough and was for some time contented to live in that private retired manner, but like fire that is kept close, will blaze when it can get out, so she could not endure to live long without being in action. She had a mind to blaze abroad in the world a little; her inclination or rather Fate forced her, and act she must; wherefore she waited her opportunity when she might get some prize and so march off with flying colours.

She waited the coming of the next quarter day when his rents were to come up, which were brought accordingly, but secured as I have already told you. She knew not how to engage him to bring it home, lest he should distrust her, and if it lay long there, he would fetch it away in parcels; wherefore she knew not what course to take, but Fortune put an opportunity into her hands by his coming home one night so drunk that she was forced to put him to bed, where when he was laid and she found by his snoring that he was fast enough, she examined his pockets, and looking into his letter case among his papers, she there found a bill upon a goldsmith in Lombard Street for a £100. This she secures and puts all up again; and although her bed-fellow sleeps hard, yet she takes little rest for thinking how she should finish her design. For she doubted that the next day upon examining his papers, which he often turned over, he would miss the bill and presently go to the gold-smith's and prevent her receiving of it; wherefore she con-cluded it absolutely necessary to hinder from that by getting him out of the town, but how to do that she did not pres-ently know, but at length considering that he had a very loving friend that lived about eight mile off, she resolved to send her bedfellow of some errand thither. Wherefore early in the morning before he was willing to awake, she called on him, telling him the day before in his absence Mr. such-a-one his friend had been there and must needs speak with him that day. "Now," said she, "I thought fit to call you thus early that you may have time enough to go and return again before night, for you know that I cannot be content without your company." He, hearing her discourse and not having any occasion to hinder him, soon rises, and taking leave of her, begins his journey.

No sooner was he gone but she makes ready for hers,

and being dressed she takes coach for the goldsmith's. When she was almost come thither, she drew out the bill to look on it, and it was well she did so, or else all her project would have been spoiled, for she intended to demand a just £100, when looking on the back side of the bill, she found that £20 of the 100 had been received. This startled and troubled her to think that she was £20 worse than she thought for, but she was glad she saw it before she came to the goldsmith's who might else have distrusted her, had she asked for the full £100. She, being now come to the goldsmith's shop, told him that she came from such a gentleman who had such a day left a £100, but had received £20, and he being sick, had sent her for the £80 remaining. There was no distrust nor no cause for it; wherefore the money was paid and the bill delivered up.

She, being now mistress of this rich cargo of £80 in money, the jewel of £50 which he had given her, and several other rings, pendants, and necklaces to a good value, was resolved to march off, leave her old friend, and seek a new, or at leastwise new quarters; but she was much disturbed and vexed that she was disappointed £20 in her expectations, and thought how she might make that good; and being now resolved to leave her old lover and therefore to make the most of him, and knowing that she had time enough by reason of his being out of town, she therefore returns to her lodging and, not having the keys, breaks open the locks of a trunk and box and rifles them both, where she finds twenty pieces of old gold, a golden seal, an old watch, and some odd pieces of plate. These and all things else of any worth she takes, and then without taking any leave of her landlady, she again takes coach and marches off to a new lodging at another end of the town where for some days she keeps close.

And now I have related this story of her, is she not a base, ungrateful woman thus to leave a man who so handsomely provided for her? Had it not been better for her to have continued with him, who loved, tendered, and would always have taken care of her and kept her from running into those lewd courses that she since then committed? Was it not enough for her to take the gentleman's bill and all his money, but also afterwards to go back and take his gold which he valued, it may be, more than the worth, but above all things his seal of arms, which it may be had descended to him from his ancestors and which he would not have parted from for forty times the price? This she must needs think must much discontent him, considering the trouble and necessity she would put him to, till the next quarter day, until when he must stay without money or be forced to borrow. All these things she knew, but no consideration weighed with her as anything. All was laid aside to perform her will and to be, as she reckoned, revenged for the £20 she was disappointed of. Well, let her go for a base, lewd woman, but time will come that she must repent this unhandsome, ungrateful action. And thus you see how dearly this man paid for her wanton company. If he had any music he paid the fiddler soundly, or she paid herself; his sweetmeat cost him sour sauce, and so will hers in the end. But she had much more work cut out for her to do. This was but one of her first projects and was not likely to make much noise, for the gentleman for shame would not speak much of it in public, only to some private friends, and from one of them I had it. If he had made it public it would have availed him little; he should only have been laughed at, and therefore silence was best in the case.

Our Counterfeit Lady having thus overreached her old lover and having taken a convenient lodging, it was not long ere she had a young one, who you shall see she used no better than the former, but first when she took her lodging pretending she was a virgin and newly come out of the country upon some extraordinary occasion, she wanted a maid to wait on her. She, therefore, desires her landlady to help her to one; she soon furnished her, but not to her content, and several she had before she was pleased. They had one fault or other, and she found they would not be for her purpose, but in conclusion one she had that very well pleased her and, indeed, was as cunning and subtle a bag-

gage as herself, and was afterwards very assistant to her in
her affairs. She being provided and fitted with tools, a convenient lodging and fit servant, it was not long ere she fell
to work. She was very careful to keep herself out of idleness
and to contrive how to get more money before what she
had was gone.

She had already given out that she was a country gentlewoman, had a £1,000 to her portion left by an uncle
that she could command when she married; that her father
was able to give her more and would do so, too, if she
would consent to marry with one in the country whom he
well liked and had provided for her, but she, wholly dis-
liking him, had chosen rather to leave her father and come
to London than abide at home and be so importuned by
her father and hated lover; and that for her maintenance
she had the interest-money of the £1,000 quarterly paid
her. This was the story she framed, and to make it the more
feasible she contrived letters to be often brought her as if
sent out of the country from a kinswoman, who gave her
constant intelligence how affairs went about her father and
lover; and these letters, being loosely laid about her chamber, were seen and perused by her landlady. She was so
reserved and retired that she went seldom abroad, and then
masked, veiled, and coached, and kept very good hours
and a handsome decorum in all things.

The landlady where she lodged had a kinsman of a very
good fortune who came often to visit her and so by that
means had a sight of our Counterfeit who was very wary
and shy of being seen of any, and that occasioned this
young man to be the more inquisitively curious. He knew
no more than what his kinswoman, the landlady, told him,
and all things corresponding to her discourse it was taken
for authentic; and he, believing her to be a fortune suitable
to his quality, sought all means to court her. She, as shy as
she was, was however so civil out of complacency to her
landlady to suffer herself to be treated by this young gallant, and in fine drew him on to be her affectionate lover.
She knew her distance and kept that, engaging him to the

same, and he respectfully obeyed her. He presented her with a watch which she after some seeming refusal accepted, and now being free in their converse, she told him all the sad story of her father's harshness in seeking to force her to such a match as she hated. Her suitor pitied her in that, and made a free tender of his love and service, telling her that he had £500 by him in money and £200 *per an.* and that he would gladly enjoy her to wife with her bare £1,000, and leave her father's good will to time. She thanked him, but withal seemed very unwilling to marry without her father's consent, for by that means she should lose a £1,000 more, which he could and intended to give her. Our youth heard and believed all still, offering his love at the terms aforesaid.

As they were one day discoursing of these and such like affairs, a porter knocks and brings a letter; the maid receives it and brings it to her mistress who presently opens and reads it, but she had no sooner finished her reading, but she pretending to be amazed and affrighted cried out, "I am undone," and was so ready to fall into a swound that her servant was forced to apply things to recover her. Her lover was all this while by her and comforted her with the best words he could, desiring if she pleased to understand the occasion of her present distemper. "Sir," said she, "since you are already acquainted with most of my concerns, I shall not make a secret of this; therefore, if you please to read over that letter, you will know the present cause of my affliction." He, having her leave, took up the letter and read thus,

Dear Cousin,

Although I have taken pen in hand with a resolution to write to you, yet I almost resolve against it, knowing that you will receive much trouble at the intelligence I shall give you, but there is somewhat in it that may turn to your advantage, which I pray make your best use of, and let that give you some consolation for the other trouble; and now I have provided you in general

for ill news, know that your dear brother and my loving cousin is dead. I know he was dear to you, and
therefore his loss will the more sensibly afflict you, but
withal you know that by his death you are the only
heir after your father to his estate of £200 *per an.* This
may give you some pleasure, but what I am next to
inform you of is the worst news of all, and that is this,
that your hated lover hath been so importunate with
your father, especially since your brother's death, that
now your father is resolved you shall be married to
him. Your brother who was used to be your friend to
dissuade your father from violence being dead, it is
believed your father will take no refusal of you, especially since he says now you, being his heir, are to receive the greatest part of your portion from him. And
therefore you shall obey him in order to these resolves.
He and your lover are preparing for a journey to London where they will be in few days, and they know
where to find you out, I doubt to your trouble, unless
you can in obedience to your father's commands throw
off the aversion you have for your lover. I shall not advise you, but thought good to let you know of this
alteration of your condition, that you may not be
wholly unprovided how to dispose of yourself, which
God grant may be for the best. Those are the prayers
of

Your loving and affectionate kinswoman,
R. F.

Our young lover, having read over his lady's letter, found
that she had cause to be afflicted and that he was concerned in the matter. He was glad to hear of her additional
fortune, but doubtful that her country lover would deprive
him of her; wherefore after some words of comfort, they
fell to consultation of what was necessary; and to be brief
in my relation, it was thought wholly necessary to change
her lodging, and not knowing where better to be, he made
her a tender of his, which he could commodiously spare,

having two rooms on a floor. This was that which she aimed at, and therefore he without much difficulty persuaded her thereto, and so they the next day removed accordingly. He gave her the accommodation of the fairest room of the two which was to the street side and was better furnished than the other which was backwards and where his man had lain, who was now mounted up into a garret. He removed only his trunk into his back chamber, leaving all things else in the fore-room. Here our Counterfeit and her maid lay, but her business being to come at this trunk where she supposed his money was, she was not well pleased that it was removed, and therefore resolved to be lodged where that was. For this purpose, one evening, when they were ready to go to bed, she complained of an illness in her head, and that she was so disturbed by the noise of the street that she could not sleep, and therefore desired to change lodgings with him. He made some excuses that it was not so commodious, but she still urging the inconveniency and noise, he was content, and only changing the sheets without removing anything else, for that night they changed lodgings, he telling her that the next day he would cause several things that lumbered up the room to be removed to make it as commodious as might be, but she purposed to save him that labour, and therefore a bottle or two of wine being drank in her new lodging, they for that night parted, he to his bed to sleep, but she was otherwise employed.

Her maid knew of her design and assisted in it. They resolved not to go to bed that they might be ready so soon as the doors were open to be gone. They lay down by turns for some hours in their clothes, but towards morning they fell to work and soon broke the trunk open. There they found a £100 in a bag and some suits of clothes. They searched for gold which they knew he had, but that being portable, he carried it in his pocket and so they missed of it, and only the silver was their prize, which so soon as it was day and the doors open they slipt away with, leaving our poor lover to look for his money & his mistress, who with her woman (for maid I cannot truly call her) were gone far enough. Thus did she overreach both old and young, still coming off with flying colours, and as yet acted pretty honourably, only cheating those that intended some project upon her; but ere long she, being flushed with success, attempted to cheat anybody, friend or foe, rich or poor; all was fish that came to net whether salmons or sprats; for she would play at small game rather than stand out. A silver tankard or beer-bowl was prize with her; nay, rather than lose her labour, a pair of sheets and pillow-biers would serve the turn. But before she declined to these poor things, she had some more considerable projects; one whereof was of notable, subtle contrivance, and thus it was. She had often changed her lodging, and by her woman's means had gained some ranting acquaintance which had been of hers, so that money flew away apace; and they knowing that she was somewhat bare of money as well as they, but still their wits were as plentifully furnished as hers, they set them (the only tools they had) to work, to raise a new stock, and having considered of many ways they resolved on this.

She one day told her landlady that a country gentleman of her acquaintance, being unacquainted in the city, had happened into a pitiful alehouse where falling sick he soon died; and some friends of his and she together had thought it very inconvenient to bury him from thence, and not knowing any place so fit, they desired to bring his dead body to her lodging to bury him from thence; therefore, she desired her leave and assistance in accommodating her with necessaries, and she should have a piece for the trouble of her house. The landlady hearing of profit soon consented, and that evening the corpse, in a very handsome coffin, was brought in a coach and placed in the chamber, which was the room one pair of stairs next the street and had a balcony. The coffin being covered only with an ordinary black cloth, our Counterfeit seems much to dislike it. The landlady tells her that for 20 shillings she might have the use of a pall of velvet and, for as much more, some scutcheons of the gentleman's arms. Our Lady was well pleased with the pall, but for scutcheons she said they would be useless in regard the deceased gentleman was unknown, but she desired that the landlady would send for the pall and withal accommodate the room with her best furniture, for the next day but one he should be buried. This the landlady performed, getting the pall of velvet, and placing on a sideboard table two silver candlesticks, one silver flagon, two standing gilt bowls, and several other pieces of plate. This was for adornment and to be used in serving the wine the next day, but the night before the intended burial, our Counterfeit Lady and her maid within the house handed out to their comrades without all the plate, the pall of velvet, and all the other furniture of the chamber that was portable and of value, leaving the coffin and supposed corpse, and she and her woman descended from the balcony by help of a ladder which her comrades had brought her.

The next day the landlady, opening the door, found all was conveyed away but the coffin; when calling some friends, they opened that and found in it only brickbats and hay, such a quantity as might make it weighty enough for a dead body. This was the adventure of the coffin which was so talked of and, indeed, was one of her masterpieces, and she carried it off very cleverly. The plate was converted into money, and the pall of velvet into a loose French coat and mantle for herself, and velvet coats for her confederates, who being all rogues alike were in one livery. They sang "Oh be joyful," whilst the landlady and arms-painter sang *Lachrymæ*, and this adventure made work for the lawyers as well as the tailors, for the arms-painter went to law with the landlady for satisfaction for his pall of velvet, which lately cost him £40. But let them agree the matter as well as they can, our Counterfeit and her companions agreed to act more villainies; and she, seeing that her stolen French coat became her so well, purposed to have a new gown of the same price, and having projected the way how, she soon put it into execution in this manner.

She and her waiting woman took coach and went to Lombard Street where at a mercer's shop they alighted, desired to see several sorts of silks, which were showed to her Ladyship, who at length likes of some for her purpose. She beat the price as low as possibly she could that she might seem to be a good paymistress, and at last they agreed for £6. She then pulls out a purse wherein she had about 20 shillings in silver and several pieces of gold, but seemed so troubled to part from her gold that she, rather than do so, desires the mercer to let his servant ride along with her in the coach to her house and she will instantly pay him in silver, telling him that she should suddenly, and it may be presently, lay out more money with him for a kinswoman she had at home who, it may be liking of her silks, might presently bespeak some of him of the same. The mercer, being willing to accommodate his customer and to gain more, ordered his servant to attend her; whereupon they being all coached, the coachman was ordered to drive home, but they had not gone far, but our Counterfeit, bethinking her of some present business, altered her orders and commanded the coachman first to drive to the Old Exchange, and said she to her waiting woman, "Now I am out, I will go up into the Exchange and fit myself with a set of knots suitable to this silk." "That will be very convenient," replied the woman, and therefore being come to the Exchange and the coachman opening the boot, she alighted, saying to the mercer's man, "Friend, you may sit here in the coach while my maid and I go up & buy a few odd things & will return instantly." The poor young man thought it was good manners to obey her Ladyship and therefore sat still, permitting her woman to take the silk to match with ribbons, as they said, and so they tript it upstairs, leaving the young novice to take a nap in the coach; but he might have taken a long one, if he had stayed till their return, for although their business was soon dispatched, yet they came not back. No, they returned another way. All that they did there or intended was to walk halfway round the Exchange to the other door and so, descending and taking coach, drove home to their lodging where they fell into a great fit of laughter, to think what the poor fellow would do and how he would answer his master. How he came off you may imagine, but he waited long in expectation of her Ladyship's return, and then examined the coachman of his Lady, who could give as little account of her as himself. Only, the coachman first discovered they were both cheated, and the young man not knowing how to excuse his folly to his master, as his best expedient, gave the coachman twelvepence to go home with him and certify his master how the case was, who understanding the cheat was forced to sit down with his loss.

Our Counterfeit, having made silk enough at one heat for a gown and petticoat, caused it to be made up, and bragged of her fair undertaking to her comrades, telling them that it liked her very well, although it was the cheapest gown she ever wore. "Well," said one of her male companions, "I dare undertake within one week's time to be master of a better, and that at a cheaper rate, for your silk came from the mercer's, and I intend to have some at a better hand, an easier lay, play the good husband and have it from the weaver himself that makes it." "That would not be amiss," said she, "and, indeed, although I want no gowns, yet I long for a piece of silk so purchased at the first hand; therefore I pray make trial of your skill." The other replied he would not fail, and therefore thus he executed his project.

He walks into Spitalfields and inquires for a broad-silk weaver, a Frenchman, and finding such a one, he, knocking at his door and being brought in to him, tells him that he belonged to such an eminent lady, naming her, who had ordered him to find out a Frenchman, a broad weaver, that she might buy of him some silks, for said he, "My lady hath been deceived by her mercer who sells her English silks for French, and therefore I had orders to find out a Frenchman." "Well, sir," replied the weaver, "what would your lady have?" "A right French farendine,"[22] replied the cheater. "I can furnish you with the best in England," said

the weaver, "of the very same making as such a great lady
had," and thereupon brings out several sorts and pieces.
They discoursed of price, and the weaver asking 11 shillings a yard, the cheater replied that his lady had ordered
him to give 10 shillings per yard if it were a right French
farendine, and to buy the whole piece. The honest weaver,
being willing to take money, tells him that indeed if he did
sell it so, it was as cheap as the mercer's gave him, who
bought all he made all the year round. "That may be,"
said the cheater, "but then I suppose you trust six or twelve
months whereas now here is good ready money." " 'Tis
granted," replied the weaver. "That, and that only, is the
reason why I shall be willing to take your money." "Well,
then," said the cheater, "since we are agreed, I will have
all the piece, being forty yards, and you shall have your
ready money. Only, I must desire you or your servant to go
home with me to my lady who at the first sight will pay
the price we have agreed upon."

The old weaver, having formerly been choused and had
tricks put upon him, was shy and unwilling to go from
home, but the thoughts of £20 together ready money induced him, but that he might be the more sure, he was
resolved to take his man with him to carry it, and then he
did not question but they two should be wise enough to
prevent any trick that should be put upon him. He therefore delivering the silk to his servant, they walked out together to the other end of the town, when coming to a
great gate the lady's pretended gentleman entered, and desiring them to walk in the courtyard, he goes in, stays some
little time and returns, saying, "Sir, my Lady is not yet
stirring, but will be presently; wherefore if you please, we
will go over the way to the alehouse, take a morning's
draught, and by that time she will be ready, and you shall
be dispatched." To this the weaver consented, and they
took a room next the street. There they sat about a quarter
of an hour, when over comes a fellow bareheaded. "Now,"
said the cheat, "I believe my lady is up, and I am sent
for." Upon this the fellow without a hat enters. "How now,"

said the cheat, "what news?" "Why, Mr. Thomas," said he, "my Lady is ready and would have you bring over the silk, and she will send the money." "You see," said the cheater to the weaver, "that I told you true; it would not be long ere she was ready. Therefore give me the silk, and I will go over and fetch the money. Ralph," said he to the other, "do you stay and keep the gentleman company the while."

The weaver, as wary as he was, was now blinded. He saw everything carried so cleverly that he had not the least distrust, but the bareheaded fellow sitting down and drinking, he delivered the silk to the other who goes directly in at the great gate, and the weaver, seeing that and having the other fellow with him, thought all was well, but he did not find it so. For they sat drinking so long that the bareheaded fellow began first to complain, saying, "I wonder our Thomas stays so long. I am sure my Lady will give him the money at the first word if she be at leisure. I therefore wonder at his stay." "And so do I," said the weaver. After some little longer stay the weaver seeming troubled, the bareheaded fellow said, "I will go over, if you please, and see what is the matter." "Do so," said the weaver. "But do not stay." "No," replied he, but he intended not to be so good as his word, for he was glad he was thus discharged, and going in at the great gate he was no more seen.

The weaver sat in great trouble, doubting somewhat was the matter, and vexing that he had delivered his silk. At length he calls for the people of the house and asks them if they knew not the men that were with him. They replied, "No." What not know my lady's men Thomas and Ralph that were there with him? "We know none of them," replied they. "Nor know not what lady you mean." "My lady," replied the weaver, "that lives over the way at the great gate." "Sir, you are mistaken," said the people of the house, "for we assure you there is neither lady nor lord there at present; all are out of the town but a housekeeper and one boy." "Then I am cheated," said the weaver. "But I cannot conceive well how that can be, for I saw them both go in, and neither of them yet is returned, for I watched them." "If that be all your hopes," said the host, "you will be deceived, for there is a passage through into the back street." "Nay, then," said the weaver, "I am certainly cheated and cannot help it." But to satisfy himself further, he went over with the host and found the passage was as he had related, and nobody but an old woman and a boy in the house, who could give no account of the people he inquired after.

There was no remedy but patience, and that the weaver was forced to, & to return home with a light purse and a heavy heart, and he was not so troubled, but our Counterfeit Lady was as well pleased with the handsome performance of her friend who gave her a particular account of the management of the affair. He commended his wit, and so did she, too. But she told him that she should never be at quiet until she had acted somewhat that might be equal to it and, considering of what she told him, that she would put the cheat upon the very same man, the honest weaver. "Nay, if you can do that," said her confederate, "then I shall yield you the priority, but I doubt you will find it a very hard task to outwit the weaver who is bitten so considerably already, and who stands warily on his guard." "I am resolved," said she. "I will attempt it," and so she did in a short time after.

She, being acquainted with the place and person, takes coach and goes thither, but first she provided herself of a convenient lodging, for that is the principal matter in the case. Being thus fitted, she boldly goes to the weaver's and desires to see some silks, which he shows her. She likes them, and the price they agreed upon. Nothing was remaining but to pay for it, but examining her pocket, she had nothing but gold, and not enough of that neither; wherefore she tells him that he must either go or send with her, and take his money. "You must pardon me, Madam," said he. "I shall not let my goods go out of the house before I have my money." She demands his reason; he tells her he had been several times cheated, and among other cheats, he relates the last, which she knew as well as himself. She seems to wonder at the contrivance, and exclaims against the cunning, subtle wickedness of the world, and tells him he had been well enough, had he kept his wares in his own hands and presented them himself to the pretended lady, but to trust another was the ready way to be cheated. "Very true," replied he. "I know it to be true to my cost, and therefore shall not venture myself nor goods out of my own house." "What not with a woman?" said she. "I have nobody with me, and I will pay you before your goods go out of your sight. I shall be at one word, here's one, here's 'tother, and besides it will not be very inconvenient for you, for you may ride in my coach with me."

"Well, Madam," replied he, "I believe you are an honest lady, and I dare trust myself in your company." And thereupon taking up the silk, he went with her into the coach. She, seeing that she had secured him thus far and not questioning but she could finish her project on him, was resolved that she would exceed in her first purpose and that he should have a companion in his suffering; wherefore asking him where she might buy some good gold and silver lace, he directs to a place, as he says, a friend of his. Thither the coachman was ordered to drive, who did so, & she, seeing and liking the commodity, agreed for as much as came to £20. She tells that man, as she had done the weaver, that he must go or send with her and receive his money. The lace-man, seeing his friend the weaver there, not doubting anything, did not think it necessary to go himself, but sent his man, supposing him to be sufficient, and so they entered the coach, ordering the coachman to drive to the lady's lodgings.

Thither they came, and she conducts them upstairs, calls her waiting woman to bring a bottle of wine, that is brought, and they drink. She fetches a bag of money, supposed to be £50 or £60, chinks it on the table, but being about to open it, calls to her attendant to bring pen, ink, and paper, and says to the weaver and lace-man, "I must desire you both to write down the quantity and prices of your goods, that I may have no mistake, for I buy half of it for a niece of mine, who is above in her chamber." They were content with this and began to write. Her bag of money and hand on it was still on the table, and then she calls to her attendant. "Here," said she to her, "carry this silk and lace to my niece, and see how she likes it." The attendant takes it away, and one of the two had now made out his bill, and the other begins to do so. She takes it in her hand as to peruse it, walks three or four steps towards a curtain, and turns in there. The other had by and by made his bill, and they both expected the return of the lady with the money, but she intends no such matter. They had seen their last of her. To conclude, after much stay they call and knock, and that so loudly that one from below came up, asks what is the matter. They inquire for the lady, are answered, they know nothing of her, but thought she had been still with them. They draw the curtain and search the room, but find nobody, but to their great grief see a door and a back pair of stairs, which they concluded was the way she and her woman went. The weaver inquires for the lady's niece, but can find no such party. He charges the people of the house with the cheat; they deny all knowledge of it, and tell him that she was a stranger to them, having lain there but three nights. He fumes and frets, but to no purpose; for upon further inquiry he finds the people innocent, & therefore he and the lace-man return without money. The weaver is very angry, and the lace-man more than he, charging him with the miscarriage. This enrages him, but all to no purpose, for he is forced to sit down with the loss, only resolving for the future not to trust out of his house.

In the meantime our Counterfeit and her attendant got home to her old quarters (for she continued her old lodging, only taking this, as finding it convenient for her design), and there she lays up her purchase, much rejoicing that she had exceeded her confederate in her undertaking; and he that evening coming to her, and she relating her particular adventure, did conclude himself outdone by her, and that she had far outstripped him, not only in the affair of the weaver, but in that additional adventure of the lace, and that now she was capable of any undertaking. She was as well pleased with these praises and commendations as she had been with her purchase, which was now to be made up into clothes for her, and having enough and to spare, she promises her attendant a gown out of it. She had money enough to pay a tailor, but it went against the grain to think of parting from any money, where wit would serve the turn. Nay, she should not so well like of her clothes, if she did not wholly cheat for them, and therefore she was resolved to give no more for the making than the materials had cost her, and that was a little wit, which she thus set to work.

She must again take a new lodging and, therefore, went upon the hunt to inquire for one. She saw many, but liked of none, till she came to a tailor's house, and understanding his quality, though the lodgings were dear and not so convenient as she desired, yet she dispensed with that and agreed upon all terms. She gave herself out to be a country gentlewoman, newly come to town, and that her trunks would in few days be brought to her. She one day went abroad and at her return tells her landlady that a scurvy mischance had befallen her, for her trunks with her clothes, and other things which she had expected, were left behind and would not come in a fortnight, and that she, being to be visited within three days, was much troubled at the disappointment, and that she was so concerned that she would instantly go and buy silk for a new gown, if she could tell that her landlord would be at leisure to make them by the time appointed for her visitants. The landlady replied, yes, her husband should in such a case as that lay by all other work to accommodate her. Our Counterfeit, hearing this, takes coach with her maid and, pretending to go buy silk, goes to her old lodging and takes as much of her late ill-purchased commodity as would make herself and attendant, gowns and petticoats, and so returned.

By this time the tailor himself was come home, and his wife having acquainted him with their lodger's occasion, he offers his service. She produces the silk; he likes it and commends her pennyworth, and takes measure of her and her maid, for the mistress says the maid's sweetheart was one of those that was to visit her, and therefore it was convenient for her to be as handsome as she can. She says she will pay for both, and produces much gold, and is on all occasions free in showing her necklaces, pendants, rings, and other jewels. The tailor, believing he hath an excellent job of work, falls closely to it and, by the assistance of his servants, gets both the gowns and petticoats finished by the day, against which time she bespeaks of her landlady a fish dinner, as she says, to entertain her friends, gives her 20 shillings to buy the fish, and desires her to dress it and provide all things necessary, and she will in the evening pay it. All is provided according to order, and the visitants came, ate up the victuals, and drank off a large quantity of wine which the landlady sent for. The landlord is fuddled, and the landlady goes up with him to get him to lie down. In the meantime (the entertainment being kept in a room belowstairs) our Counterfeit Lady seeing the coast clear, and all things as she would have them, she and her associates (who all came for the purpose) slip out. Neither did they go empty-handed; one carries a silver tankard, another a silver salt, and the rest, all that they could lay their hands on; and the lady's attendant in the rear carries her lady's and her own old apparel made up into a fardel. They clap all, and themselves, into a coach, and so march off. And thus much for the adventure of the tailor.

And now, Reader, let me tell you and assure you that these three last adventures, two whereof were with the weaver, and the third and last with the tailor, are certainly true, for they are both my relations and lately gave me this account of their misfortunes, which you may understand to be very considerable. For would it not anger anyone to be twice cheated by back doors, as the honest weaver was, and yet all things were managed so well that there was not the least cause of suspect. To see and hear money, and be ready to tell it, was such a disappointment as could not be imagined and could not be contrived, but by such a crafty slut, with the assistance of that foul fiend, who I think always attended her.

The tailor, too, was much disappointed of his good customer. All he had for workmanship, and other necessaries for two gowns and petticoats, was only his share of a fish dinner. The fish indeed she paid for, but she left him to pay for the sauce, which I am sure was sour in his stomach a great while after, and then it was that laughter and joy was turned into sorrow and mourning, nay, and further, into bitter cursing, for this honest tailor was one of those that at her trial about her two husbands was so joyful at her deliverance. He then commended her for a brave woman and said it was much pity that she should suffer for that fact, but now he was in another tale; he said it was pity she had not been hanged seven years before. Since that time he knew her, though his eyes were then blinded, one would have thought he could not have been so mistaken in his lodger, for he had seen her at her trial and after that in her public acting at the theatre, but now he did not remember her, nor could not imagine who she was, till in some few months after, she, having played some more such projects, became famous for stealing tankards, &c., and then he too late remembered that his lodger was the very same German Princess, but she had such an art in disguising herself that it was very difficult to know her. She could upon occasion alter, not only the air of her countenance, but also some of her features would seem to be different. To conclude, she had such a face, such a carriage, and such a tongue, as would deceive a very piercing eye, as experience hath already demonstrated. She, being thus bravely come off, had no need at present to seek out for more purchase, and commonly she did not seek for any because it fell out ready to her hand; the bird usually came into the net of its own accord; and her manner of living being altogether upon plots and devices, and she always like a cunning gamester, looking to her hits, did let few blots[23] escape her, but was still contriving how to win the game.

Among the rest of her contrivances, I shall acquaint you with one of a different nature and quality from what I have already related to you. For although she did often act her tricks over several times, yet I shall relate them but once, lest I should seem tedious, and what I intend for your *divertissement* should prove your trouble, & that I may come to matter of fact, I shall thus proceed. Our Counterfeit had for some time lived privately at home in her quarters, if I may term that to be private when she was visited frequently by her comrades, such as were as good as herself of both sexes, but she went abroad but seldom and then only to divert and air herself. But now being weary of her retirement, she went to the Exchange to buy gloves, ribbons and such like toys, and which was somewhat wonderful, she paid honestly for them; but it was still out of design, for she seldom acted anything that was good, but it was for some ill intent. She only paid for this small parcel that she might cheat for a larger, and thus she did it.

She acted several parts, but all in a splendid gallant garb which now she was weary of, and therefore intended to put herself into mourning, which she was resolved somebody should pay for. Her clothes being fitted, she wanted a set of mourning knots, ribbons, hoods, scarfs, apron, cuffs, and other mourning habiliments. She therefore sent her woman to the Exchange, to the shop where she had laid out money and was known, desiring them to bring all such sort of trinkets to her lady instantly, for her father was dead, and she must put herself into mourning. The woman of the shop instantly looked out three or four of a sort of all these commodities, and sent them by her servant to see which she would like and bring the rest back, but she was mistaken. None was to return. No, our Counterfeit was resolved to show her a trick, and it was as good for much as little, and as soon done. When the things were brought, she pretended to be so indisposed that she could not at present look on them, but sent word that at noon she would dress herself, and then when she was fitted with what she liked, she would send back the rest, and money for what she had. This answer was sufficient at present, but not satisfactory in the main, for the next day the Exchange woman sending her servant to see what her Ladyship had liked, answer was given that she went out, and came not home that night. Neither did she the next, nor no more thither; for she, having another part to act, left her quarters, and so the Exchange woman lost her goods and customer.

Our Counterfeit, being now habited in sable à la mode, became the talk of those that saw her, for as yet she had not given out at her new lodging what she was. She knew not whether it would be most for her advantage to pass for a maid, wife, or widow, and she was ready to represent any quality she pleased. She now walked abroad attended by her woman into Gray's Inn Walk, where she was gazed on by all, everyone inquiring who was this unknown lady, but she intended to continue so for some time. There was at the same time walking a young gentleman in mourning, too. He was known and talked of to be a rich heir and a well-moneyed man by the late death of his father; he was a student in the law, and of able parts. All this she understood, and this was the trout she intended to tickle. This was the prey she hunted after, his ready money made her fingers itch to be at it, and therefore she also gave herself out to be a rich heir, hoping that she should make a younger brother of this young lawyer. But she was mistaken. He was otherwise designed; he courted a lady who lodged not far from her lodgings, and she found by his often passing by her lodgings what his design was. She therefore, understanding that one of her strings had slipt, and that she could not draw him in as a suitor to her, she therefore consulted with some of her confederates and resolved on another course, which thus she effected. She now gave out that she was an heir to her late-deceased father, but that she had an husband who, being an extravagant, she did not live with him, and that her father had given all his estate to her, so as her husband might not enjoy it; but that her husband threatened and prosecuted her, and her chief business was to take such order in the settlement as her husband might not disturb her, and to this end she wanted counsel of lawyers to advise with.

This was her pretense, and this was laid to get in with the young lawyer, to whom she went and related this story. He gave her the hearing, and asked her several questions, which she well enough answered, but he told her that he could not satisfy her in all particulars unless he saw the writings. She was at a loss in this, but said she would get them and come again. So giving him 10 shillings for his fee, she left him. She made several errands to him, and still giving him money, she became familiar, and he entertained her in his bedchamber, where his beloved chest of money was, but she had no opportunity to come at it. She told him she should ere long have her writings, which she durst not keep in her lodging, lest her husband coming should seize on them, and thus she spent some time, till at last she saw there was no good to be done at his chamber, and therefore she intended to make her own lodging the scene of her undertaking.

All parties and things being therefore ready, she one day, seeing him go by, watched his return and then desired to speak with him. He, distrusting nothing, walked upstairs and was conducted into her bedchamber. A bottle of wine was brought, and she drank to him, causing him to sit down, and some discourse they entered upon about her pretended law affair. She enlarged upon the subject and spun away the time, till on a sudden her woman, who was below, came running up, crying, "O Lord, Madam, we are undone, for my master is coming." "What shall I do?" said our Counterfeit. "Why?" said the lawyer. "I mean for you," said she. "What excuse shall I make for your being here? I dare not tell him your quality and business, for that would endanger all, and on the other side he is jealous of his honour, too. Therefore, good sir," said she, "step into that closet, till I can send him away."

The lawyer, being surprised and not knowing what on such a sudden to do, did as she desired, and she, locking the closet and drawing the curtains of the bed, went to the chamber door to receive her counterfeit husband, who was no sooner entered the chamber, but having heard the noise of drawing the curtains, cries out, "How now, what means this? Have you been lazing on your bed and, be hanged, let me see if you have not a companion." When looking there, he sees the bed all tumbled and places as if two had been lying there. Wherefore he cries out, "Oh, you have a companion. Where is he? Let me see the rogue, that I may sacrifice him to my just anger. Ah, you whore, have I now caught you? Is this your retired modesty?" "Truly, husband," replied she, "you are mistaken. There is no such party here." "There is, you base woman," said he, "and I will find him to the shame and confusion of you both." And thereupon he, searching behind the hangings, found the closet door, which in fine he forced her to open, and there discovers the young lawyer, all pale and trembling.

At the first sight of him, out flew his sword, but the wife flew between them, and a companion of his seized his sword endeavouring to pacify him, but the more he endeavoured it, the more enraged he appeared so that at last his wife confessed that indeed she had abused him, but desired pardon for herself and friend, who seeing himself trepanned began to speak and tell the truth of the story and what his business was there. But he had been as good to have said nothing; all was to no purpose. There was sufficient testimony; the bed, the drawing of the curtains, his being hid, and above all her confession were sufficient to contradict all he could say. Therefore nothing would serve but blood or other sufficient reparation for his honour, which at last his friend propounded should be in money and named £500. This was a tall sum and frightened the lawyer, but he, considering the many inconveniences he was fallen into, was in the end brought to pay £100 down instantly, which he sent his man for, and then he was discharged from his imprisonment. Glad he was that he was gone, and they as glad that they were rid of him; but doubting some afterclap, and that the lawyer after second thoughts might return and trouble them, they therefore thought it necessary to change their quarters. Wherefore the pretended husband, continuing his huffing humour, would have his wife away with him, and so they instantly removed.

And now, Reader, let me tell thee that as our Counterfeit's father, the fiddler, did often in his lifetime strike up that merry and well-known tune called "The worst is past," so I on the contrary do assure you that the best of your sport and of my writing is past. I have little more of her adventures to relate, nothing but what is ordinary, except her two last adventures of the apothecary and watchmaker and some few silver tankards and beer-bowl adventures, and then I must conclude with her; but although the best of our writing is past, the worst of her adventures are to come, which I shall thus relate to you.

She had thus fortunately enough performed all the aforementioned projects: success had flushed her, and she finding with how much ease she gained money, she was as free in spending it. She knew she had the same tools, her wits, to work with, and so long as they lasted, she assured herself of a brave livelihood and therefore sought no other way, took no other course to live by; but her money being gone, she attempted to get more, and her ordinary course was this. She, pretending to be some country gentlewoman, would take a lodging, carry herself very demurely, keep good hours, and although she went abroad about her urgent affairs in the daytime, yet she still returned early at night, would hold any discourse with her landlady or landlord, and pry into the affairs of the house, and be sure to mind what plate was stirring; and if there were a silver tankard, that she would assure herself of, by pretending sickness in her head and stomach and desiring a posset which was commonly brought her in the silver tankard; some she would eat, and the rest must stand by for her breakfast the next morning. And thus would she become mistress of the tankard, which with herself would the next morning be invisible, for she would be sure to be up early and watch her opportunity to give her landlady the slip. Neither did the tankard alone serve the turn, but if there were any chest, trunk, or box in the room, she would break it open and rifle it of all that was considerable and worth her carriage. This was her trick for tankards; this was her usual common way to serve her landladies, and this she did so often in so many places that it is admirable she should escape. I can name at least half a score of these tankard-adventures in several places, and all performed much after one and the same manner, in Covent Garden, Milford Lane, Lothbury, New Market, and several other places; and for one of these adventures was she at last taken and indicted, found guilty, condemned, reprieved and banished to Jamaica, but before I let her pass from England I will relate another adventure of hers and a petty one, wherein she took much pains for little gains, to show you that she would play at small game rather than stand out and that she would not be daunted nor put by her undertaking, she could not endure to be baffled.

She came one evening into an alehouse near West Smithfield, being scarfed and masked, and pretending to be very cold, was admitted to the kitchen fire. She calls for a cup of ale and her landlady; one was brought, and the other came, desiring to know her pleasure. "Only," said she, "to have your company, for I cannot drink; I do not so much value that as your fire, being newly come to town, just now alighted out of the coach." "From what country, I pray?" said the landlady. From such a place in Essex, naming it, said our Counterfeit. "Oh, dear," said the landlady, "I know the parson of a parish close by!" naming it. "And so do I," said our Princess, "and he is a brave preacher; I love to hear him," and much more she and her landlady enlarged upon this subject, in all which discourse

she was very confident. And now she was not only acquainted with the landlady, but her daughter coming into
the kitchen, she enters into a dialogue with her, who being
at work upon a point lace, she looks on it and much commends it, telling her that she would come again suddenly
and show her work, and thus she invites herself into an acquaintance, and finding there was no good to be done at
present, she paid for her drink and departed, but came
again the next evening, and calls for more drink, and enters into a familiar discourse with the landlady. She en-
larging and sitting there a great while and being troublesome, the landlord takes her into examination what she
was. She replies a maiden gentlewoman which had a £1,000
to her portion in her own hands, and lived upon the
interest-money of it. "Who gave you that portion?" said
the landlord. "My father," said she, "who allows me to receive the interest-money of it, and truly what I do not
spend I bestow upon the poor and other charitable uses."
"Away, away," said mine host, "I cannot believe any man
to be so mad as to leave a £1,000 to your dispose. Neither
do I believe you to be such a person as you name yourself.
If you were, you would not sit tippling here at this time of
the night." The host, having given her this tart discourse,
left her; and so did she the house in short time after, but
was not in the least daunted, but made excuses for his
peevishness.

One would have thought that this would have beat her
off for coming hither any more, but it did not. Now she
was resolved not to lose her labour nor to leave things done
by the halves, and it may be she was resolved to be revenged of her host; for the next morning she comes again
early before the mistress or master was up, calls for a pot
of ale and a toast. The maid brings it her but pours it
out into a pewter pot. "Alas," said our Counterfeit, "what
do you do, maid? You know I cannot drink in pewter. I
hate it above all things, and I know you have plate enough
in the house; therefore fetch some, or else I cannot drink
one drop." "Truly," said the maid, "my master carries all

the plate up every night. He is not up yet, but if you please, I will go up and fetch a beaker." "Do so," said she. The wench went up and told her master and mistress that the gentlewoman was there below and wanted a silver cup to drink in. "She shall have none," said the man. "Why?" said his wife. "She is a cheat," said the man. "No," said the woman, "I cannot believe it, but to be more sure I will go down and watch her." And thereupon she leaps out of the bed and, with her clothes half on and half off, went down.

By this time the lady had dispatched her drink and was contriving how to secure the cup, but the landlady came and prevented her. Withal seeing that her drink was off, she went to take the cup out of her hands. She was unwilling to part from her cup, therefore said, "Nay, Madam, what do you mean? Now you are come down I will have the other pot of ale to drink with you." The landlady, being willing to take money, was content; her maid was stept out of an errand, and a neighbour's maid came for some drink; she therefore herself went into the cellar to draw for her guest and neighbour's maid, leaving them together in the kitchen. She was but just down in the cellar and was beginning to draw the ale when she heard one tread, and being jealous of her guest, ran up immediately to see if all were well, but she found that the bird was flown. She asked the maid where was the gentlewoman. "I know not," said the maid. "She stept to the door, as she said, to see what weather it was, and I saw her no more." "Good lack, my beaker," said the woman. "Where is it?" "I saw none," said the maid. They both looked for that and for our Counterfeit, but they were both invisible, neither to be seen nor heard of. And now her husband, being come down, understood the case and was very angry, but to no purpose. It was too late. They were both troubled the more because it was an ancient piece of plate worth about £3, but more or less, old or new; it was gone and no more to be heard of.

And now, Reader, I have no more projects to relate to you, for it was not long after this that she was taken and secured in Newgate for one of her tankard-adventures. She had used so many of them that she was at last caught. She had lived like a duck hunted by the spaniel, who had often forced her to dive and hide herself, but at last she must be taken and the sport at an end. She was indicted for stealing a silver tankard, was found guilty, and condemned to be hanged, but had the mercy of transportation, and was two days before Shrovetide, in the year 1670, sent on board a ship at Gravesend bound for Jamaica, so that from her banishment to her late death was under two years.

How she behaved herself, and what new projects she had in these two years, is the intent of my future discourse, which I shall briefly relate to you. There were about twenty other felons went with her the same voyage, who were put on board on Shrove Tuesday, 1670, two days after her. She, being a person of quality, had the liberty to go alone, and they followed, and all performed their voyage together. How she behaved herself in this voyage I know not but from her own relation which said that the other felons had a design of murdering the commander of the ship and some of the other officers, of seizing the ship and steering their course another way. The design was communicated to her, who seemed to approve of it, but soon after acquainted the commander therewith, who finding the danger he was in, hastened to the next port, and there furnishing himself with irons, caused all his felons to be sufficiently shackled & otherwise secured, and so they ended their voyage. And for this piece of good service to the captain, she was in much favour with him and the governor, where she had her freedom to dispose of herself.

She who had been so famous in England was well enough known there, and for the present was courted and treated by all, but this was not to last; there was no work for her to do. There was no thought of drawing in another Lord Carleton to marriage. No acting on the theatre. No young novice to cully and draw in. No old man to keep and maintain her, till she serve him a jade's trick, rob him, and run away from him. No suitor to persuade to entertain her in his lodgings, till she robbed and fled from him. No pretended burial to cheat for plate and a pall of velvet. No mercer's man to leave at one door of the Exchange, whilst she goes out at the other. No weaver nor lace-seller to cheat by wholesale. No tailor's house to lodge in, where she may get her clothes made, and march off without payment and with a further prize. No Exchange shop there to cheat of ribbons, hoods, scarfs, and other habiliments. No young lawyer to draw in, trepan, and hector out of £100 at once; and to conclude, Jamaica afforded her no several lodgings to cheat of tankards, nor alehouses to make beer-bowls and beakers in. There being none of this sort of trade to be dealt in at this place, she knew not what to do; she was out of her element, like a fish out of the water. In the time of this her exile, we had a letter from her, from Port Royal in Jamaica, to all her fellow sufferers in Newgate; wherein she, or the author that writ it, gives a drolling, romantic account of her voyage thither, arrival there, and several other fabulous fancies, which letter being first printed in the year 1671 and now again printed and added to a book of hers, called *The Memoires of Mary Carleton*,[24] and being known to be only a piece of romantic wit, I shall not recite it here, lest all the rest of my relation be suspected to be only my own invention; therefore I shall pass that by and proceed to matter of fact.

How long she continued there I know not, but she said, all the while she was there, she was sick and attended by two physicians. She still kept her state in all places, but the air of the climate not agreeing with the constitution of her body and, indeed, there being little for her to do, and her fate so ordering it that she was not to die there; she therefore takes shipping in order to her return. I remember that some persons of quality being at sea in a terrible tempest, it was the opinion and fear of most in the ship that they should suffer shipwreck and lose their lives, and accordingly prepared for death. When one gentleman among the rest cries out, "Fear not, friends. I dare warrant, you will escape this danger, and that we shall come safe to

land." "What reason have you to hope it?" said the rest.
"I am confidently sure of it," replied he, "for here are two
fellows of the ship's crew that will never be drowned, for
I am very sure they are born to be hanged; they have hanging countenances; every feature in their faces tells me that
they will be hanged. Now, therefore, if we have them in
our companies who are born to be hanged, what need we
fear to be drowned?" This was that gentleman's frolic. Now
if those who sailed with our German Princess had but
known of her fate, they needed not have feared drowning.
Whether they were in any danger on that account, I know
not, but she endangered her neck by her return. Whether
she first landed in Holland, and so from thence came
hither, I know not; neither is it much material. But hither
she did come and fell to her old trade, so that it was not
long before we heard of her. She had her old tools, her
wits, to work with, and besides that, she had not lost all
her time at Jamaica: she had gained some acquaintance
there who at her return sent letters by her to their friends
in London. These letters did her some kindnesses, for by
virtue of them she had some business. She was entertained
and treated by the friends here, for their sakes from whence
she came. You may be sure she told her tale plausibly
enough and pretended to be of quality, so that she was
admitted into their houses, where she served two or three
some of her tankard-tricks, seeing an opportunity, seized on
a piece of plate and marched off. To one she pretended she
had not yet received money for the goods she brought over
with her, desires his assistance, pretends a present occasion
for a small sum, which he lends, and then she gives him
the slip. Many of these petty cheats she puts upon her new
acquaintance, but at length, being resolved upon a better
game, she thus begins.

She takes lodgings somewhere about Westminster, and
knowing she can do little without help, she entertains an
old woman of her acquaintance to be her attendant, or assistant rather, in her new design. They both inquire if there
be any young rich novice thereabouts that she may cully-

draw into some considerable adventure, and upon inquiry they find that there is a young man, a shopkeeper, by trade an apothecary, who was rich and covetous; him they think to be a subject fit for them to work upon. Our Counterfeit Lady herself keeps close, but the old woman is sent on many an idle errand to the apothecary's shop. She wants pomatum, mithridate, diascordium, and several such well known medicines; he furnishes her with them, and she gets acquaintance with him, and watching her opportunity, she discourses with him of several matters. Among the rest, she asks him why he does not marry. He replies, "The times are hard, trading dead, and housekeeping chargeable." "That is true," said she; "but all this may be supplied by a good rich wife." "Yes," said he, "a good one and a rich one, too, were a brave thing worth the having, and I should gladly embrace such a fortune." "Such fortunes there are, and such a one I can help you to."

The young man, hearing the old woman's tale, was well pleased with the discourse, which they continued, and he urging her to know who and where she meant. He by degrees draws this intelligence from her that there is a young gentlewoman of her acquaintance, that is niece to a rich eminent citizen of London; that she hath £2,000 to her portion in her uncle's hands which must be paid at the day of marriage; that her uncle kept a very strict hand over her, not permitting her to go much abroad; but however that she sometimes gave her a visit, she having formerly been nurse in her father's house, and that she complained of her uncle's severity and was minded to alter her condition, and indeed willing to marry with a husband that would take her from her uncle's severe usage. The apothecary was marvelously well pleased with this old woman's story, believes it all, and being told the name of the citizen and his niece, he instantly goes into the city and makes inquiry of both. He finds that there is such a citizen, that hath such a niece, that hath such a portion, and the citizen is described to be such a person as the old woman had related, and indeed every particular was according to her re-

lation, so that he questioned not but that there was such a
gentlewoman that had such a fortune; and he hoped he
should have the good fortune to have her.

This made him very eager and earnest to see the old
woman, that he might know when he might see his intended mistress. The old one was not long absent from
his shop, but came and was soon taken on one side by the
apothecary, that he might ask some more questions, which
she answered cunningly enough, and thereupon he promises to give the old woman great matters, if she will bring
this match to pass. If she will help him to get the gentlewoman, she should have some of the old angels. "Well,"
said she, "I will have no hand in the match, unless you
can love one another. When you have seen her, if you can
like her, and when she hath seen you, if I can find by her
that she can love you, then I will tell you more of my
mind, then I will make my propositions." "Very honestly
said," replied the apothecary, "but when shall I see her?"
"I expect her daily," said the old woman, "and so soon as
she comes, I will bring you into her company."

Thus she said, and so she did, for our Counterfeit who
was to personate the citizen's niece was not far off, and
therefore the sooner to be procured, and was brought into
the apothecary's company. Their first interview was but
short, the lady pretending haste to return to her uncle's.
The apothecary courts her and desires her further acquaintance. She promises nothing, but passes some few indifferent compliments, and so they part. And now the old
woman hath somewhat to say. She goes to know the apothecary's mind, who was all on fire to proceed, and promiseth
her anything; she shall have her own terms, if she can but
bring this matter to pass. The old woman remains indifferent and says she desires nothing, if she does not effect his
desires; but if she doth, then she hopes he will remember
her. "Nay," said he, "that you may be upon sure terms, I
will instantly seal a bond of £100 to pay you £50 at the
day of marriage." The old woman is content and accepts
his offer, promising her utmost assistance and withal tell-

ing him that she hopes to manage it so, as it shall be done without much difficulty; for she tells him that she finds the lady had a good opinion of him, and then let her alone to increase it. Thus did these two make their bargain; neither was it long before the apothecary and the Counterfeit had agreed upon theirs, for after some several treats and meetings, he still pressing her to be married and telling her that he loves her, can, and will handsomely maintain her, and that he is not quite destitute of an estate, having some hundreds of pounds by him ready money, and a good profitable trade, & very well furnished, and withal that he was a good husband. "I but . . . ," said our lady, "I question not all this, but I doubt I shall still be in the same condition and be kept bare of money. My uncle hath money enough of mine in his hands, but he will spare me none, or very little. He will not let me have sufficient to buy me clothes and other things befitting my quality, and that makes me so unprovided at present, and he for to justify his niggardliness urges the same argument as you did, good husbandry; and you having commended your own good husbandry, I doubt I shall find you guilty of the same sparingness towards me, and that you will not afford me wherewithal to maintain me as I ought." The apothecary, hearing this discourse, and knowing to what it tended, and being resolved to please her in all things, that he might testify what he had said was true, that he was of a noble temper, he presently fetches 200 pieces of gold and, throwing them into her lap, says, "There, Madam, you may see that I do not belie myself in reporting of my estate. I give you this, and can show you much more; and that you may have a taste of my liberality and love towards you, I present you with this as a token of my love, and leave it to be wholly disposed of as you shall think fit."

Our Counterfeit, being well pleased, was resolved to please him and therefore replied, "Well, sir, I am very well satisfied of you, and am content to be ruled and ordered by you in all things." He, being overjoyed, pressed her to speedy marriage, which was consented to and performed

accordingly, and he bedded with her, and so she left him
for the present, ordering him in a few days to come to her
uncle's and demand her and her portion. This was good
advice, and the apothecary purposed to follow it; but now
our Counterfeit and her old woman, having performed
their project, they change their lodging to another end of
the town, leaving the apothecary to get his rich wife where
he can find her; they laugh at that which will ere long make
him cry. For at the time appointed he walks into London
and goes to the citizen's house, the pretended uncle of his
wife. He, believing he should have some falling out, resolves to bear the first brunt with much bravery; and therefore coming to the speech of the old man, he peremptorily
tells him that he comes to demand his wife. "I know not
what or who you mean," replied the citizen. "I mean," said
the apothecary, "your niece, Mrs. ——, who is my lawful
wife, for I have been married to her and bedded with her
some days since." "I cannot believe it," said the citizen. "I
doubt you are mistaken, for my niece hath not been abroad
in that time, and therefore this is some idle story." "It is
very true," replied the apothecary, "and I do demand her
of you and, with her, £2,000 which you have of hers in your
hands as a portion." "I do not deny that," replied the citizen, "but I doubt I shall keep it out of your hands." "But
I hope," said the apothecary, "you will not deny me my
wife, and then as for the money I shall find a way to take
course for it." "I will give you the satisfaction of showing
you my niece," said the citizen, "but I hope she is no wife
of yours," and thereupon the old man went in and called
his niece, telling her that she must come to her husband.

The young gentlewoman was at a loss and wondered at
her uncle's discourse, who tells her again seriously, she must
go to her husband. She replies she knows not what he
means; and the old man, telling her the absolute demand
of the apothecary, charges her with it. She denies it, as well
she may, and is unwilling to go and see this bold pretended
husband of hers, but at length her uncle leads her out to
him saying, "Well, sir, here is my niece. What have you

to say to her?" Our apothecary, seeing the maiden and doubting that they did put tricks upon him, tells them that they are deceived in him, to think to serve him so. He knows his wife well enough, that this is not she, but that she is in the house, and he will have her. The old man, now believing that the apothecary is either a madman or a deceived man, tells him that he believes somebody else had cheated him and put this trick upon him and not he, for he had no other kinswoman but that here present. The apothecary, doubting somewhat of the matter, told the whole tale to the citizen, who now fully concluded he had been cheated. He only pitied him and advised him to go home and make some further inquiry. He did so, but to little purpose. The old and young were both gone and left him to a fruitless repentance.

This is the story of the apothecary so well known and talked of. But although the story is related generally in this manner and is written thus by others, yet I have been told, and by those, too, that pretend acquaintance with the apothecary, that it was not just in this very manner, but that our Counterfeit Lady acted the same part as the old woman did in this relation and that she procured another baggage of her acquaintance to represent the citizen's niece, that this was acted at our Counterfeit's lodgings, and that she had the bond of £100 to pay £50, though I suppose the bond was never paid to either. And that our Counterfeit, being fearful of making any more marriages with herself, procured one of her acquaintance to act that part, who deceived the apothecary, for instead of a young virtuous virgin to his bride, he had a rotten jade to his bedfellow that since hath cost him some physic in his own cure of that disease which is commonly gotten by such kind of bedfellows. But whether it was thus or as is afore-related, matters not much, but in general cheated he was of his money and his expectations of a rich wife, and that by the contrivance of our Counterfeit Lady, who now rants it among her companions as long as this money lasteth, not questioning but to get more by the same means as formerly;

and she would often bolt out of old quarters, seek and find a new one, where she would be sure to march off with a silver tankard or some such purchase. Many of these she thus purchased, but still using the same way.

I omit the relation and come to her last trick, and so shall conclude. The scene still lies westward, and near Charing Cross was the particular place where she takes her lodgings for herself and a pretended maidservant. She understood the quality of her landlady and the other lodgers in the house, but principally of a watchmaker who not only lodged abovestairs but had a shop below. She quickly acquaints herself with him and her landlady and, being earnest in her business, makes haste to put it in execution. Therefore, three or four days after her arrival there, she invites the watchmaker, who was a bachelor, and her landlady to go see a play at the Duke's Theatre. She tells them it is recommended to her for an excellent play, and that she desired their companies and would pay for them. They accepted her offer, and taking a coach, together they went.

Whilst the actors were employed in acting there, her agents were as busy at home at her lodging; for a gentlewoman came to inquire for her, whom her maid tells that her mistress is not at home but will return ere long, and that if she please she may stay in her chamber and rest herself the whilst. She took her counsel and was conducted upstairs to the chamber and left there. The maid comes down, and the landlady's maid asked her how she durst trust anybody in her mistress's chamber alone. She replies it is her mistress's sister, but she lies, for it was as errant a baggage as her mistress; they might be sisters in iniquity and quality, indeed, though they were not by consanguinity. For this woman's name was Herne or Keeling; by both these names and indeed several others she goes by, but these are the most usual. While she is employed abovestairs, our Counterfeit Lady's maid entertains the landlady's maid belowstairs with a bottle of wine. They were merry while the other breaks open a chamber-door and a trunk, from whence she takes above £200 ready money in

gold and silver, and about thirty very rich watches, so that
the prize was in all valued at about £600. She, being possessed of this, comes downstairs and tells the maid she can
stay no longer for her mistress, but would return another
time, and so she departed.

The play was by this time done, and our Counterfeit desires her friends to go to the Green Dragon Tavern in Fleet
Street, where a bottle of wine being called for, she pretends
an excuse to step aside, and so downstairs she goes and
hastens to her lodging. Her servant tells her all is done,
and then she knowing it was time for her to be gone, away
went she and her maid, and were no more seen in those
quarters. And the watchmaker and his landlady, distrusting
somewhat by her sudden departure, after half an hour's
stay, went home after her, but they came too late. All was
done and gone, and he found out his loss to be as considerable as I have related it. The news of this loss was
soon spread abroad. Neither was it long before it was well
enough known that our German Princess was the principal
actress. She was known, but it was too late, and not to be
met withal at present. This purchase was so considerable as
one would think that she might leave off. Whether she did
or intended it, I know not, but it was not long after, before
she was taken.

The pitcher had not gone so often to the water but it was
to come broken home at last. Search had been made for
her in several places, but she was far enough off out of the
way. She left the west; though it had been lucky, yet it was
at last fatal to her; and now she settled southward. She
crossed the river of Thames, and takes lodgings in St.
George's Fields in Southwark, where she for some time was
as safe as a thief in a mill, but her appointed time was
drawing nigh; her glass had but few more sands to run.
And I do not hear of any more projects that she acted; this
of the watchmaker was the last, especially of any remark.
As the world had been several years troubled with this
subtle female thief, so we also had men of the same good

qualities: for one Mr. Freeman, a brewer in Southwark, was robbed of goods to the value of £200, and one Lancaster, a notorious felon, was suspected. Alderman Freeman, being desirous to meet with his goods again or at least with the thief, employs one Fisher, bailiff of the hundred there, to seek after him. He, being promised good payment, makes diligent inquiry in all suspected places. Among other places, he comes to the house where our Counterfeit Lady was. He sees two or three fellows belowstairs who, upon inquiry what lodgers were in the house, sneaked away. The landlady said there was none, but Fisher seeing these fellows gone and hoping to find more above, he, without any leave or more questioning, runs up two pair of stairs where he finds our Counterfeit Lady walking in a nightgown. He knew her not, but being curious and suspicious of everything, and seeing some letters lie on the table, he had the curiosity to cast his eye upon one which was directed to one Mr. Hyde. He takes it up, and our Lady, seeing him, endeavours to get it from him; but he thereby growing more suspicious, and knowing there was one of that name prisoner in the Marshalsea, and hoping to get some light into his present business, as believing this Hyde might be concerned in the late robbery, he therefore opens the letter and reads it. Although it contained nothing of that concern, yet he thought [it] good to let Mr. Lowman, the keeper of the Marshalsea, know of it; and he, being not far off upon the same inquiry, was presently sent for. When he came he knew not his old acquaintance, the German Princess; for he was turnkey of Newgate when she was prisoner about her marriage with Carleton, although he knew her then well enough. Yet at the first sight he knew her not, but upon some little discourse he knew her, and told her she must go along with him. This was ill news to her, but he would be obeyed, though he had no warrant nor, as he said, no thoughts of her at present; but he had heard of her late practices, and believed he should do good service to the public in apprehending and securing of her. Therefore away she is forced to go along with him and was lodged in the Marshalsea. The news of her apprehending was soon spread abroad, and a great resort was daily made to her, some out of curiosity to see her, others who had been cheated by her, to see if they could get any satisfaction; but she was too cunning to confess anything that might turn to her damage, and if any such question were asked, she would tell them that she was not in humour at present to talk of any such matters, and would be sure to deny knowledge of any person that so charged her. But however, charged she was and examined before a justice, upon the watchmaker's account, on the 17th of December last; but she continued a prisoner in the Marshalsea till the 16th of January, when by writ of habeas corpus she was removed to Newgate to take her trial at the Sessions House in the Old Bailey. During her imprisonment at the Marshalsea, she behaved herself very briskly and as if she had been innocent and unconcerned. No thoughts of death possessed her, and she was in great hopes of her life; for pretending to discover somewhat considerable, she went abroad with her keeper to the judges, but I do not hear of any discovery she made. She promised much, but performed nothing, only played with her business. Had she been true to justice in her discovery, it is possible the justice might have spared her that never spared anybody whom she could cheat, so that now she cheated herself of her life, as she had cheated others of their goods, for which facts she was on the said 16th of January brought before the court at the Old Bailey.

The judge asked her if she were the same woman that commonly went by the name of Mary Carleton and was not long since transported. She replied, "I am the same person." She was then asked the reason of her so sudden and speedy return. She replied she had something to discover that troubled her conscience; she was desired to declare what it was. To this she answered, "It is not convenient to unveil my thoughts about this concern in so public a place, and therefore I humbly desire further time till the next morning," which was granted her.

The next day she was again brought to her trial where she was arraigned and indicted for stealing a piece of plate from one in Chancery Lane, of which fact she was found guilty by the jury. She had now but one shift more and that was an old Newgate trick, to plead her belly, that she was with child; whereupon a jury of women was found out and sworn, who after an hour's private debate brought in this verdict, "that she was not quick with child"; and thereupon sentence of death, according to law, was passed upon her, and [she] was presently sent back to Newgate to prepare herself for the other world. And now after this sentence she was quite altered; she was of another note; she had not been so frolic and merry before, but now she was as melancholy and sad. She had the day before answered all questions in a drolling merry way, and now she can say nothing for sighing. When she was the day before at the Sessions House, some gentlewomen discoursed with her, and one told her that she wondered that a person so rarely qualified and gifted should be guilty of such poor beggarly shifting tricks as stealing anything that came to her hand. She readily replied, "Ladies, your failings consist in 'falling,' and mine in 'filching'; yet if you will be so charitable to forgive me, I will freely forgive you."

On Thursday night after she was in her lodging in Newgate, several persons visited her there; one told her that she must think of death. "Yes," said she, "that is no hard matter. I am very well satisfied in my condition." "You have good friends," said he. "Yes," said she, "one good friend here," laying her hand on her belly and meaning a child there, but said one, "You have not seen your husband a great while. How then will the court believe you to be with child?" "Good lack," replied she, "is it such a matter to be with child, because I have not seen my husband?" These were her replies, and in this manner she answered all her visitants, and when some who were appointed by the court came to her from the bench to know what great matter she had upon her conscience to relate, she could say nothing to them but trifled, telling them the story how she preserved the captain at her going to Jamaica, as you have already heard, and pretending that she had other treasons, but all was but to trifle away the time in hopes of a reprieve.

There were several visitants with her of both sexes, and among the rest I myself went on the Saturday night, but then she was in her melancholy mood. She was sending to the Marshalsea for some things she had left there, and for want of which she had not been in a naked bed those two nights since she had been in Newgate. She complained of some hard usage, and that people were so numerous and troublesome in their visits that they would not give her time to repent, but would have her to die with all her sins. She then said that it was a great thing to die, a harder matter than she had thought it. There [were] two women with her, one of which was a witty baggage. For she made a speech which tickled the ears of all that were present, talking of the frailness of human nature, and that these crimes, which men would slip through and make nothing of, were accounted highly criminal with women; but before the great tribunal in heaven, men and women should then have equal justice, adding that it was an unworthy action in men to come only to behold that poor soul there as a wonder, when indeed she was more like a looking glass. "Yes, indeed," replied the prisoner. "I am very like a looking glass wherein you may all see your own frailties." The other woman added more to her discourse, that she was a stranger and had seen the prisoner but once before, and that it cost her 2 shillings her admittance. So after some little stay, she took leave of the prisoner and departed.

I observed that there were two very near her, who spake in French to her, who I then believed and since have had farther information that they were Roman Catholics. They had several private dialogues with the prisoner and then also went away. When another friend in my company discoursed her, telling her of death here and Judgment hereafter, and advising her not to believe any Roman Catholics, and that none was able to save her but Jesus Christ the righteous, who had suffered for sinners, and that the merits of all others would little avail her, she seemed to be very well satisfied in what was said to her. And I, being near her, told her it was a great work she had to do and that yet she had time to repent of all her ill deeds to a merciful God, who refused none that came with a true repenting heart. She replied, "The Lord grant me true repentance." And some other discourse we had suitable to the condition she was in, which she seemed to be very well satisfied in; and truly I believe she was truly sorrowful, for she was heard to sigh very often and cry out, "Oh that I had my days to live over again, but I do not desire it." Yet did she seem very desirous to live and troubled that the women who were of her jury did not favour her as they might, and then she might have had more time. She was like a piece of wax fit to receive any impression, and God knows whether the sparing of her life might not have been to her prejudice, since I believe she thus prepared herself for her change, and it is thought and hoped that she was truly fitted. She continued in this frame of spirit to the very last, spending all the daytime in discoursing about her present condition, and most of the nighttime in prayers. She was not lodged as other condemned prisoners are, in the dungeon, but in a fair room abovestairs, although strictly guarded. Indeed the profit paid for the charge well enough, for great was the concourse of her visitants, and many gave money for their admittance.

Many reports have gone of her that she was very frolicsome during her imprisonment. I was told that while she was at the Marshalsea, two or three gentlemen came out of curiosity to see her and prevailed so far with her keeper as to go forth with her to a tavern, and that she as soon as she entered, told the master of the tavern that she would have him send so many dozen bottles of wine and such a quantity of neats' tongues and other junkets to her fellow prisoners, and that he should be paid before she went out of the house; that her orders were obeyed and she was treated by the gentlemen in a very handsome manner, asking her several questions which she pleasantly answered; that a reckoning being at last called for, it was answered £30. "How so?" said the gentlemen. "We have not had above 30 shillings here, and that we are willing to pay." "But, gentlemen," said she, "I hope you will pay for me, too, and I did bespeak as much as you hear of and sent it to my fellow prisoners that they might be the better for me, & gentlemen," continued she, "you came purposely to see me, and to hear of some of my tricks, and now I have showed you. Therefore without more questioning you must pay the reckoning."

This is a story that I have heard of her, as done at the Marshalsea, and that she acted it over again at Newgate, but I cannot believe it and am confident no such thing was done at Newgate; she was not in so merry a mood; for after her trial, to her sentence, she was another creature. I am sure she was much dejected and very humble when I was with her. I believe she had no wild, wanton thoughts. She was as clouded in her spirit, as she was in her face, for her hood was still over it down to her mouth, and she very rarely turned it up; and her speech was very low and faint, broken and interrupted with deep and often sighing; and she was in a manner constantly attended by one of these Romish priests on one side of her, and her sister on the other.

Thus did she continue till the day of her execution, which was Wednesday, the 22nd of January, and then she seemed to be much altered, for she was very cheerful and pleasant in her countenance and appeared to be so in her mind; for she did not sigh so often as before, and her speech was less interrupted. She seemed to be not only very willing, but also very desirous to die, saying she had no hopes nor thoughts of a reprieve, and that she was truly willing to leave this world wherein she had found nothing but misery, to go to the other where she hoped to find mercy. At the hearing of the passing bell, she showed signs of joy, crying out, "Lord Jesus, I come to thee. Help me, Lord, in my extremity, and do thou overcome nature for me. Thou that hast overcome sin and death for me, assist me against nature that does cling to me and is unwilling to leave me."

I told you in the beginning of this treatise that she was born on the 22nd of January, but it was *stilo novo*, so that she was born on the 11th day, but it was on the 22nd day that she was baptized. Whereupon she made a considerable remark, saying, "This day was I baptized, and before night I expect to be sprinkled with the blood of the Lamb, which will be a second baptism." Some time before her going to execution, the priest, her ghostly friend, left her, but she first gave him a testimony of her religion by lifting up her hands and crossing herself, and did not deny to those that asked her that she was a Roman Catholic. At her friend's departure, she said to him in French, "My friend, the good God bless you," and so they parted. She gave order to her sister and a kinsman about her burial, giving them money, and they lamenting her sad and deplorable condition; she desired them to rest satisfied and content, as she herself did, entreating them not to continue their grieving which was great trouble to her.

And now her time being almost come, the master of the prison ordered her irons to be taken off, which had been put on but on Monday night before, for what cause I know not, and being ready to go, took out her husband Carleton's picture, saying, "This picture hath been my companion in all my afflictions and miseries, and I desire it may be buried with me," giving it to her sister; but soon after she took it again, and pinned it on to her left side, and wore it so to Tyburn. She was now led out of her lodging into the Common Hall to have the halter tied about her, which was done, and there she met with five young men who for several facts were to suffer with her. She was the eldest of the six, for the other five could not make 120 years. They were all much of her temper and humour, and indeed more unconcerned and insensible of their condition, for they went into their several carts as if they had only been going to return again; but she employed all the time of her being in the cart in meditations and reading in two popish books which she had in her hands, one entitled *The Key of Paradise* and the other *The Manual of Daily Devotion*, which books when she came to the gallows she delivered to a friend in the cart. By the way as she went in St. Giles Street the cart stopped, and she had a pint of canary, one glass full of which she drank off, delivering the rest to one in the cart. Soon after her arrival at Tyburn she was lifted out of the cart into another, where all the rest of the prisoners were, and there she was tied up, and then she took her husband's picture and put it into her bosom. Then the sub-ordinary [assistant to the ordinary—the prison clergyman] coming into the cart to them, asked them all twice if they had anything to say before they departed this world. No answer being made, he began his prayers; which being ended, another person also desired to pray with them. This was granted, and when he had finished his prayer, Mary Carleton desired the liberty to speak to the people, and being permitted so to do, she thus began. "You will make me a precedent for sin. I confess I have been a vain woman. I have had in the world the height of glory, and misery in abundance, and let all people have a care of ill company. I have been condemned by the world, and I have much to answer for. I pray God forgive me and my husband. I beseech God lay nothing to his charge for my fault."

A gentleman, hearing her speak of her husband, asked her if she desired anything to him. "Only" (said she) "my recommendations, and that he will serve God and repent, for I fear he wants sober counsel, and I beseech God lay nothing to his charge upon my account." "You are in perfect charity with him?" said one. "Yes," said she, "and with all the world." And thus the cart being ready to be drawn away, she began and continued in pious ejaculations, saying, "Lord Jesus receive my soul. Lord have mercy upon me. Christ have mercy upon me," and thus she continued till the cart was gone and she ended her life. After she had hanged about an hour, she was cut down, and her friends having paid all due fees for her body and clothes, they put her into a coach which carried her to her coffin not far off, and being put into that, she was the next day buried in St. Martin's churchyard.

Thus have I brought this unlucky woman from her birth to her burial. As she was born obscurely and lived viciously, so she died ignominiously. Such crimes as she was guilty of deserve such end and punishment as was inflicted on her, and without repentance and amendment, infallibly find them here and worse hereafter. The only way, therefore, for Christians to avoid the one and contemn the other is with sanctified hearts and unpolluted hands still to pray to God for his grace, continually to affect prayer and incessantly to practice piety in our thoughts and godliness in our resolutions and actions; the which if we be careful and conscionable to perform, God will then shroud us under the wings of his favour, and so preserve and protect us with his mercy and providence as we shall have no cause to fear either Hell or Satan. But if we give ourselves over to ill company or our own wicked inclinations, we are infallibly led to the practice of those crimes which, although they may be pleasing at the present, yet they have a sting behind, and we shall be sensible thereof when we shall be hurried to an untimely end, as you have seen in the vicious life and untimely death of this our Counterfeit Lady.

FINIS.

THE TRIUMPH OF TRUTH
(1664)

Anonymous

FOREWORD

As in the case of the German Princess, the Colonel James Turner affair follows a threefold pattern: the crime, the journalistic pamphlets, and the fictionized criminal biography. Whereas the pattern is intricate in *The Counterfeit Lady Unveiled*, it is relatively simple in *The Triumph of Truth*.

The crime was a London sensation. Four men, working according to a prearranged schedule and possessing inside knowledge, burglarized the home of the wealthy merchant Mr. Francis Tryon, late on a Thursday evening, January 7, 1664. The chief suspect, at the outset, was the victim's trusted friend Colonel Turner, solicitor and man-about-town.

Londoners reacted immediately to the crime. The Exchange hummed with "great talk" about the valuable jewels and ten hundred and fifty pounds that had been stolen. Pepys was personally convinced that the Colonel was guilty: "a mad, swearing, confident fellow, well known by all, and by me." The excitement was heightened during the three-day trial by the culprit's bravado, his erratic but ingenious defense, and especially his tiresome "romantic"

stories. However, after he was sentenced and was waiting
in vain for His Majesty's mercy, the doomed Colonel turned
public sentiment in his favor. Even the hostile Pepys,
among the twelve thousand spectators at the gallows, declared, "A comely-looked man he was, and kept his countenance to the end: I was sorry to see him."

The crime had all the elements of a shrewd plot, violence, and human interest to make the next phases of the
pattern inevitable. Shortly after his execution on January
21st, the hawkers were selling the news reports: *The
Speech and Deportment of Col. James Turner* and *A True
and Impartial Account of the Arraignment, Trial, Examination, Confession and Condemnation of Col. James Turner.*
Without much delay, there quickly appeared the full-
blown criminal biography, *The Triumph of Truth.* That all
three pamphlets were published speedily in this order is
attested by the advertisement on the last page of *The
Speech and Deportment.* Here, *The True and Impartial Account* is described as already licensed, but *The Triumph of
Truth* is only "now in the press ready to be published." The
pamphlets, moreover, were the handiwork of the same two
publishers, Nathaniel Brook and Henry Marsh—names that
one also notices in the imprints of the Mary Carleton narratives. Two other pieces dealt with Colonel Turner's crime:
a third news report, mentioned by the bibliographer W.
Carew Hazlitt, and a second criminal biography, *The Life
and Death of James, Commonly Called Colonel Turner*
(1664).

What makes *The Triumph of Truth* worth reading today
is its fairly persistent effort to interpret the central character. The narrator poses as an investigator who pursues
the "verities." He aims to see his subject as a man and not
as a monster; he deprecates those who observe "Machiavel's
rule, to throw dirt enough upon him, for that some would
stick"; he very emphatically labels the misdemeanours that
are "conjectural," as distinct from those that are "real." Like
Bunyan in *Mr. Badman,* he must discredit the report that

his criminal was "the head of all the highwaymen in England." Despite this alleged aim of truth-seeking, the author of *The Triumph* utilizes a technique of conscious fictionizing that is similar to Kirkman's in *The Counterfeit Lady Unveiled*. He creates his central character—as a schoolboy and as an apprentice—in the image of the picaresque rogue. And he does this in the face of totally different information available to him from the trial and from the news reports. In revamping Turner's pre-Civil War career, the "intimate friend" of *The Triumph* tries to unify the character of his rogue by providing him with "a bloody morning" to foretell "a dismal afternoon."

As a Royalist in the "uncivil Civil War," the Colonel continues to behave like an anti-hero. He develops now the macabre humour of the typical picaresque villain. Nicknamed the Plunderer of the North, he displays a cavalier's courage only during profitable raids. War to the Colonel is an outlet for his restless ambition to win "high estate" and escape the restrictions of a middle-class trade. After the war, he longs for the old comradeship. Like a seventeenth-century Robin Hood, he is "very charitable to poor distressed Cavaliers." He pays for the lawsuits of poor men out of his own pocket, in order thereby to lure clients "amongst the great ones." Cavaliers like the Colonel also pose a real threat to society. As Pepys's Puritan friend pungently remarks in the *Diary* (November 9, 1663), "the others [Cavaliers] go with their belts and swords, swearing, and cursing, and stealing; running into people's houses, by force oftentimes, to carry away something . . . and concludes . . . that the spirits of the old parliament soldiers are so quiet and contented with God's providences, that the King is safer from any evil meant him by them one thousand times more than from his own discontented Cavalier." In Chapter 7 of *The Triumph*, the Colonel is especially discontent. His bitterness is perhaps best reflected in *The Speech and Deportment*, where he tells how distraught he is "to see all manner of business in tumults and disorders, and sin, and all manner of wickedness." He then continues, "When I was a boy, there were no such doings. My father, I told you, was a minister. There were eight or ten gentlemen, adjoining families, who kept a house of hospitality, loving friendship, peace and quietness; but now there is no such thing in the world. It is a new world, a world of malice and difference." To the modern reader, the Colonel is a not unfamiliar type—the veteran dislocated by war who cannot adjust to a brave new world.

The Triumph of Truth should attract the modern reader by its description of the criminal's progress from trial to execution. In spite of tedious moralizing, the piece does rise to dramatic moments like the Colonel's protest against "the Hole of Newgate." The procession, the confession from the cart, the grim joking with the hangman—these were once realities. The Hanging Match used to be the favorite amusement of a race "that had not yet learned," as G. M. Trevelyan once wrote, "to dislike the sight of pain inflicted." *The Triumph of Truth* has even greater interest as a crude and perhaps accidental venture into fiction to depict the criminal as a product of vast social change.

ABOUT TURNER: *A Complete Collection of State Trials,* comp. by T. B. Howell, 1816, Vol. VI; *The Complete Newgate Calendar,* ed. J. L. Rayner and G. T. Crook, The Navarre Society, Ltd., 1926, Vol. I; James Granger, *A Biographical History of England,* 3rd ed., 1779, Vol. IV; "Colonel Turner Tells His Own Story," in *The Oxford Book of English Talk,* ed. James Sutherland, Clarendon Press, 1953.

THE TRIUMPH OF TRUTH: *in an Exact and Impartial Relation of the Life and Conversation of Colonel James Turner, Which He Imparted to an Intimate Friend, a Little Before His Execution*

Chapter I

The Birth and Breeding of Col. James Turner, His Marriage, and First Taking Up of Arms

As the memory of good men ought not to be buried in silence, but that men by reading their heroic actions may be stirred up to an emulation of virtue, so the remembrance of the wicked should not be forgotten, that men by reading the punishments of vicious livers might be deterred from the committing of lewd actions. And herein examples work more with the people than precepts, especially when men eminently known come to be examples of justice. For the terrors of punishment work more with many to deter them from vice than the promise of reward doth excite others to the pursuit of virtue. To this end is the life of this person set forth, that others by his extravagancies and the evil effects attending thereon may learn sobriety and to live a regular and well-ordered life. In the pursuit of our intended design, we shall avoid all unnecessary impertinencies and, with as much brevity as may be, declare to the world what are known to be verities concerning the whole progress of his life and conversation; and herein we are resolved to steer an even course, neither swerving to the one hand nor the other, for favour or envy, that so avoiding this Scylla and Charybdis our relation of him may find free acceptance with all people.

James Turner (commonly called or known by the name of Capt. or Col. Turner) was born about the year of our redemption 1608. He was the son of a reverend divine, minister of Hadley in Middlesex, not far from Barnet, of which he was parson above forty years, being a divine of the primitive stamp and temper that expressed his faith by his works, a friend to the poor, a mediator in any differences among the rich, eyes to the blind, and feet to the lame, in short (according to his ability) none more forward in good works than he. This his son, James Turner, he brought up to school for the attainment of some sufficiency in learning, where he first began to show his pranks, which were so unhandsome that his very schoolfellows took such a dislike of him that as much as in them lay they shunned his company.

Afterwards, for his future fortune, he bound him an apprentice to a seamster (or one that sells linen clothes ready made) at the lower end of Cheapside, near the Mitre Tavern, which time he served, though with much regret to his neighbours who likewise by reason of his unlucky actions had ever an evil opinion of him.

For to relate the mad figgaries[1] he had during his apprenticeship would of themselves make up a sufficient volume: no unhappy action done, wherein he had not a hand, if he were not a principal; yet was he always so cunning to carry on his business that his extravagancies were by his master rather deemed youthful excursions or harmless figgaries than any innate mischief or wilful acting of what was bad, though others of his neighbours had a contrary opinion, and by a bloody morning did foretell a dismal afternoon.

His time being out, he married a gentleman's daughter of Shasten in Dorsetshire, one of the Foyles, a family of good account in that country. Afterwards; he set up for himself in the Round Court in St. Martin's-le-Grand near the Shoemakers, which trade he continued for some short time. But the small profit redounding from a private shop was not correspondently agreeing with those high chimeras his vast imaginations had prompted unto him; and his ambition soaring a higher pitch, he resolved to throw his chance in Fortune's lottery. The times then suited well to his purpose, being those fatal days wherein the nation was engaged in an 'uncivil Civil War; and first (as nearest) he sought to ingratiate himself into the Parliament's side, endeavouring an advancement under them, and was very active to promote his own interest, thinking by taking up arms to have brought him to have wound himself out of many troubles which his litigious nature and vexatious spirit had brought him to. But a turbulent person hath many enemies, who prevailed so far that he was in danger to have been taken by the officers and sergeants-at-arms, so that he was forced to make a virtue of necessity and, abandoning London for the amendment of his fortunes, to turn Royalist.

Chapter II

His Actions in the Army, with Some Mad Frolics Which He Committed

His first appearance in the King's army was very low, accompanied only with three or four companions. But being a Londoner, he was the more welcome; and having gotten a commission, he made use of his wits to raise a troop, commanding many of the countrymen who lived in the villages to ride with him to Newcastle, which they were persuaded into upon promise they should not stay above three or four days. Whereupon getting ammunition for a whole troop, he became a captain under the Marquess of Newcastle. In this military condition he continued four years, during which space of time we cannot greatly applaud his manhood, for we hear of no wonders performed by him. Nor was his courage so great, but that (I conceive) the Iliads of his valour might be comprised in a nutshell. His chiefest valour consisted in plundering, for which he was called "the Plunderer of the North." In this action being very busy one day in a town in the North, a party of Parliament soldiers came in. He was so busy at his work that had not one cried to him, "Col. Turner, Col. Turner," he had been taken, so that for his refuge, he was forced to run, and that with all the speed he could. Yet did he receive one shot in the neck, which was all the wounds he could ever boast of.

One thing very remarkable is commonly reported of him, namely, that during his command, he sent a warrant to a constable to provide quarters for him and his men and, over and above, for himself in particular, a handsome lass. The constable was willing to obey him in the one, but having not such a command as Mr. Turner, could not tell how to satisfy him in the other. Whereupon he was threatened to be hanged, and being of a foolish temerity, to avoid what was afterwards the destiny of the Captain, he permitted him the enjoyment of his own wife, whom he [Turner] kept three or four days; but afterwards (as being contrary to the rules of war) he was called to an accompt for it, when to justify himself he sent for the constable's wife, whom he belike had so pleased that she cleared him of any incivility to her, before the Council of War.

> *Thus Women (if they list) can hide men's crime,*
> *And none shall e'er be hanged before their time.*

But one exploit he used much to boast of, which we will relate, leaving the reader to believe as he pleases, namely, that he being with a party of men gathering of contribution near to Newbury, he was set upon by a party of the enemy's horse of far greater number than they were. But according to his order, making fast their bags to the bows of their saddles (which proved a defence to their belly and groins), he gave them a desperate charge and very manfully hacked their way out quite through the enemy, both men and money coming safely off to Wallingford Castle.

> *Thus some can boast, although they make a lie on't:*
> *For evermore the knight must beat the giant.*

It is likewise reported that in a skirmish betwixt some small parties near Stevenage in Bedfordshire, he was beaten and taken prisoner. For his ransom he gave a ring with a stone in it, which he said was worth £100, but the victor afterwards found it worth no more than 5 shillings. But this rodomontade humour was not so much to be blamed in him, it being for his liberty.

During this War he had plundered and laid up much money for his future occasions, whereas the other Royalists, instead of getting, lost almost all they had. Here we may commend his providence, though we must condemn his conscience, in plundering for his private gain his own countrypeople.

The War now being expired, he with several other gentlemen, for some facts they had committed, were kept prisoners at York. Their crimes were some misdemeanours during the War. All the gentlemen saving only Turner pleaded Not Guilty, but he (whose indictments were said to be no less than sixty-five, he himself telling the judge that if he stayed one hour longer there would be no less than ninety-nine) pleaded Guilty and, the day of his trial, had as many dishes of meat as there were indictments against him, all carried up in sight of the court, and withal laid a wager of £5 he should be hanged that assizes. Being demanded his reason therefore, he said, if he lived he did not value the £5, and if he died it would serve to buy gloves and ribbons for his friends; which frolic together with his plea to the jury, viz., whether they would not have done the same if they had been under the like command, brought him off clear without the least fine or damage, whereas the other gentlemen, who pleaded Not Guilty and stood to the defence of their cause by disproof of witnesses, &c., were by the jury found guilty and lost their lives.

Chapter III

Turner's Returning to London, His Ways to Enrich Himself, and of the Great Port He Lived In

Soon after this, he returned again to London, and knowing it in vain to strive against the stream, he resolved for his profit to have a seeming compliance with the adverse party, sitting amongst the Committees of Goldsmiths and Haberdashers Hall, upon Compositions for Delinquents'

Estates;[2] but those foxes were too cunning to be deceived, and the place of such great profit as it was coveted after by some of their own gang, and he being known to have been one of the other side, he was forced to abandon that employment quite.

Thus did he run divisions like a dog in a halter, for his active spirit would never be at rest, well knowing that idleness is the mother of poverty; and having gotten some small store of money formerly in the army, he spared for no cost either of clothes or otherwise to bear a port equal to the best; and having thereby screwed himself into the acquaintance of some men of good account, he pretended to a great perfection of skill in all affairs. And first he began to manage poor men's causes whose charges he disbursed out of his own pocket, which won him very high commendations and was very acceptable to injured people, who very much applauded him for it.

This brought him into more employment amongst the great ones so that what betwixt broking and soliciting he grew very famous and withal got store of money, for the condition of some people is so given to contention that they will do no right nor suffer any wrong; and where such seeds of division are sown, there the lawyers reap golden harvests, so that now he flaunts it with the bravest. Taverns and ordinaries are daily frequented, rich and costly garments provided, high-prized jewels daily worn, not a dinner could be made under seven or eight several dishes of meat, not the least journey gone without a coach. Yea, nothing wanted which might conduce to an outward happiness. And that he might be the more taken notice of, he kept a high-prized gelding with which he ambled up and down the city, and was so bold that upon the King's most happy restoration, when the lords and gentry went to meet him, he thrust himself into the company of the barons, riding most sumptuously in his footcloth, attended by his footboy; but being known by the marshal, that it was only the ass that marched in the lion's skin, he was by him sufficiently caned for his audacious boldness. Yet notwithstanding this check, he always afterwards kept up a stately port so that none was more notice taken of than he, for had he come by in his coach (as he often did) in the night, upon Col. Turner's name, the very watchmen would tremble, whom yet he would often reward with money: but his terrible oaths, being so habituated to swearing, would make a good Christian quake to hear him. But though his vices were very great, yet had he many things in him worthy of commendation, being very charitable to poor distressed Cavaliers whom he would entertain at his own table, and if it were his chance to be in their company with him at taverns, he would pay their share out of his own pocket and lend them money besides.

> *High active spirits commonly excel*
> *Either in doing ill, or doing well.*

Hitherto no great blemishes were laid on his practice, which now began to be very great, being acquainted with most of the moneyed men in London. His frequent dealings were in the sales of lands decreed in chancery and the recovery of right and title to lands unjustly holden from the true heirs, in which he had such a multitude of business that he kept two clerks constantly a-writing or running about his business. He also dealt very much in jewels, by the sale and bartering of which to persons of quality he gained exceedingly, so that his incomes were valued at £700 or £800 a year; yet by reason of his extravagancies we cannot conceive he laid up much for his posterity.

But in prosecution of his designs he met with many opponents, particularly one Batchelor who lived near Fenchurch Street, who having (as he thought) received some wrong from Colonel Turner, got a friend of his to write a pamphlet[3] against him, wherein amongst other base passages this was one, viz., "This same Turner was knighted in the field for slaying, killing, and undoing the good and well-affected people of this nation, a most dangerous and active fellow, and for his services so rewarded," &c. This he did out of revenge to render him obnoxious to the

Usurper, though it proved rather to his reputation, he himself taking great delight in the repetition of it; nor would ever contradict it, but would say, if he had an estate of lands and value, he would soon be a knight; but his condition as a broker and solicitor would not comport thereunto.

Chapter IV

Some Conjectural Misdemeanours of Mr. Turner, with Some Other Mad Frolics Performed by Him

Several other matters are by common report laid to his charge, viz., that one Mr. Clench of Cambridge, having occasions for money, borrowed £400 upon a farm called Bendish in that county and made use of Mr. Turner for the procuring of it, who pretended that because his lands lay so far distant, he [Mr. Clench] must give bond together with personal security for the payment thereof at the appointed day. But Mr. Clench, upon the payment of the money, only took up his mortgage, but forgot the bond, which was afterward sued and recovered against him. Another story is reported of him, that he should deceive a young gentleman of £60 upon promise of procuring him a mandamus from the King for a fellowship in Cambridge. Also, another rumour is commonly spread abroad, namely, that by his procurement he should supply the tyrant Oliver with £20,000 to pay his soldiers, who were then in a condition of mutinying. But for the truth of these, I shall desire the reader to suspend his belief, being cautious in our relation to cast any just aspersion upon the dead.

But another thing real we shall impart unto you, wherein he received a foul check, namely, in his dealing with one Mr. Galilee in Finch Lane who pretended a right to an estate of an £100 *per annum* in Norfolk; and hearing of Col. Turner's abilities, bargained with him for the sum of £50 paid ready down to prosecute his title, and did afterwards pay him several sums of money incident to the charges that belonged thereunto: which suit being commenced in the Exchequer (according to the customary proceedings of that court), a lessee was named which was one Sampson, and he by the appointment of Galilee, as Turner affirmed. But before it came to a trial, Galilee sold his right, so that Sampson was overthrown, and an execution for costs taken out against him, who thereupon made his application to Galilee that now disowned the matter and said he never named him upon that account. Hereupon high differences rose betwixt Turner and Galilee, who brought an indictment of barratry against Turner and swore it himself with an attestation of several other witnesses, which put Turner to great trouble; and notwithstanding he produced several persons for testification of his honesty, yet the jury found him guilty, but the court was not so well satisfied therewith. Whereupon the business was referred to Sir William Wild, who awarded Turner that he should pay to Galilee either £40 or £50, the whole charges amounting to not less than £300.

To allay these and some other troubles which he had, he had many comical frolics, of which to relate one or two may not be unpleasant to the reader. He, having one time made one of his company dead drunk, caused the bell to be tolled and sent for a chimney sweeper to be his doctor and the searchers to view his corpse, giving them 12 pence apiece for their pains.

At another time, having occasion to go to Colchester upon the arrest of a certain man, he took for his assistance some officers from the Compter,[4] as special bailiffs (which he many times before had done). Having done his business, he bought a pipe of canary of his landlord of the house and gave it freely to all comers, and from thence carried his company to Bishop's Stortford in Hertfordshire where in the like frolics he spent £40 more.

Another of his frolics was at Colchester aforesaid where he hired a wagon to carry away all the dead he should kill, and to affright the people, caused all the swords that

belonged to his company to be hanged drawn, out of the
window, which so amazed the man of the house that he
commanded his hostler to stop up the well in the yard with
hay that none of the slain might be put in there.

This his ungoverned prodigality brought him of late out
of money, which (as I conceive) was the occasion to make
him undertake this dishonest shift to piece out his ruins by
base attempts rather than to sink obscurely into a gaol,
and there lie an object of misery. The manner whereof we
shall declare unto you.

Chapter V

An Exact Relation of the Manner of the Robbery of Mr. Tryon

About Christmas last, he consulted with some persons
about this grand robbery and had gotten for his turn three
men fit for the purpose, viz., one William Turner, a butcher,
James White, a solicitor, and another person, White's
friend. The main of their design was to be carried on by
Colonel Turner himself, which was for the robbery of Mr.
Francis Tryon, a merchant in Lime Street,[5] with whom
Turner was very intimate, and knew all passages belonging
to the house. Upon their first meeting for the undertaking
of the business, one of their company being drunk, it was
laid aside for that time, White (one of the actors) protesting he would not venture his life with one in his condition.

But not long after, viz., the 7th of January, they met
again at the Red Lyon in Bishopsgate Street, where they
dined together, and then resolved upon the robbery that
night, appointing to meet there again by six of the clock
in the afternoon; but coming thither, the room was taken
up by other guests, wherefore they went over to the Four
Swans or Green Dragon and there stayed till eight o'clock;
from thence they removed to the New Market in Leadenhall where three of them sat upon the stalls till the Colonel

went out for intelligence, who after half an hour's space returned, bringing them word that the man and maid were both gone out and that now was their time. Whereupon away they went, and coming to the place, Col. Turner unlocked the door (having before got the impression of the key in soft wax and had one made answerable unto it). Then went they up the stairs, Turner leading the way, and in the kitchen lit a candle, and so went immediately up to Mr. Tryon's chamber where two of them put a cloth into his mouth and bound his hands and feet, whilst Turner at the bed's feet took the keys of his warehouse and counting-house out of his pocket; and whilst they were busy in gagging him, he in the meantime searches the closet where he finds the jewels and pockets them privately, not acquainting his companions therewith. But there was store of money beside, with which they severally loaded themselves, to the value of £1,023. This was done all in the space of an hour's time, which money they carried to one Nicholas Higginson's house at Lousy Lane in Dukes Place, which they hired some days before, pretending it for the use of a master of a ship, his mate, purser, and boatswain. The next morning Turner fetched away the money to his own house, giving to White and his friend only £20 apiece for their pains, and promised William Turner £100.

Soon after they were gone, Mr. Tryon got the gag out of his mouth and, though bound, tumbled out of his bed, in doing which he fell upon an earthen chamber pot and hurt himself sorely, but recovering his legs and getting to the window, called out, "Murder and thieves," which being next the street, his neighbours heard him and with a crow of iron broke open the door (for Turner had locked it after him) and unbound him. Then did they see how he was robbed, but the man and maid being missing caused some suspicion of them, who presently after came, pretending they had been at supper at Col. Turner's, which was not so. Whereupon a constable went to examine the business, who found Col. Turner and his family in bed, who likewise (upon the request of the constable) went along with him to Mr. Tryon's where he kept such a bustle about the business that his too overmuch diligence gave him cause to be suspected; which suspicion was afterwards aggravated by his listening to hear when others were examined, the man and maid being at that time thoroughly sifted by Sir Thomas Aleyn, who took a great deal of pains in the business. However, Turner was let go that night and in the morning betimes removed the money from his own house to the house of one Mrs. Fry, a sempstress at the lower end of the Minories, pretending it to be the money of a merchant newly broke, who having a wife and seven or eight children desired to have it secured.

This business Mrs. Fry reveals to a kinswoman of hers in the house, who having been formerly a servant to Alderman Love and hearing of Mr. Tryon's robbery, suspected the money was not well gotten and thereupon acquainted her master, Alderman Love, of it, who as speedily informed Sir Thomas Aleyn thereof. Sir Thomas therefore, taking a footboy with him, speedeth down, and in the way meeting with Major Tasker, desired his company to go along with him, which he accordingly did; and entering the house of Mrs. Fry, found Col. Turner with his hands in a chest wherein were two wallets of money, one of a £100 the other £200. Sir Thomas took the keys from him and, going into another room, found two wallets of money more. Then was a constable called for, and Turner being examined whose money it was, he said he had received it of a goldsmith, but could not tell his name. Being further asked why he should remove his own money, he answered he only did it for two or three days, till this foolery was over.

Whilst thus they were arguing the matter, John Turner the son (who had helped to bring the money thither), hearing how the business went, got out by a back door, and leaping over a pale behind the house, made an escape; but the Colonel, though he pretended he were in pursuit of the thieves and therefore desired freedom to go about it, yet would not Sir Thomas grant it, but calling for a coach (in company with Major Tasker and the constable) brought him to Mr. Tryon's house, telling him he had brought him £500 of his money and did not doubt but also a person that could help him with the rest he had lost; but Turner having spoken with Mr. Tryon in private, upon promise of helping him to all the next day about four or five o'clock in the afternoon, he was permitted to go at liberty.

The next day he went to the Exchange, as he formerly used to do, where about two o'clock he was arrested in the streets by the two coles[6] (at the suit of four officers of the Poultry Compter who had bailed him to a writ of one Mr. Van de Burgh, a Dutch merchant) who carried him to the Hoop Tavern where they stayed him. In the meantime his wife brought the jewels to Mr. Tryon's so that he had all his again. But the matter was so apparent against Mr. Turner that Sir Thomas Aleyn by warrant committed him to Newgate, whither he was carried about one or two o'clock the same night, and January the 15th and 16th he was arraigned for the same at Justice Hall in the Old Bailey, where he was by the jury found guilty, and on the 19th day of the same month had sentence of death pronounced upon him.

Thus though that felons to escape may hope,
At last they are rewarded with a rope.

The same day Col. and William Turner were by Sir Thomas Aleyn examined apart, who finding their design fully discovered, declared the manner of it as we have mentioned it unto you.

Chapter VI

The Passages Betwixt Col. Turner and Mr. Ordinary of Newgate, with the Manner of His Going to Execution

Soon after his condemnation, Mr. Weldon, the ordinary of Newgate, went unto him, telling him he was a

dying man (being dead in law), and very earnestly pressed
four things unto him.

First, that as he was an open sinner, so that he would
make open confession of his sins, urging to that purpose
the saying of the wise man in his book of Proverbs: "He
that hideth his sins shall not prosper, but he that confess-
eth and forsaketh them shall find mercy."[7]

Secondly, a hearty contrition for his enormous offenses
which had brought that just judgment of God upon him.

Thirdly, a restitution, for words without deeds [were]
but a feigned and hypocritical repentance. And,

Fourthly, charity, to forgive others, as he would that God
for Christ's sake should forgive him.

He pressed much to him the message which the Prophet
Isaiah brought to Hezekiah, viz., "Set thy house in order, for
thou shalt die and not live."[8] He told him that by "house"
was meant not only his temporal but his spiritual body;
that the body in respect of the soul was but as the shell
to the kernel or as the jewel to the case which enclosed it;
what a small minute of time he had left him betwixt that
& the infinite space of eternity; therefore what great need
he had to make the best improvement of that short time,
with many other such like speeches which wrought very
much upon him, declaring by many outward signs a real
sorrow for his heinous crimes, not only weeping bitterly,
but by many expressions declared his hearty, unfeigned
contrition.

Afterwards on Tuesday he desired to receive the Sacrament. The ordinary asked him (because he would have no
more wine than needed) how many would communicate
with him. He replied, his wife and two sons. But they,
being asked, did refuse, Mrs. Turner alleging she was not
in charity with some persons whom she imagined too eager
in prosecution of justice against her husband; but Mr. Ordinary pressed so much a necessity of her reconciliation and
gave her such sound advice that she willingly embraced to
be partaker in that Holy Ordinance, but their two sons did
not receive it.

Whilst thus he prepared himself for death, he was not negligent in using all endeavours for the prolongation of his life. To this end he desired Mr. Tryon to accompany his wife with a petition to his Majesty for a reprieve, which they accordingly delivered upon their knees in the Long Gallery; but the King told them he could not do it, having received such an account of him from the judges and magistrates of the city of London; and being humbly requested for a respite for some few weeks, he would not consent for so few days.

This not prevailing, he desired Mr. Ordinary to move the Lord Chancellor in the business, propounding two reasons to persuade him thereto: the first was the shortness of the time which, he alleged, was very quick, considering that load of sin that lay heavy upon his conscience; and the other was that he had the estates of two or three widows in his hands, which by reason of his sudden cutting off might be much injured thereby. But notwithstanding these plausible pretenses, it would not hinder the execution of justice.

But one thing we had almost omitted, namely, that when Mr. Ordinary preached on the Sunday, treating of a thorough and sound repentance by which they might obtain pardon for their sins, the Colonel interpreting that to be meant of his corporal body, which Mr. Ordinary spake in reference to his spiritual condition, when the sermon was ended he seriously asked him if there were a pardon for him or no.

But no doubt the man was thoroughly convinced of his crime and the heinousness of it, and spent the whole day in sorrow and mourning for his offenses; and therefore those are much to blame who reported him to be drunk that day, that he ranted and swore: "Damn him," and "sink him," he would have a pardon though it cost him £5,000. But such is the nature of some base lying spirits to insult over men in misery and, when they cannot touch their bodies, brand them as much as in them lies, in their very memory.

To confirm the truth of these passages concerning Mr. Ordinary with the Colonel, we shall give you a letter from his own hand, which he [the ordinary] wrote to a person of quality here in London who desired of him the relation of the whole business.

Here follows the letter:

Sir,

My occasions have been extraordinary, so as I have wanted a convenient opportunity of recalling the several passages that were between me and Mr. Turner, I shall begin. After he was cast, I attended him to the press yard and told him that shortly the sentence of death would be denounced against him. He answered, "I dread not death, I have looked death oft in the face. I pray, sir, pray for me, that I may not faint when the day of death comes." I told him death was the king of terror, and a man had need of a strong faith to shield him against the fiery darts of death from hurting the soul. He replied, "Sir, we shall have time to talk of these things Monday or Tuesday. I pray," said he, "call upon me as oft as you can." Tuesday night I waited on him and told him, "Colonel, I am come to repeat the sentence justly denounced against you by the judge, and I assure you, you shall die and not live. Therefore, my advice is to set your house in order." "What do you mean by that?" said he. "My meaning is your outward affairs relating to your family, and in satisfying those that have entrusted you: but principally the closet of your soul, to see that it be furnished with the Grace of Almighty God, as faith, repentance, &c." "I pray, sir," said he, "direct me, for I believe I am not a man for this world." Sir, I should have told you that Sunday in the afternoon he came to chapel, carried himself very soberly, heard my sermon attentively, which was out of the book of Numbers, Balaam's wish, who I told him had lived a curser, a ranter.[9] He [Turner] desires, "O that I might die the death of the righteous and that my latter end were like his." He gave me thanks for my sermon and told me he hoped it would do his soul good.

I told him meditation was the way to make the Word fruitful. I desired him to dismiss the company that frequented him and to do as Hezekiah: when sentence was passed, he prayed and wept sore. "Pray to God for pardon of sin, and bathe the feet of your Saviour with your penitential tears, and your Saviour will bathe your soul in the fountain of his most precious blood." "Sir," said he, "I shall take your advice." Notwithstanding, company pressed on him.

Wednesday I visited him with the rest of the prisoners in chapel, prayed and advised them, where I met with a true penitent Jane Cradock who had spent all her time after sentence in mourning and lamenting. I returned to Colonel Turner. He gave me 10 shillings for my sermon and some other moneys to hire a coach to speak to the Lord Chief Justice to allow him a longer time for his repentance and preparation to die, and to satisfy four widows who had entrusted him with large sums, £4,000, as I remember. I went to the Lord Chancellor where I found the judges moved in his behalf, but his request could not be granted. Die he must the morrow by eight of the clock or time usually appointed. I gave him notice thereof. His reply: "Lord God, I have been a great sinner, and shall I have so small a time of repentance? God is more merciful than man, or I have no hope." I told him it was not the length of time, but the truth of repentance God looked at; a moment's true repentance, the Thief's case was accepted. "Be as penitent as he, and you shall not fail of remission, the proof whereof will be by the concomitants, confessed restitution, forgiving others." "I shall do all and observe," said he, "your method." I prayed God to assist him in this his conflict.

Thursday I came to him. I found him very pensive. He desired the Communion. We made a pause at

last, having prest him to restitution; he promised he
would to his power. I found by him his power was
small. He had lived high upon the estate of others, as
I perceived by some passages that dropt from his
lips. Therefore, I told him, where you wanted a power,
the will was accepted. I demanded who would receive
the Communion. He answers, himself, his wife, his
sons and daughters. I demanded whether his sons and
daughters had received the Communion before. They
answered, no, some of 'em; others were not prepared.
His wife also refused to receive with him, but we persuaded her to join in that sacred performance with her
husband; otherwise it would be adjudged she had no
charity for him. He importuned her and saluted her,
so she came after consecration. I administered. When
the cup was delivered to him, I found a heart of stone
become a heart of flesh, and the blood of Christ melt
the adamant. For before he received, he broke forth
into this speech, "Lord Jesus, dear God, I pray that
this blood may not seal up my damnation who have
been a great offender. Lord, thy blood is able to save
me. O God, thou never didst cast away penitent sinners. Let thy blood seal up my salvation, dear Lord."
So he drank it, and after said, "I have comfort in my
soul." He was very attentive to the admonitions of
myself and Lord Bartlet's chaplain, who went with me
in cart. That is all I can say who am

Your loving friend,
John Weldon,
Ordinary of Newgate,
& Deputy to Clerks, &c.

Thursday morning being come (the fatal day appointed
for his execution), he was very intent upon his preparation
for another world and spent the morning wholly with the
ministers and in taking leave of his wife and children, to
whom he gave many good and wholesome admonitions.
About 10 o'clock both the sheriffs came in person to con-

duct him to the place of execution. Coming out of the press yard and seeing a cart there prepared to carry him, he was somewhat abashed and desired of Sir Richard Ford (one of the sheriffs) he might have a coach, which was denied, Sir Richard telling him the King had ordered it otherwise. Then did he desire he might walk on foot, but that neither would be granted. Whereupon he went up into the cart, and being by the officer ordered to sit in the body of the cart, the usual place for offenders, he desired to be permitted to ride on the copse,[10] but that also was denied, and so he was tied according to the custom of felons. There rode with him in the same cart Mr. Ordinary of Newgate and another minister. Great was the confluence of people all the way he passed along the streets, the windows being so thronged as hath not been known in the memory of man upon the like occasion.

Being come to the place of execution (which was in Leadenhall Street at Lime Street end, where a gibbet was erected), he called the executioner unto him and told him that his friends desired his clothes, and therefore in consideration of them, he gave him 50 shillings, and half a crown besides to drink. He also gave 15 shillings to the sergeants and yeomen there present, to see his body and clothes delivered to one Mrs. Smith, a neighbour that lived hard by. Then looking round about upon the people, addressing himself to the sheriffs, he made a long speech, the substance whereof is this.

Chapter VII

The Speech of Colonel James Turner at His Execution, with His Character, as Also an Example of His Horrible Swearing

He confessed that it was the greatness of his sins that brought him thither, the greatest of which was prophaneness, blaspheming God, and taking His name in vain; that

he was much addicted to company, yet never accompanied
with thieves or such base inferior people, but by hearing
others swear got a habit of it, though inwardly he detested
it. That for the fact which brought him thither it was of
his own contriving, and that his two sons John and Ely
were ignorant of it, and therefore desired they might be
released. That his father was a reverend divine, a gentleman of good life and conversation. That his wife was descended from a family of repute in Dorsetshire, one of her
uncles having lent the late King £8,000. That his wife now
being brought to this distress, his two children might be
released for her comfort, and not to add affliction to her
affliction. That he was afraid the crying sins of this nation
(without God's wonderful mercy) would bring some heavy
punishment upon it. That the dislike of the disorders in
the world hath made him many times wish himself in his
grave. That being a boy, men were more friendly & given
to hospitality, but that now the world was full of malice
and difference. Then did he free himself of some calumnies
cast upon him and gave account of his service under the
old King. Next did he fall upon the occasion of his coming
thither, imputing it to the just hand of God for his sins,
desiring all people to take warning by him; that had he not
been arrested at that sad juncture of time, Mr. Tryon had
had every pennyworth of his goods and money again, desiring God to forgive them that were the hindrance thereof.
Then did he vindicate himself of some other calumnies cast
upon him, namely, concerning that sad fire in Lothbury,
of which he protested his innocency therein, as likewise
some money that was lost in Coleman Street, which he
averred he never knew of. He also purged himself of an
imputation laid upon him concerning a gentleman of his
own name that lay in his house, as if something should
be put into his drink to dispatch him out of this world
(the gentleman dying suddenly), of which he likewise declared his innocency. Next did he give some brief account
of his faith and profession: how he had been bred up in the
Protestant profession and was a zealous practicer of the rites

and ceremonies belonging thereunto; that he was truly and heartily sorrowful for his sins, desiring of God the forgiveness of them. That he had made a true and faithful confession and restitution so far as in him lay, that his repentance was not feigned, desiring to be with Christ in glory, and that he was in perfect charity with the whole world.

Next did he free himself of some imputations that he was drunk the Sunday before in prison. He desired some order might be taken concerning the Hole in Newgate that poor prisoners might have some boards to lie down upon them in ease, that they might not be so tormented when they should be preparing for their ends. Afterwards he desired them about him to join with him in prayer, in which he earnestly begged for the forgiveness of his sins, praying heartily for the King's Majesty and all the royal family, as also for the magistrates and ministers of the land. That God would provide and take care for his wife & children, thanking him for that space of time for repentance, and that he was not cut off by sudden death, desiring God through Jesus Christ to wash away his sins and receive his soul.

Then did Mr. Ordinary of Newgate pray with him. Afterwards he had some private ejaculations wherein he expressed much sorrow for his sins and earnestly begged pardon for them. Then taking his leave of the sheriffs, desiring to be remembered to the lord mayor & the rest of the aldermen, he addressed himself for his last minute, still earnestly begging of God for mercy and desiring for his comfort the doctor to read to him those verses in the second of the Hebrews, being the 14, 15, 16, 17, and 18 verses.

Next did he give 40 shillings to a minister to be given to the poor of that parish, and 18s/6d more for his wife, to be delivered to his young son's schoolmaster.

Afterwards he directed the executioner to take off the halter from his shoulders; which being done, he took it in his hands, kissed it, and put it about his neck himself, and having fitted his cap, went out of the cart (wherein he made his speech) upon the ladder, where the executioner tying the rope and pulling it something too much, he very smartly said to him, "What? Dost thou mean to choke me? Pray, fellow, give me more rope. How long hast thou been executioner that thou knowest not how to place the halter?" Then bidding the executioner not to turn him off till he gave him a sign, he again fell to prayers; and desiring the Lord to receive his soul, upon the sign given, he was turned off the ladder.

After some short time he was cut down, and his body conveyed to the house of Mistress Smith, a neighbour nearby, where it continued till ―― ―― when it was buried very decently at the parish church of St. Andrews Undershaft.

And this was the end of Mr. James Turner, a man who by the course of nature might have lived many years longer. He was a person of a middle stature, something corpulent, but active, of a cheerful countenance, which he kept up even to the very period of his life, not much changing to the very last. He was one very loving to his wife and indulgent to his children, of a high spirit which, having not an estate answerable thereto, caused him to fall into many errors. His vices were great and many. Yet were they not without a mixture of virtues and other good qualities. He was much addicted to the sin of swearing, a vice which hath in it neither profit nor pleasure and, unless a man be wholly given up to wickedness, cannot but strike the conscience with much regret in the committing of it. He was very charitable to the poor, especially to such who had formerly been able to give themselves. But his thoughts were vaster than his estate, and therefore (as I formerly hinted) I am persuaded the occasion of this his last wicked act was to have wherewithal to keep up that state and grandeur he had formerly lived in, fearing nothing so much as to strike sail and stoop to the privacy of an ordinary way of life. Many were the troubles he had passed through, which we may think he rather desired than studied to avoid. As some men delight to fish in troubled waters, so did he take pleasure in divers and intricate troubles, though I conceive the profit arising by them was the greatest motive to make him undertake them. For his valour, we find not much commendation of him; yet do not I think he was a coward, as some have aspersed him. Indeed (as I said before) his vices were many and great, especially that horrid sin of cursing and swearing, whereof we shall give you an example, as a warning to all those who are addicted to those horrid crimes, which we received from the hands of one who knew all the passages for truth.

About September, 1662, Col. James Turner sent to a citizen of London to come to him to the Castle Tavern in Cornhill, who found a gentleman with the said Turner, to whom two captains also came. Turner entreated the citizen he sent for, to move a company, of which the citizen was a member, to give out of their bounty £10 to release a prisoner out of the Fleet, which was by him promised and some few days after granted by the said company, and the prisoner set at liberty. Turner swore very much without any provocation. The citizen told him if he continued to swear, he would not stay in his company. Whiles they were drinking, a blackamoor-boy of some fourteen years of age brought pipes and small beer. Turner swore and curst the boy, and said he was like the Devil, for which the company did much reprove him. The drawer, standing by, said the blackamoor was to be baptized the next Lord's day with his master's child, his wife then lying in. The citizen, to try the blackamoor's fitness for baptism, asked him who made him. He answered, "God." Turner very furiously replied and swore desperately the Devil made him, earnestly saying and swearing, "You rogue, the Devil made you. God never made you." The citizen desired Turner to forbear his swearing and had much ado to get him to be quiet. Whilst he asked him further interrogatories, the blackamoor replied Christian-like answers to the questions of who redeemed him, who sanctified and preserved him, wherefore God made him, and several other Christian-like answers the boy gave, till he came to answer to the priestly, prophetical and kingly office of Christ. Turner still continued vehemently cursing and swearing against the boy.

It being now near ten o'clock at night, the four gentlemen present and also the drawer and the blackamoor, Turner sitting with his face against the casement, therein came a mighty great flap or stroke upon the window as if two great wings would have drove the window into the room upon the company, which made them all in a great amazement. Whereupon the citizen ran to the window, opened the casement, but could not see anything as the cause, not a quarrel[11] broke, nor any dirt upon the window. Turner gave over cursing and swearing, and sat as a man ready to sink into the ground, that one of the captains told Turner, "This is because of your swearing and cursing." The window was near a story from the yard, which belonged to the tavern, and a shed of boards from it downward, that in no probability any man did it.

Chapter VIII

Col. Turner Vindicated in Several Aspersions Cast Upon Him

Hitherto have we given you a narrative of his life and conversation which, as it was bad, so have some men endeavoured to make it worse than it was, rendering him rather a monster than a man, and upon slight conjectural grounds have added stuff of their own brain to make it pass with the more likelihood, so that what at first was but a molehill soon becomes a mountain, according to Ovid,

> The thing at first invented great doth grow,
> And everyone doth something add thereto.

As may be instanced in their calumniation of him that he should take £200 of the Lady Hewyt to procure a pardon for her husband and that he never did anything in the business, which when he heard of (being when he was in

Newgate), he sent one Mr. Gray of Blackfriars to the Lady Hewyt's, being thirty-two miles off, with all the speed he could, for a certificate under her hand to quit him of that aspersion, which she accordingly did in a message to the King, the copy of which letter (as I received it from Mistress Turner) I shall give you verbatim, viz.,

To the King's Most Excellent Majesty:

Whereas I have received intimation that your Majesty is informed that James Turner, Gent., prisoner in Newgate, did receive £200 in order to the saving the life of my late dear murthered husband, Dr. John Hewyt, and did nothing therein but kept the money.

These are humbly to certify your Majesty that I never knew or heard that the said James Turner was employed thereabouts. Nor did he ever receive any such sum of money of me, or any other to my knowledge. Nor do I know him. And this I do upon the request of the said Mr. Turner make bold to attest under my hand this 18th day of January, 1664.

Mary Hewyt

George Gray maketh oath that he did see the above-written certificate signed and acknowledged by the Lady Mary Hewyt.

Jo. Bramston   George Gray

But that the saddle might be laid on the right horse, the truth is it was one Col. Whetton, a person very intimate with the Usurper, who by fair promises got £235 of the Lady. She so dearly affected her husband that she would have parted with her whole estate to have saved his life. This Whetton pretended that a £100 of it was for Secretary Thurloe who, he said, was likewise to be instrumental towards it, but Thurloe cleared himself of it by a letter so that the whole blame lies upon Whetton.

Another calumny is commonly reported of him, that being beyond sea with our now Gracious Sovereign, he should deceive him of some sums of money wherewith he had been entrusted. But this is easy to be refuted, it being well

known he was never out of England and so by consequence
could not be culpable of that offense. I should, therefore,
advise people not to be too credulous of every report they
hear of him as that, which some have confidently reported,
because he always kept two or three geldings "he was the
head of all the highwaymen in England," and that under
pretense of soliciting men's businesses, which occasioned
him to stay out late some nights, it was only a cloak to
blind the eyes of the world when he was abroad upon
worse matters: insomuch that the tanners of Rumford and
other market-folks, since his death, have been bold to say
that "they hoped now they should ride safe home since that
great robber Turner was dead." But for these and such like
conjectural stories, I shall desire the reader to suspend his
judgment till time (the father of truth) shall bring things
to light.

For that of one Marshal, concerning some money that
was lost in Coleman Street, as also that he should cheat a
woman by a false deed, there is so little of likelihood in
them that were it not only to stop the mouths of some who
are apt to believe every false report, I should not so much
as once mention them.

Therefore, though his vices were great, yet we ought not
to lay other men's faults upon him only upon supposition,
which is no evidence in law; and of the two, ought rather to
judge the best or at least to weigh and consider thoroughly
the contrary reasons, lest we come under the lash of the
poet,

> He that doth judge and will but one side hear,
> Though he judge right, he's no good justicer.

But it is a known observation that in such calamitous
cases more is commonly charged than proved, and it may
be his adversaries observed Machiavel's rule, to throw dirt
enough upon him, for that some would stick. For I have
observed that let a lie be invented, though never so ridiculous, it shall meet with some fools that will believe it.
Witness that story about ten years ago of the great giants

coming into England. No doubt his crimes were very great, for which we may judge his excesses were the greatest occasions of them. In the meantime, humanity commands us to think the best of him and to pity his wife and six children whom he left behind him, the only remains of seven and twenty by one woman, whereof two he left behind him in prison upon account of the same fact.

But one thing is known to many for a truth which indeed comes near to inhumanity and barbarousness, namely, his preserving some of the fat or other parts of the corpse of divers persons lately executed for treason (as those who have seen it with him have informed me), which though pretended to be used for the making an excellent medicine he had for the gout, yet it is a most unmanly thing to have no reverence to human blood, though in persons justly punished.

Nor could this person, who had been so litigious in his life, rest free from suspicion after his death, a common rumour being bruited that he was not hanged till quite dead, but that afterwards, by means used to him, recovered again to life.[12] But this story being most of all ridiculous, I leave to be believed by those that are more credulous than myself.

I shall conclude with a merry Epitaph which was made by an ingenious person upon him, leaving it to the reader to judge of it as he pleases.

Here lies the carcass of a wretched wight,
Who at noonday did bid the world good night.
Of what sect he was of, there's few can tell:
He (like Erasmus) hung 'twixt Heaven and Hell.
Valiant by consequence he must be said,
He scorned to die (like cowards) in his bed:
And whereas others run from death's embrace,
He boldly went to meet him in the face.
Lastly, his courage was so mighty, too,
He did what all that saw him feared to do.

Postscript

Let the reader take notice we hear there is a rumour of a false copy which is likely to come forth. Let him beware of it, lest it abuse the memory of the dead.

FINIS.

JACKSON'S RECANTATION
(1674)

Richard Head

FOREWORD

Richard Head's best-known book, *The English Rogue Described, in the Life of Meriton Latroon* (1665), was his first venture into fictionized rogue autobiography. It was so successful that in 1674 the author reworked portions into another very similar piece, *Jackson's Recantation.* Head's keen interest in certain types of criminal activity, as these two pretended autobiographies show, grew out of personal experience. Even in its own day, *The English Rogue* was suspected of relating incidents that had actually happened to the author.

The book was responsible for considerable misinformation about Richard Head. Biographers inevitably saw him as the image of his anti-hero, Meriton Latroon. According to one stubborn tradition, the opening chapters depicted his own early life in Ireland. He was born there around 1637. At Carrickfergus, when Head was four, his father (like Meriton Latroon's) was murdered by Irish rebels. The boy escaped with his mother, traveling from town to town and coming eventually to England. He may have lived awhile, as did Meriton, with gypsies. An early biographer,

John Aubrey, accepts this story and adds appropriately
(for Meriton was cross-eyed) that Head "looked like a
knave with his goggling eyes. He could transform himself
into any shape." At Oxford, he is supposed to have attended his father's college, New Inn Hall, but left, for lack
of funds, to become an apprentice to a Latin bookseller in
London. He tried his hand at translating a poem by
Sinibaldus, *Rare Verities, or The Cabinet of Venus Unlocked* (1658). Next, opening his own bookseller's shop in
Little Britain, he was admitted a stationer on June 4, 1660.
Throughout his life, it seems, he neglected business for
pleasure. To avoid creditors, he retired to Dublin, where
he wrote a comedy, *Hic et Ubique, or The Humours of
Dublin* (1663). Back in London as a bookseller, he was
again ruined by gambling. Altogether, writes Aubrey, he
"broke two or three times."

His dissolute habits impressed all his contemporaries
who wrote about him. William Winstanley noted Head's
fondness for "that accursed vice of play," and Kirkman
(who played up his friend's vices to publicize *The English
Rogue*) hinted that he was "indeed guilty of some petty
waggeries" recited in the book. Although Head had never
been "upon the pad," said Kirkman, he was often cheated
at gaming and was "guilty of female frauds." Not all of
these innuendoes can be believed. But Head *was* suspiciously sensitive about charges that the scandalous parts of
The English Rogue were autobiographical, and he *does*
dwell upon card cheating in *Jackson's Recantation*. According to Winstanley, in 1686 Head was at last cast away at
sea on a voyage to the Isle of Wight. In a copy of *News
from the Stars*, a manuscript note provides a final com-
ment: "Rich. Head, a broken bookseller & the author of yͤ
English Rogue, writ this; he turned Papist in his voyage to
Spain, was drowned."

Living a life of "many crosses and afflictions," Head was
compelled to turn to "scribbling" for the booksellers at
20 shillings per sheet. Between the years 1665 and 1677,
he produced eight books on the subject he knew best—

crime. More than any other Restoration author, he commanded a whole arsenal of criminal lore: the habits, temperaments, and language of beggars, gypsies, thieves, shoplifts, padders, and highwaymen. In addition to *The English Rogue* (Part I) and *Jackson's Recantation*, he wrote or compiled such books as *News from the Stars* (1673); *The Canting Academy, or The Devil's Cabinet Opened* (1673); *The Complaisant Companion, or New Jests . . . and Pleasant Novels* (1674; retitled *Nugæ Venales*, 1675); *Proteus Redivivus* (1675); *The Miss Display'd* (1675; retitled *Madame Wheedle*, 1678); and *The Life and Death of Mother Shipton* (1677). Deserving special attention is *The Miss Display'd*, the "biography" of a still living "notorious Irish-English whore." In focusing upon a real criminal for its subject, the book bears a strong resemblance to *Jackson's Recantation*.

That Richard Head wrote *Jackson's Recantation* was never questioned by William Winstanley and Anthony Wood, or by later critics. Only recently, Patrick Pringle, in an exciting book, *Stand and Deliver: The Story of Highwaymen*, has argued for another author. He ingeniously theorizes that Jackson's ghost writer was Samuel Smith, the Newgate ordinary, whose pseudonym, Samuel Swiftnicks, endorsed the postscript. No mention is made of Richard Head's claim, or of the many similarities between *Jackson's Recantation* and Head's acknowledged book, *The English Rogue*.

The close connection between the two books is very significant. Borrowing unabashedly from *The English Rogue*, Head transformed episodes to fit Jackson that were originally meant for Meriton Latroon; he plagiarized whole passages, even verbatim. Jackson's prison lament, his remorse and guilt—these and other dramatic moments were first experienced by Latroon (Chapters 59, 65). The "autobiography" in *Jackson's Recantation* is thus demonstrably a veneer for consciously written fiction. The few events that actually happened to Francis Jackson, alias Dixie, are very slightly treated in the *Recantation*. The highwayman's story, however, can be pieced together from other sources. On March 16, 1674, Jackson and his gang (Captain John Williams, James Slader, John White, and Walter Parkhurst) robbed the Windsor coach in broad daylight. Two days later, after a coach robbery near Staines, they fled from town to town, hotly pursued by a posse. At Hampstead Heath, in the evening of March 18th, they made a bold stand against two hundred irregulars. Slader was fatally wounded, and Jackson murdered one of the pursuers. Captured and brought to Newgate gaol, the highwaymen awaited trial. Meanwhile, Londoners were reading *Bloody News from Staines, or a True Account of Five Notorious Highwaymen.* The four surviving culprits were then tried at the Old Bailey, and "on 11 April convicted of fifteen indictments for robbery and murder, and sentenced, three to be hanged at the usual place of execution and Jackson to be gibbeted at Hampstead." So states the official State Paper. Captain John Williams told the story next, "to prevent false reports of them when they are dead," in *The Confession of the Four Highwaymen.* The last of the publications, advertised on May 26th, was *Jackson's Recantation.*

As an experiment in handling point of view, *Jackson's Recantation* represents a notable advance in the writer's conception of fiction. The author is completely effaced. The mask of a real criminal "talking out" his guilt is never once dropped. When Jackson finishes, Swiftnicks (another real criminal) vouches "this is no fiction, but a true relation." But since Richard Head wrote the entire piece, the "autobiographical" form itself becomes a major fiction. On the other hand, it is true that chinks appear in the mask. The calloused criminal slips at times into the prosiness of the Oxford-educated author. Out of a printed source, *Bloody News from Staines,* Head lifts the description of highwaymen as "riotous caterpillars" who prey upon "the fruit of human industry." In his title and the long section of "notable instructions for your future caution and preservation," he pilfers a popular early-seventeenth-century poem, John

Clavel's *A Recantation of an Ill-Led Life,* but he atones for petty larceny by bringing the highwayman's techniques up-to-date.

In spite of these lapses in point of view, *Jackson's Recantation* has exciting moments: the consternation of the bedraggled youth when he finds the long purse, the antics of the hard-to-please mistress, and the crafty seaman's prank. Subtleties of tone are attempted—for instance, when a knight of the road asserts that keeping a miss is "agreeable to the custom and honour of the times, and should we throw any 'approbium' upon it, it would reflect upon ourselves." Social protest breaks into the narrative—against "silly, old, decrepit" watchmen, the "terrestrial Hell" of prison, easily secured pardons, and a severe law that did not fit the punishment to the crime.

ABOUT HEAD: James Granger, *A Biographical History of England,* 3rd ed., 1779, Vol. IV; William Winstanley, *Lives of the Most Famous English Poets,* 1687; Anthony Wood, *Athenæ Oxonienses,* 3rd ed., 1817, Vol. III; references to R. C. Bald and Strickland Gibson in bibliography "About Kirkman," on p. 7 of this volume. ABOUT JACKSON: Charles G. Harper, *Half-Hours with the Highwaymen,* Chapman & Hall, Ltd., 1908, I, 356–86; Charles Hindley, ed., *The Old Book Collector's Miscellany,* Reeves and Turner, 1876, Vol. VI; Joan Parkes, *Travel in England in the Seventeenth Century,* Oxford University Press, 1925, pp. 183–84; Patrick Pringle, *Stand and Deliver: The Story of Highwaymen,* W. W. Norton & Co., [n.d.], ch. x. OTHERS: Richard Head and Francis Kirkman, *The English Rogue,* Dodd, Mead & Co., 1928.

JACKSON'S RECANTATION, *or the Life & Death of the Notorious Highwayman, Now Hanging in Chains at Hampstead. Delivered to a Friend, a Little Before Execution; Wherein is Truly Discovered the Whole Mys-*

*tery of that Wicked and Fatal Profession of Padding
on the Road*

How vain are the thoughts of such who, whilst youth
and strength accompany them, never consider they are a
mere statue of dust kneaded with tears and moved by the
hid engines of restless passions, a clod of earth which the
shortest fever can burn to ashes, and the least shower of
rheums wash away to nothing. Instead thereof they bounce
so high, and make so great a noise in the world, as if both
the globes (those glorious twins) had been unwombed from
the formless chaos by the midwifery of their brain.[1] Such
was my disordered fancy, and my actions being attended
still with successes answerable to my desires, I thought myself (notwithstanding my vicious practices) one of Heav-
en's favourites and, by the eloquence of my own vanity,
persuaded myself that the machinations of my brain were
able to unhinge the poles. But Heaven thought fit I should
no longer reign in pride and arrogance, and therefore committed me into hands of justice to be punished to the
demerits of my crimes.

Being here confined in this terrestrial Hell, surrounded
with horror and despair, my conscience started out of her
dead sleep and demanded a severe account of what I had
done. Guilt instantly did stop my mouth, and having not a
word to say for myself, I wished my production (as my
actions) inhuman. Such was my deplorable destruction that
I thought I heard the howls and hollow groans of damned
souls, which added weight to one another's perpetual misery. Whilst I was in the greatest agony imaginable, a minister, or rather a charitable physician for my sin-sick soul,
came to visit me, who knowing me a notorious offender
advised me to repent, for as yet it was not too late. Hereupon he propounded several questions, endeavouring to dis-
burden my overloaded conscience by extracting from me
an ingenious general confession of what enormous crimes
I had committed. Finding this pious man had no other
design than for the benefit of my soul and knowing withal

the impossibility of my escape by reason of so many indictments alleged against me, I plainly laid open the whole course of my life, not omitting any circumstance remarkable. Having put a period to my narrative, he seemed all wonder. I perceived quickly that his amazement proceeded from the strange history of my wicked life and conversation. This wonder was soon converted into pity and commiseration that a man so young should be thus weeded out of the garden of the world, just as he is entered into the blooming springtime of his age. After he had thoroughly made me sensible of the danger that attend these wicked courses (applying his corrosives before his cordials), he then acquainted me with the benefit of true repentance. In short, it will take me up too much time to give an account of everything which was alleged either for information, contrition, or consolation, delivering that divine message with so much power and efficacy that the obdurateness of my heart was able to hold out no longer, but melting into tears, I was willing to have its flintiness broken by the hammer of sacred Scripture.

Finding me in so good a temper, he left me to God and myself for the perfecting that great work he had so hopefully and happily begun. I now condemned a saying, which I once applauded, used much by some of my dissolute companions: "he is more sorrowful than is necessary that is sorrowful before there is necessity." For had sorrow taken place, where pleasure sat regent and jostled out all consideration of the dreadful effects that attend our evil facts, doubtless we should not be made a shameful spectacle to mankind and a heartbreaking to our dearest relations. That saying of Seneca I wish I had practiced as well as registered in my memory: "When I was young, I studied to live well; when aged, how to die well."[2] As I was in the midst of these serious contemplations, my heavenly physician came again to visit me, to know and inquire into the condition and temperament of my soul, feeling in what manner did beat the pulse of its affection. Finding the constitution of my better part indifferent sound and that there were great hopes of a perfect recovery, he rendered thanks to the Almighty for his infinite mercy in looking down with pity on poor sinful creatures whom, when the law hath cast them off and banished them from this lower world, out of His mere infinite goodness receives them into his own blessed protection. To give this holy man some real testimony of my unfeigned repentance, I showed him the abstract of my life, drawn up a little before my apprehension, and did intend to have published it, resolving at that time to have abandoned all those destructive, desperate courses which I formerly followed by padding on the highway, which resolution had I kept, my country would have received the benefit without any further detriment to me either in life or reputation. Now, since I have no other means left to satisfy in part the injuries I have done my countrymen, let this ensuing discovery not only extenuate my manifold offenses, but more especially be the medium of preventing the like hereafter. In the first place give me leave briefly to acquaint you with some remarks in the series of my short life, and in the next place let me lay down some notable instructions for your future caution and preservation against highwaymen, those devouring and destroying caterpillars of a corrupt and polluted nation.

I say little of my parents more than that they were too indulgent to me, supplying my youthful extravagancies with money continually, in such superfluity that my invention was frequently puzzled to find out ways for quick dispatch. These unnecessary expenses took up so much time that there was little left for my study, so that I became as deficient in acquired learning as my parents grew indigent in their estate by my profuseness and debaucheries, whilst with tears they lamented their poverty occasioned by their foolish indulgence, and deploring my future sad condition, foreseeing or fearing the dismal catastrophe which inevitably attends such irregular pranks and wild practices. Death in pity came and closed their eyes that they might not see what otherwise would break hearts. By the loss of their breath, I found the want of their kindness, and having not that supply of money, the sole composure of that flambeau which lit me to all those several extravagancies my disorderly passions, my disorderly will prompted me to go to, I then did cast about what course to steer. My scandalous deportment made me an exile to civil society, and the frequent disobligations I threw on my nearest relations made me an absolute stranger to their families, whereby I was reduced to great extremity, so that necessity, the mother of ingenuity, was constrained to pump every day for some new stratagem to appease a stomach in an uproar for the want of sustenance. Which wanting the accustomed pampering even to satiety made me frequent the eating society so long, till I had eaten quite through my credit and devoured my clothes to boot.

My breeches were so jagged and tattered (that I may say without offence to the reader, though jocosely) they looked somewhat like those that are now called à la mode, and seemed as if my arse, according to the proverb, was hung with points. My hat broadbrimmed, broader than the broadest once in fashion, in pure love and kindness, would have flapped o'er my shoulders to have hid the shame and confusion my face was in, that my own eyes (as well as others') should see my coat becullendred[3] or like a well boat, and though it had as many holes as, or more than, Argus had eyes, yet wanted one to find out some pitiful soul that would intend relief to a wretch so miserable. Had not this misfortune befell me, I should have thought it a thing impossible for a man to live so well, and so ill, in that short registry of time. But now when nothing but despair attended me, being altogether unfit for human society and so out of conceit with myself that I thought myself unworthy of a foreign plantation, and therefore to that end would not apply myself to some merchant; nay, I could not think Hell's imp, a kidnapper, would take of me any cognizance, as I walked very early (for the hardness of my lodging would not suffer me to lie long, and modesty would not permit to be seen lying on or under a stall, unless the

sun had been up to have warmed my chilly limbs, be-
numbed by committing incest with my Mother Earth).

I say, being thus early up, I timely met with a long
purse lying neglected in the street, whose entrance was
on the middle like a wallet; and diving into the bowels
thereof, I found at one end some yellow dirt or excrement,
and the other white, at the sight whereof my body was
seized with a general convulsion so that I feared each member would become a traitor to [the] other in the discovery
of this prize to the right owner, and by that means be deprived of that wanted benefit. I first consulted my hands in
the concealment of this treasure. In order thereunto it was
conveyed into my pocket-holes, but I forgetting my pockets were bottomless, it dropt quite through, which I soon
snatched up, and then betaking myself to my trembling
legs, I got into the fields with an inquisitive eye and panting
heart, and under an hedge found in this purse 10 pound in
silver and 50 guineas. Burying all this money but 50 shillings in the earth, I went and bought an ordinary suit ready-
made, and this I did for fear of being suspected how I
came by the money, being indifferently accoutred. I removed my hidden treasure, thinking it not safely trusted
anywhere but about me. Now did I think I might confidently enough take a lodging, remote from those who knew
me, and having furnished myself with a chamber, I pretended to be a country-gentleman's son, who came up to
London about a suit in law, and behaved myself accordingly, not discovering the least symptom of any former
debauchery, observing very early hours for bedtime. But
not contented with that condition, I was dissatisfied till I
was in another habit, more splendid, and that I might do it
more boldly and safely, framed a lie to my landlord that
I had cast and recovered a considerable sum from one of
my father's creditors and doubted not in a very little time
to overthrow the rest.

This gained me a great reputation in the house, especially [the] seeing my money; and bespeaking a genteel
suit of clothes with all necessary appurtenances befitting

persons of quality, as silver sword, &c., I now scorned the thoughts of associating myself with those narrow-souled-plebeian-snippers, whose parents were neither able or willing to see their sons go in a garb outshining commonalty in the time of their apprenticeship, or if there be ability and propensity thereunto, or the morose master hindering it, to obstruct their servants' pride and vanity. Yet are these bondmen's boundless desires such that (though to the ruin of themselves and the breaking of their masters) they will have these gaudy outsides to pimp for their lechery and other sensualities, having moneys in their pockets (though none of their own) to pay for it. For their habiliments they purchase by exchange of their masters' goods, one with another, and the money they purloin out of the box, or one of the snipping crew shall convert a piece of goods for him into ready money and go his share. The mercer deals with the draper; and a tailor perhaps, who hath shipwrecked his conscience, deals with them both; and the linendraper, hosier, goldsmith, &c., with such-like ornamental clothing trades, are respected as very material instruments among them. Nay, they will stoop so low sometimes to chaffer for belly-timber of the choicer sort, and will bid fairly to a drawer for a flower. I might amply enlarge my discourse concerning the locusts, as how they insinuate into the maid's favour to let them out at unseasonable hours and stay up for them till it be early, to the great prejudice of their master's business the next day, and at length the wench will find for the reward of this notable piece of night service, a great belly, and when she expects to find relief from the caterwauling father, the plot is discovered, and they both turned out-of-doors, to their utter ruin and destruction. I shall desist saying more on this subject, but only advise the master to have a prudent and careful eye over his servants, checking betimes any looseness he discovers, so shall he find his business done when requisite, and they the benefit of their fidelity, by performing their trust at the expiration of their time.

Now to return where I left off. Being gallantly equipped,

I soon got new acquaintance, the most of which were intimately acquainted with the humours of the town, were incomparable at the art of wheedling, which some call complaisance. Neither were they unpracticed in any sort of game, but more especially cards and dice, both which pernicious tools they have laboured with more and taken as much pains to understand as a seven-years student hath done with *Aristotle's Organon*. One of these, whom I judged had somewhat better principles than the rest, I daily accompanied, and grew in a little time to be so familiar that we embosomed the arcanas of each other's concern without restriction or suspicion, and having tried each other's fidelity, we agreed upon a lasting league of brotherhood, and knowing that contiguity of bodies is the speediest confirmation of a desired friendship, we resolved to lie together.

Now were our thoughts and actions like the air to all, as free to one another; and although in love there should be no competitor, yet such hath our freedom been that frequently the subject of our amours hath been one and the same person, whom he first knew and loved (as he said) beyond any of her sex, and I wish he had still loved her without me. Then had not those resistless charms, enthroned in every feature of her face, so bewitched and infascinated my reason that I undervalued the greatest danger for her sake. Nor did I scruple to undertake anything for her satisfaction, as I shall hereafter declare more at large for the reader's satisfaction but to my great grief, she being the cause of mine, as such loose ambitious women are of thousands of men's ruin and destruction.

My new acquaintance, finding me but raw and ill-experienced in the crafts of this subtle world, undertook to be my tutor and read his lectures to me every day. What his mouth did not inform, his actions instructed me in. When I was abroad, I observed his deportment to a hair and took wonderful delight in imitating his insinuations, whereby I had wriggled myself into what tavern-credit I pleased without being great with the vintner, though much in his books, but by being inwardly acquainted with his wife or ingratiating myself into the favour of his daughter, if barkeeper; for then I knew the money's going all through her hands, she might perform her part well enough in the art of conveyance, as well as the most experienced scrivener about the town, and with lesser noise and trouble. The purchase of these favours, though at first they cost a considerable sum, yet I found by computation the annual income recompensed the cost.

He made it his business to inquire out impotent men who had buxom, lusty wives. If shopkeepers, he commonly bought commodities of them as an introduction for his dealing in one not to be sold because the master keeps it for his own use, and so according to each several trade or profession, he squared his designs so that frequently they took effect, unless the premises were prepossessed by a brother of the same quill.

The next thing he taught me was to game, and made me so great a proficient at it that I could nick the nicker[4] sometimes, by which means I was taken for a brother at the ordinary, and by frequently dining there, and conversing, and practicing with the rooks, I went my share in a bubbling and had an interest in several taverns near the ordinary where the poor cully was inveigled in, and afterward under the pretense of great kindness, then wheedled into play, and in a thrice the woodcock deplumed, and not a souse left to give a linkboy to light him home.

In this sort, I as greedily hunted after prey as the Devil doth after usurers' souls on their deathbeds.[5] Nor was the ordinary the only pond I fished in, for I found a playhouse sometimes convenient for my purpose, also cockpits, bowling greens and alleys; neither must a brothel be omitted. My tackling was so good and my hooks so well barbed that after I had struck a gudgeon I was sure to hold him, though I suffered him to play a little in the stream.

If at any time I casually fell into the company of any young country-gentleman, whom his rich father had sent up to the City to learn somewhat more than the ruder country can afford, I and my companion (that brother of mine in iniquity) did first study what humour he was of. When that was known, we had an excellent art in suiting ours to his in everything. This artifice so endeared us unto him that loans of money, engagements, and such easy requests (as we called them) were seldom denied; and lest at any time he should repent him of those excesses in expense and high debaucheries we constantly drew him into, by any serious reflection upon what was past, we kept him by turns always in a high pitch of drinking, and like a careful guardian to some wealthy heiress, we could not endure he should be out of our sight lest falling into other company he might be snatched out of our hands by some other Craftsby, and so we lose our expected booty.

Having thus by much sweat and industry adapted and wrought him to such a soft and waxen temper that we could make him wear what impression we pleased to lay on him, we then boldly venture abroad with him, having taught him to wear fine clothes and to leap out of one fashion into another so often, till he had quite lost the knowledge of himself and the latest habit à la mode. Having made our youngster believe himself in Elysium, and thought that he enjoyed more delights than the Turks believe their paradise affords after death, we then bethink ourselves how to conclude the play, the prologue to which are these our seeming kindnesses, and you would think them not small when you shall see us strive who shall first lend him money upon his least pretense of want thereof; carry him to very handsome, lovely women, and then with leaving him alone to the full fruition of his amorous desires; assist him in all quarrels, but most of them of our own making; if challenged, secure him and his honour safe, whilst we pretendedly fight for him, and it may be return from the supposed field to his chamber (where he waits till the danger is over) with a hand bound up in a scarf, where his rogueship, my beloved brother, begins a formal and serious speech telling him what bloody work there had like to have been, how strenuously and resolvedly his cause was fought, to the loss of some blood on his side, but it

was no matter; there is more still left at his service, and
such like fair, deluding pretenses. Hereupon this country
cockbrain, transported with the consideration of such great
effects of friendship, expresseth how much he is obliged.
Nor can the obligation be cancelled. However, he will study
to be grateful, and in the first place promises to pay the
chirurgeon liberally to cure a wound (was never made);
next gives him a silver sword to wear for his sake, which
the receiver promiseth shall be worn on no other account
than for the defence and preservation of the giver. These
and the like were but the petty forerunners of greater kindnesses we expected to receive, which must be effected in
their proper time and season. As thus, when we prompted
him to change of apparel, the mercer (who trusted him),
knowing his father to be wealthy and him heir to the estate, gave us credit also upon his account; and now and
then, by a whisper in the ear, he was advised to remember
Mistress B—— or Mistress F——, a petticoat or some such
thing she wanted, which was done accordingly, and delivered into our hands, but went not out of them without
a consideration. By this you may understand our gallant
also was instructed in the art of whoring, and so exact an
observator of his mistresses that he was forced to keep a
commonplace book, wherein he writ the names of those
bona robas alphabetically digested, and that he might presently recall to his memory their several complexions, he
affixt to each name a little lock of hair which he took from
the person, *in perpetuam rei memoriam.*[6] When all his
money is spent, his credit gone and destroyed, and his
father hearing of his extravagancies and what dissolute,
desperate company he keeps, then we think it is time to
vanish, or disappear, and leave our cully in his fool's paradise, to be handled at the discretion of his creditors.

Whatever we got by these indirect courses, we equally
shared, and thus continued a twelvemonth together, acting
many rogueries not all of a complexion, for we were now
thorough-paced in all manner of villainy. Nor could it be
expected that our actions should always meet with success;

for we were several times in gaol, and once I had like to
have lost my life for robbing a coach near Barnet, and
without question the law had then put a period to those
evil practices, had I not restored the major part of the
money and goods to the right owner, on this condition: at
my trial they should forbear bringing any evidence against
me, and so I was then acquitted by proclamation.

So fair a warning, one would think should have put a
stop to such proceedings, but it signified nothing to me.
I rather think it was the cause of my hardening, for I
thought with myself: Why may not I escape another time
in the same manner? And that which much augmented this
senseless security was the frequent pardons granted to the
most notorious malefactors, not once or twice, so that from
thence grew a kind of proverbial saying amongst the scoutmasters of the road:[7] he can't be hanged (without treason
or murder) who hath £500 at his command. Besides, the
impudence of my fellow prisoners did much increase my
own, and made me boldly look upon my irons, and presently stare my friends in the face who came to see me,
without a blush.

Being abroad again, I thought of nothing but my profit
and pleasure, but pursued them with too much precipi-
tancy. No villainy lay fairly in my way, which I did not
think myself fit for, and was still encouraged to go on by
my comrade, and was commonly in the van upon any desperate exploit, having the knowledge of my weapon, and
could use it as well as the best experienced master of the
science in the town.

Now as ill luck would have it, my constant companion
died, leaving little behind him but his wench, whom he
bequeathed to me, enjoining me to have a special care of
her he so highly prized in his lifetime. I accepted of the
legacy and took possession immediately, without a forcible
entry, for she made presently a willing surrender. " 'Tis pity
she's a whore," for impartially, I may say it, her beauty is
scarcely to be paralleled, nor her disposition, being highly
ambitious, sensual and insatiate. To oblige them all in some

measure, I performed as much as I could, expending all I had then by me, unlawfully gotten; and fearing I might lose her beloved society, for want of continuing my wonted kindnesses to her by presents, treats, and dalliances, I made the last serve for all till I had found out some less dangerous expedient than padding to satisfy her enlarged desires, and that which pricked me forward was her coldness more than usual to me, which coldness did increase my fire, making me resolve the perpetration of anything, [rather] than to be treated by her with so much indifference.

In the first place, I went and renewed my acquaintance with an ordinary, [who] shall be nameless, and there I rooked sometimes at one table and sometimes at another, but by reason of the scarcity of fair gamesters, little was to be got. Many times I waited an hour or two before I could see one strange face come in, and if there did, immediately at his appearance the rooks were all alarmed, and though before they were busily pecking at one another for a shilling, they now desist their thoughts, being wholly employed who shall first make prize of him. Now by reason of late sittings up, there and in an adjacent tavern I frequented in hope of booty, I was quite tired out and resolved to go thither for the time to come upon a double account. The first was to win by play; secondly, if little could be got that way (for I was generally known an expert nicker), I might then observe who carried off good sums of money and, by following them in the dark, take my advantage in some convenient place, and there dispossess them of it, which I have frequently done, making choice of the darkest nights for my purpose, for winter is the proper time for a gaming ordinary.

I found it unsafe to take this course any longer, yet now and then got a considerable booty, which when I carried as a tribute of love to my fair mistress, no frown could sit upon her brow, all feigned anger was banished from her countenance, but she was all complaisance. And but that I loved her in a more than common manner, her overloving

and petulant deportment would have raised in me a humour rather loathing than loving.

So various and villainous were the pranks I committed
daily that now I was forced, like a bat, never to flutter or
stir abroad till the dusk of the evening. If I did, it was the
greatest caution imaginable, and then, too, I never stayed
long in a place, for fear some or other had dogged me in
order to my apprehension. Thus did I skulk here and there
like the dogs in Egypt, as it is reported, who when by
thirst they go to drink of the River Nile, lap here and there,
and dare not stay long in a place, for fear the crocodiles
that lie lurking within the banks should pull them into the
current.[8]

My wench, seeing what straits I was put to for her maintenance, which was none of the meanest, for the whore, if
she dined with me without something extraordinary and
wine to boot, I had better at night to have lain in a tumbril,
and if my overmuch kindness had pampered her too high
with meat or drink that was provocative (being of herself
naturally salacious), with more ease I might have lain between the sheets with red-hot Proserpine, and therefore
when I perceived some symptoms, which I used to mark,
appear, I disappeared, and sometime after sent her word
I should not lie at home. I say, my miss seeing all my
stratagems would not answer her expectation, she resolved
to desert me when I least dreamed thereof; and now I
cannot choose but rail at her whole sex, for her sake, rewarding my kindness with so much baseness and ingratitude. For as she carried away all I had left, so she left me
something that was none of my own, a swinging clap, which
laid me up in pickle above six weeks before I was cured.
At the expiration of which time, walking in Hatton Garden,
I met with three or four of my old acquaintance, knights
of the road, and all of a gang, men of such undaunted
resolution and irresistible courage that threats of death, or
extreme torture (I am confident), would no ways dull the
edges of their stout and matchless spirits.

After a few ceremonies at first meeting, it was concluded

we should drink a glass of wine, and the next tavern must be our council-chamber, where in private we might consult what was best to be done. I was demanded how I had spent my time since my first gaol delivery. I told them, who blamed me much for my undertaking such mean things as pilfering up and down and making seizures of such petty things a generous, bold soul would scorn to take notice of. They condemned me not for keeping my whore, but that I did not keep her more under. The thing is laudable, said one, to have a miss, though he hath a very handsome wife of his own, and is agreeable to the custom and honour of the times; and should we throw any "approbium" upon it, it would reflect upon ourselves.

"Come," said another, "we trifle away time; let us fall to business. It is a good while since we shared a booty. Let us lie no longer idle, and if our brother will accompany us, instead of picking up here and there crowns and angels (a thing beneath us), let us resolve at 'Have at all,' a five-hours' adventure may make us possessors of £500."[9]

I told them I was unprovided of an horse and other appurtenances necessary for the design. They presently told me I should be supplied, and so I was accordingly, and as well provided for our intended expedition as any of them.

The first robbery that I committed, I told you, was on a coach near Barnet. The second was this. We were four in company and took our road towards Maidenhead, more for intelligence sake than for any present booty. In Maidenhead we dined, and towards four o'clock in summertime we traveled on for Reading, making a little halt by the way at Maidenhead Thicket, expecting there to light upon some prize. Having waited an hour or more to no purpose, we proposed to distribute ourselves and ride into Reading singly, and that two should lie in one inn and two in the other for the better benefit of observation.

My other two comrades lay in an inn where they were intimately acquainted and were winkt at by the master of the house, the servants also being at their devotion, by whose means they understood that there was a gentleman in the house who the next morning with his man would set out for Marlborough and that it was thought by the weight of a small portmanteau it must be money that caused it to be so heavy. We, on the other side, could make no discovery till after supper, and then we heard what our hearts desired.

An attorney was in the company, and amongst other talk, he said he was bound for London to be there at the term, and asked the master of the house (who was acquainted with him) whether he had any service to command him thither, for in the morning he would set forth. Whereupon, said I, composing my countenance, "I am sorry I have not the happiness then tomorrow to have your company, for I must ride a contrary way to Bristol."

"Say you, sir," said he. "You seem a civil gentleman, and I am sorry, too; and as a stranger, I wish you so much good will. Have a care of Marlborough Downs; there are a parcel of whippersnappers have been very busy there of late." Hereupon I startled and seemed to be very much concerned. The attorney, perceiving that, called me and told me if I had a considerable charge, he willed me to secure it some way or other, for I should certainly lose it. I thanked him somewhat coldly, as if I suspected him some subtle, insinuating spy. He thereupon, to free me from any such jealousy, put his hand in his pocket and pulled out a bag wherein were an 150 guineas, saying, "These I will so conceal in the saddle I ride upon that I will defy all the damned highwaymen in England to find them out. I have past them several times in this manner, with good sums about me, and for your further belief I will show you in what manner."

I gave him a thousand thanks and assured him I would follow his advice. Now did I not know without suspicion how to get out and inform my comrades of this discovery. Just in the interim a note came from them to meet them at such a place, and so pretending business in the town, I went to them, where we concluded that I and my fellow should rob the Marlborough traveler, and they two should rob the attorney, which the next morning was performed, the attorney thinking the Devil had given them information where his treasure lay. We came not off so well, for though we gained the booty, which was sixscore pound in silver, yet I was shot in the arm and so stiffly opposed by the gentleman and his man that had we not shot his horse in the head, and so fell instantly dead, they had either killed or taken us prisoners. This being done, we met at the place appointed the last night for our general rendezvous.

The next time that we went upon the same account we met with a pleasant adventure, for after we had robbed several to the making up of a sum above £180, we were all strangely robbed of it by one.

Hearing some seamen were to be paid off at Chatham such a day and knowing that London is the center that attracts and invites them to spend their hard-gotten money, we went down to Shooter's Hill and hovered thereabouts till evening, but got little booty. The next day towards the afternoon we picked up a great many stragglers and robbed them of their money, some more and some less, but when there [were] four or five in a body, nay, if but three, we shunned them as much as they would have done us, had they known what we were. At length a parson coming from London fell in amongst us, whom we robbed without any respect to his coat. Neither could we have judged by the meanness of his habit and the poorness of his horse, with the shortness of his journey, that he could have had above an attorney's retaining fee about him; but thinking to make some speedy sport with him (and so dismiss him) by searching his pockets, the attempt was no sooner slightly made (and had never been prosecuted) but that he roared like a town bull, he was utterly undone. Then did I search him thoroughly, and from that time afterwards in all my robberies I learned to search so strictly that sooner might the Pope turn Quaker than for any of them to conceal a penny from me; and seeing what severities my unconscionable and cruel companions used to those seamen, who had ventured their lives for their King and country, and at last to be deprived of their long-looked-for reward, taught me to be as deaf, too, when the poor traveler cries, "I am undone"; and my heart in process of time grew flinty and not to be moved with sighs and tears.

This parson had £15 about him, all which we took from him, but returned him 20 shillings, if he would engage on his word, nay, swear that he would inform none he met with what had happened, or following us by hue and cry, or by general raising of the towns about us near adjacent.

The parson, minding more the loss of his money than the breach of his oath, meeting with a seaman (as we were informed afterwards), advised him to turn back if he had any money, for but a little before there were a parcel of rogues that just now robbed him of £15 and will infallibly do the like to him if he proceeded farther. The resolute seaman would not believe the parson, thinking it some idle chimera of his own invention, and so went on his way, and the parson on his. Coming up to the seaman we bid him stand, who asked us what we meant. We told him that we wanted money. "Alas, gentlemen," said he, "it is true I have some which I received for my pay in his Majesty's service, and therefore it is pity to take that from me which I am carrying home for the maintenance of my poor wife and children." If he had persuaded an angel to have been his orator and pleaded in his behalf, it would have been all one, for no other sound pleased us but that of his money. When he saw that there was no remedy, he delivered all that he had, which was £65. "Now, gentlemen," said he, "let me beg one request of you, and that is, since I dare not go home to my wife and at present know not what course of life to steer, admit me into your company. You see I am limbed well enough, and I have courage and strength enough to qualify me for your occupation." We asked him whether he was in earnest. He swore a hundred oaths he was in earnest and was ready to be tried at that instant, insisting farther that he was greatly in love with a trade that could get as much money in six minutes as he could do in three years.

I was then purse bearer; and finding we had done enough for that day, we appointed a place to meet at, and so distributed ourselves for the present. Only, I had the charge of the seaman, who was wretchedly mounted, and therefore I needed not to fear him. Besides, as we rid along, I bound him over and over again by oaths to stand to what promise he had made us. At length, riding in a lane, suspecting nothing in the least, he turns his little hobby upon me and seizing my bridle before I was aware, claps to my breast a little ugly, brass-barreled pistol, and swore as bloodily as if he had been one of the trade above twenty years: if I would not instantly dismount, he would send a bullet to my heart. I saw by his frightful countenance that there was no dallying, so I dismounted and gave him my horse; and he in kindness bid me take his: such a beast I never saw on a common, so poor, so weak that I was thinking to commit my safety to my own, and not to his legs.

You may imagine what a sweat I was in being thus dismounted, for having committed so many robberies that day, should I be met by any of the country, they would conclude me one of the robbers, seeing a man so splendidly accoutred, riding on a beast hardly fit to feed crows and ravens.

The night coming on favoured me, and I got among my associates; and now I shall give you leave to guess whether their laughter or sorrow was greatest. First, that a stout thief (for so I was accounted) should be robbed by a hobbyhorse and a potgun. And, secondly, so much money lost, when secured beyond the probability of retaking.

We heard the seaman, after he had paid himself, summoned in such brethren as had been robbed by us, and none else (but the parson) and returned them their money.

Should I enumerate all the rogueries and robberies I committed, either singly or with others, relating in what manner they were done, I shall waste too much time and miss of that design which I purposed to myself, which is the general good of my countrymen. Wherefore I shall pass them all by, not so much as mentioning the last robbery

I was guilty of near Colebrook, when pursued by the country, opposed and apprehended by them, to the loss of our own and the blood of some of them. The manner whereof is too generally known to be again repeated, and therefore leaving this and the like stories, I shall insist on, as is more profitable, and therein discover, first, what a highwayman is, how bound by oath, what order is prescribed, in what manner they assault, and how they behave themselves in and after the action. In the next place, my best endeavour shall be to dissuade these desperadoes to desist robbing on the highway by showing them the certainty of their apprehension one time or other, and though they may a long time prosper in that vile course of life, spending high and faring deliciously, yet every bit is attended with fear. Neither is their sleep less unquiet, starting ever and anon by some horrid dream, so that I cannot say, when they go to bed, they go to take their rest, but only to slumber out the tedious minutes of the gloomy night in horror and affrightment. I shall insist on other dissuasions by showing them the misery of a prison, by putting them in mind of their wretched and cursed ends, which they vainly jest at by presuming on some examples of grace, and the reward of their wickedness in the world to come. Lastly, instructions, not only for the honest traveler that he may pass in safety, but for the innkeeper to distinguish highwaymen from guests that are honest. All these I shall with sincerity run over particularly.

Highwaymen, for the most part, are such who never were acquainted with an honest trade, whom either want of money or employment prompt[s] them to undertake these dangerous designs; and to make their persons appear more formidable and to gain respect, they dub one another colonel, major, or at least a captain, who never arrived to a greater height than a trooper disbanded or at the utmost a life-guardsman cashiered for misdemeanour.

Having made up a party, ere they proceed to act their villainies, they make a solemn vow to each other that if by misfortune anyone should be apprehended, he shall not discover his complices, and that if he be pressed hard to particularize his companions, he must then devise names for men that never were, describing their persons, features, and discovering their habitations, but so remote one from another that the danger of the trial may be over ere sufficient inquiry can be made.

And further, to procure mercy from the bench, there must be a plausible account given how you fell into this course of life, fetching a deep sigh, saying that you were wellborn, but by reason of your family falling to decay you were exposed to great want, and rather than shamefully beg (for you knew not how to labour) you were constrained to take this course for a subsistence; that it is your first fault, which you are heartily sorry for, and will never attempt the like again.

Having taken a solemn oath to be true one to another, their next business is to acquaint themselves by tapsters, hostlers, chamberlains, or others, what booties are stirring, how contained, and whither bound. But before they attempt the seizure, if any novice be in the company, then are they instructed by the more experienced, as I was at first, after this manner.

In the first place, you must have variety of periwigs planted in your lodgings; and the like you must carry abroad, if occasion require the necessity of changing the colour of the hair. Neither must you be without your false beards of several colours. For want of them, you may only cross your locks athwart your mouth, which is a good disguise. Patches contribute much thereto. And lest your voice should be known another time by him that is robbed, put into your mouth a pebble or any such like thing, which will alter your tone advantageously to your purpose.

Being thus provided, a watchword must be framed, wrapped up in some common question as "What's o'clock?" or "Jack, what shall we have for supper?" to avoid putting the traveler into suspicion; which as soon named, you must instantly fall to your work, seizing with your left hand the bridle and with your right presently a pistol. This so terrifies that he delivers instantly, for who will trust a pistol at his breast loaded with a brace of bullets, and a mouth discharging at the same time volleys of oaths that if he deliver not instantly, he is a dead man? But herein you may choose to believe him, for he will be very cautious of murder, for fear of provoking the law to an implacability, unless it be when he is beset, that rather than run the hazard of hanging, he must endeavour his escape by the death of one or more of his assailants.

Having o'ermastered them you set upon, then do you carry them into some covert, where you search so severely that nothing can be hidden from you. If in the strict inquiry gold be found privately quilted in a doublet or waistband of his breeches, I can hardly forbear smiling when I think in what manner these rogues will slave the poor man with "villain," "cheating rascal," for endeavouring to preserve his own, whilst he hath nothing else to say but that he is undone, which they regard with as little as the hangman will do them at the place of execution. Having changed your horses for theirs, if better than your own, the next thing you do is to make them swear neither to follow you nor to raise the country with an hue and cry upon you. Thus having the poor traveler forlorn away, you ride to some strange place or where you are known and winkt at, and there you share what unlawfully you got, not without the cheating one another.

Now here, by the way, give me leave a little to descant on their prodigality, after an attempt that proves successful. London, the more is the pity, is their best sanctuary; and therefore after any robbery, they commonly repair thither, having as many names as lodgings, and both as changeable as a whore's dalliances with variety of persons. Their next care is to buy variety of splendid apparel; and having bought his wench a new gown and furnished her pockets with guineas, they then prosecute to the height all manner of debaucheries, which by a mistaken name they call "the chief of pleasures." And as their whore, so must their host participate with them in their gain, else all the fat is in the fire; for the vintner, innkeeper, &c., knowing very well what they are and how easily they get their money, will be sure to enlarge their reckoning and make it swell prodigiously. Neither must this be complained of, lest they refuse to keep their counsel any longer.

All the time they can spare from robbing and undoing poor harmless men is spent in wine and women so that the sunshine of their prosperity lasts but a moment, not so long as to warm their hands by the blazing fire of their prodigality, before cold death comes and seizeth them; and how can it be otherwise expected? The pitcher goes not so often to the well, but it comes broken home at last.[10]

But before death takes them from this to carry them before an higher tribunal, there to answer for all they have acted here on earth, there is a punishment preceding this, which makes my soul startle at the thoughts thereof. It is a prison wherein are contained so many tortures, woes and pains, which I do think were enough to punish without death the greatest of offenses. Now since I cannot describe the horror of this Hell on earth, I shall admonish all to have a care that their evil actions compel them not to feel the pain, and let those who have already endured the smart thereof be deterred by those sufferings from ever again espousing such pernicious practices which may venture them into their former despicable and deplorable condition.

Having thus endeavoured to fright highwaymen by showing them the intolerable torments of a prison, besides the certainty and shamefulness of hanging and hazard of eternal death hereafter, I shall here take another course to scare them if possible, and therefore in the first place I shall lay down directions how to know them as they ride on the road, with rules how to shun them or, if robbed, how to pursue and apprehend them when they think themselves most secure.[11]

In the first place, when at any time you intend to travel and cannot avoid carrying a sum of money with you, let no person know what charge you have or when you will set forward. It is a custom, I confess (but I can assure you it is dangerous), for men the day before they begin their journey, to take their leave of their relations and friends, drinking healths round to the happy return of the traveler, who suspects not the least harm in all this, whereas it hath been known that a father this way hath been betrayed by his own son, a brother by a brother, nay, one pretendedly dear friend betray another, by discovering to highwaymen when and which way he rides, bidding them to prepare accordingly either to meet or overtake, and for the plot so laid he goes his share.

Another way of setting they have in this manner. The gang shall ride before out of sight, leaving one lusty fellow of their company behind who shall ride very softly, expecting some person or other who shall overtake him. If three or four, he singles out one he thinks hath the most money and, pretending much kindness, whispers him in the ear, saying that he likes not those men, and asks him if he knows them. If not, he adviseth him by all means to slacken his pace, for certainly they are dangerous fellows. This timorous piece of credulity thanks him for his honest care and takes his advice, and not long after brings him to the place where his confederates lie in ambuscado, who upon sight of them draws, bidding the other to do the like. And now begins a dangerous fight, as the traveler imagines, who through fear of bloodshed delivers his money and persuades his champion to do the like, who with much ado at length condescends thereunto. Having given him a private item which way they intend to ride, they set spurs to their horses and are out of sight in an instant.

Hereupon this pretender to honesty will straight persuade you to assist him in making an hue and cry, in the carrying on of which to be sure he will be the foremost as seemingly most zealously active in the apprehension of these robbers, to no other end than to lead you quite another way till his brethren be out of all danger. I knew one notorious rogue (but by his sly and crafty deportment was looked upon to be a very honest gentleman) suffered himself to be robbed with three more, by four of his own confederates. The robbery being committed between sun and sun, he with those three honest men sued the country and recovered the money they had lost.[12]

Whensoever the traveler designs his journey, let him consider the Sabbath day is a time not only unlawful, but more dangerous for robbing than any other. I need not expatiate myself on the illegality of the act, since there is a special command forbidding the breach of that holy day of rest, the violation whereof hath been frequently punished by being robbed. For to speak the truth, that day hath been and is still chosen by highwaymen for the best and fittest time to commit their robberies, first, because they are sensible that few travel then but such who ride about some eminent concern, and do suppose to that end carry a considerable sum about them. In the next place, on that day the roads are most quiet, being undisturbed with great quantities of people, and therefore rob with more ease and greater security. Lastly, they know the country will not be so forward to pursue them with an hue and cry, whereas they cannot but be sensible that a judge will hardly be induced to make the country pay the reparation of a loss sustained by him who ought to have stayed at home and perform those duties required from him proper to the day, and not wander abroad and leave his Creator's business undone, that he may do his own. If you needs must travel, you have days enough in the week to follow your urgent and important affairs with more security, the roads being then full of good company, if you will make choice of a convenient time and be cautious whom you entertain into your society.

The first caution is this: be shy of those who are overprone in pressing into your company; it is more safe to entertain such who are unwilling to associate themselves with you or, if they do, it is with such indifferency that there need the urging of persuasions to effect it. Now to the intent you may distinguish an honest man from a thief or robber, take these informations and directions. First, if you suspect your company, halt a little, and in your stay observe whether they still hold on their course, or slack their pace, or it may be alight and walk with their horses in their hands. If you observe any of these, you may conclude them the justly suspected marks of an highwayman; but these following are infallible: the putting on a cypress hood[13] or a vizard mask upon your near approach are signs they presently will bid you stand and deliver, or if before they shroud their hellish looks with those disguises, stare any of them in the face boldly, and if he turns his head aside, be thence forewarned to stand aloof and provide for your preservation. Neither is there any more certain indicium of a robber than the incongruity of his bushy beard and face, his whispering, or his more incivil prying and inquiry whither you are traveling or about what business.

Beware of joining company with one single on the road, although you have a friend with you. His pretense will be to insinuate himself into your good opinion, that having a charge about him, he is overjoyed to meet with two whose face[s] and actions discover nothing but what is honest, and in a little riding will presume to call you honest fellow traveler. In a short time it may be three of his companions will overtake you, at the sight of whom he shakes and seems to be in the greatest agony imaginable. At length he says with trembling, "In troth, gentlemen, I doubt me we are waylaid. Therefore, stand to't if you have any pistols; otherwise if you have any store of money, the best way will be to fly for it."

It may be you have those grim handfuls, death's speedy executioners, and minding well the number of those you fear will be so bold to assault you and finding no inequality, your courage probably may prompt you to an opposition if cause require; but you will then find quickly your supposed friend turn cat in pan, and be on the other side, and being thus overmatched, must either yield your moneys quietly or do worse.

Sometimes there will be one or more of these trepanning rascals, who having attired himself every way like a countryman, with rolls of hay about his legs, an old hat flapping over his eyes, with a broad leathern girdle about his middle, with great buckles, riding aside on his horse with a goad instead of a riding-rod. I say, this fellow shall ride in company with you, asking very silly questions and singing a country song to some horrible tune, all to raise laughter. When by this means he hath lulled you into a senseless security, and not suspecting in the least any harm from him, he instantly assaults you, and his complices come instantly into his succour, who surprising you thus unawares, you are without difficulty made a prey to their unlawful desires.

You see how dangerous a thing it is to travel with a charge about you in the daytime, unless you have a very circumspect care not only in your inn, but on the road. If therefore you cannot avoid traveling, and that with store of money, the emergency of your business requiring it, undertake your journey in the night, for highwaymen think that none will be so mad to ride at that unseasonable time, unless they are miserable poor. Besides, it is dangerous for them to be abroad for fear of suspicion, and that is not all neither, for how can they see to take their best advantage in the dark, not knowing how many, what men, and how armed they assault; besides, should they gain the better of it, the obscurity of the night gives them the advantage of dropping their money into a ditch or other place convenient.

Now to advise you for the best. At what time soever you ride, take notice that your high-pads do always keep their station upon your greatest and most beaten roads, whereby they have the advantage of picking and choosing. Now if you would be safe, make choice of such roads which are less frequented.

If you ride several in company, shun that idle custom of bustling up all together, when you come near any place noted for robbing, for by this means you are all catched, like a covey in a net, at once. For these rogues divide themselves and make several stands, and by this means they may set upon you before and behind. But if you ride about an hundred paces distant, one from the other, I'll warrant your safety; for they dare not set upon a scattered company for fear that some escaping, the country should be alarmed and so endanger their immediate taking.

Now should you perceive them divide as well as you, and each drawing near him he intends to set upon, you have then fair warning, and running will hardly avail anything; but fight like men, you have two to one the odds, though not in numbers, yet in a good conscience; which they wanting, their own guilt and fear fights against them and disarms them. Whilst thus you contend with them, there is hope some may come in to your rescue.

By the way, let me tell you, I have known when we have been thus engaged that some have come up to us, whom we have persuaded to keep on their way and not meddle with what they were unconcerned with; at which these base coxcombs (nay, now I must call them unworthy rascals) have quietly rid away and left those men to our mercies, or rather to exercise our cruelties upon; whereas had they sided with them, we must have fled before them. For though we had courage (it may be enough), yet we durst not fight it out when we meet with those that are bold and stout, for in so doing we not only fight them but the whole country.

By the way, let me discover an egregious fault in some men who will not only yield patiently to be robbed, but are content to let the thieves go clearly off, nay, wish they may escape, so that the country may lie liable to make good the robbery, if they take them not by an hue and cry. Nay, such is the baseness of their principles that they commonly double the sum, knowing that the hundred will be willing to compound, and thus abuse the thief and country, too.

But notwithstanding all these cautions, should it happen so that you are surprised by these highwaymen, overmastered, and that you must yield, give them fair words and, without a compulsive search, deliver freely some part of your money, with a wish that you had more at their service, and it may be they will trouble themselves no farther with you; however, if they offer, show no dislike, for if you do, it will but provoke them to the severity of a more rigorous search, to the discovery of what you had most cunningly concealed.

Have a special care that you let them not perceive you eye them too much, it being of a dangerous consequence, for by this means they either think you know some of them or are taking some remarkable signs and tokens how you may know them another time, which may endanger your life.

After the robbery committed, their usual charge is, [do] not stir from the place they put you in, till they have time enough to be gone a considerable distance; and that if they find you offer to pursue them, they will swear a thousand oaths to be your death; and being desperate, for ought I know, they may be as good as their words. Therefore, be not too hasty in the pursuit, lest it being discovered, the foremost dropping into a by-lane starts out upon you, seizeth you again, and if you escape cutting, you shall not binding, and so may be bound in a ditch till some commiserating passenger release you. Wherefore follow after at a distance, till you can procure an hue and cry, which you must direct not straight on, but 'cross the country, which is a subtle practice and their constant custom. By this means they have the benefit of resting themselves and refreshing their horses before the lazy hue and cry can overtake them. If closely pursued by it, they will frequently squat like a hare and let the hue and cry pass them, and then ride back again to the place where the robbery was committed.

Be sure in your pursuit to scour the next great right and lefthand road, and if you cannot unkennel them that night, set spies, and a thousand to one you shall see them come riding by the next morning.

If the purchase be great they seized upon, you may be then confident they will that night repair to their general rendezvous here in the City, which is their great "asylum" and chiefest place of refuge and security. The largeness of the City, and the little cognizance one takes of another therein, is the main reason why so many robberies are committed nigh London, and so few remotely distant from it. Now since twenty or thirty miles about London is the stage on which these highwaymen act their parts, I shall discover when robbed how to pursue them with hue and cry.

If you are set upon and robbed in the eastern quarter, take not that road in which you were to London, nor raise the country thereabout, for it is to no purpose; but ride with all speed to Holborn, Strand, St. James's, or Westminster, and there search with all diligence. If you are robbed towards the north, never search any place in the City, but make all convenient speed to the Bankside, Southwark, Lambeth, or Vauxhall. By thus planting themselves, they know, or think at least, they are sufficiently secure, having the City between them and you.

And now, ere I proceed, let me take notice of a great folly and abuse of the countrymen. When report is brought to a justice of a robbery done in such a place, presently a watch is ordered to stand at that place at the charge of the country. Is anyone so senseless to think those highwaymen will voluntarily ride into the mouths of those who are appointed to apprehend them? However, admit they should continue scouring that road, the watchmen are constantly fixed at one place so that but a little way out of their sight, the highwayman may do what he list and meet with more booties than if the road lay unwarded. For all travelers will covet to ride that way in which is placed a watch, for who can imagine thieves will be so bold as to rob near them, which they do to choose; for well they know that those watchmen are silly, old, decrepit men, and though a dozen of them I have seen stand with halberds in their hands, yet have we robbed before their very faces, and they stood still the while, not daring to oppose us in the least. It may be when we were gone out of sight, they would make an outcry and pretend to pursue, though to no purpose.

Once, we resolved to set upon the watch, which was done so effectually that we disarmed them and, having taken them aside out of the way, bound them. After this we per-sonated them in their places, and standing with our brown bills, as with authority, we stopt whom we pleased and, having robbed them, bid them to be guarded by the country-watch, and to secure them, bound them in like manner.

It is now high time to inform the innkeeper how he shall distinguish highwaymen from honest travelers. In the first place, observe their curiosity about their horses in dressing and feeding them. Next, you will find them asking of questions, as who owns that horse and who the other, what their masters are, whither traveling, and when will they set out. These are infallible signs of a highwayman. Nor must I omit this remark: let the hostler poise their cloak-bags, and he shall find them empty, which they carry only for show, and not to burthen their horses.

Next, let the chamberlain take notice, when he shows them to a room, that they will soon dismiss him, and after that, let him listen a while, and he shall hear the gingling of money, and if he can but get a peephole for his eyes, he shall see them sharing their booty.

It will be very requisite to inquire severally each one's particular name, and let your servants do the like. By this means you find them tripping, for they may easily forget a name they borrowed that very day.

At suppertime, let some one knock furiously and hastily at the gate. Then mark them well, and you shall see them start, their countenances change, and nothing but fear and amazement appearing in each face, by which you may positively conclude them what you before did but imagine and suspect.

If in the daytime they come into your inn, you may guess what they are by trifling away their time and staying somewhat longer than is requisite for baiting. You shall observe them sometimes looking out of the window, sometimes standing at the gate, for no other end but to mark what passengers ride by. If they perceive any person of quality to ride that way, or the garb discovers anything of a booty, you shall have them presently in all haste, as alarmed to horse, mount presently, as if some dear friend or near relation was just rid by, whom they must endeavour to overtake.

At night they will come dropping into an inn severally, in divided companies, thereby to cross the number in the hue and cry, and will, when met, subtly take no notice of one another. Nay, to blind the eyes of suspicion, they will inquire of the host what country-gentlemen their own companions are, whether he knows them or not, and if it be convenient to join in company with them. If you find they have no jealousy of them, they will as strangers compliment one another whilst any eyes are on them, but withdraw and watch them well, and you shall find them fall into their usual familiarity and will not only rejoice at the success of their designs, but laugh at the credulity of their landlord.

Much more might be written on this subject, but since it is impossible to discover the whole art and mystery of the highway trade, let this suffice, for according to the proverb, "New lords, new laws." So all new gangs have new orders, plots and designs, to rob and purloin from the honest traveler.

Postscript

Reader, let me assure thee this is no fiction, but a true relation of Mr. Jackson's life and conversation, penned by his own hand and delivered into mine to be made public for his countrymen's good, in compensation of the many injuries he hath done them. The introduction he writ whilst in Newgate, after sentence of condemnation, and desired me to apologize for it, fearing he had neither writ large enough of his true penitence nor had laid down sufficient dehortations from the commission of the like offenses. The disorder he was in, lying under the horror of a speedy and more than common execution, may plead his excuse. The plainness of his style may admit of this plea, that he aimed at (as he confest to me) nothing but the good of his countrymen and that, as he had picked their pockets, he thought it needless to tickle their ears with the gilded straws of rhetorical expressions. God, I hope, hath forgiven him his sins, and may we all amend by his errors, for which he now hangs in chains at Hampstead, a sad and dreadful spectacle to all beholders, and hoping you will pass by the faults of his writing and the press, I subscribe myself a well-willer to all,

Samuel Swiftnicks.[14]

FINIS.

DON TOMAZO,
OR THE JUVENILE RAMBLES
OF THOMAS DANGERFIELD
(1680)

Anonymous

FOREWORD

The place of *Don Tomazo* in an anthology of fiction is, at first, subject to question. One approach is to regard the book, no matter how extravagant its escapades, as straight autobiography. Thus, in the bibliographies of Hazlitt, Esdaile, and Wing, *Don Tomazo* is listed under the name of the author, Thomas Dangerfield. Also, even though the narrative is not told in the first person, the original text does betray four slips—first-person pronouns rather than third-person. Another approach to *Don Tomazo* is to call it, as the *Dictionary of National Biography* does, "a fictitious narrative with some scraps of truth" or to agree with the bolder assertion in Philip W. Sergeant's *Liars and Fakers*: "It is obvious that there is very much more fiction than fact in *Don Tomazo*." By this explanation, the Don's crimes can be viewed as the author's fantasies, and not as the hardened villain's experiences. Still another possibility is to reject altogether the autobiographical approach and to accept Don Tomazo as a criminal biography written by a person very close to Dangerfield, using a narrative technique not very different from Francis Kirkman's in *The*

Counterfeit Lady Unveiled. A look into the political background of *Don Tomazo* reinforces this third approach.

Scanty but unmistakable are the references, at the beginning and the end of *Don Tomazo*, to the infamous episodes of 1679–80 known as the Popish Plot. In November, 1680, when the book was being advertised in the quarterly issue of *The Term Catalogues*, the most sensational informer and "plot witness" was Thomas Dangerfield, alias Captain Willoughby. Capitalizing on this notoriety, the anonymous author breaks off the "juvenile rambles" on the last page, with the Don in Newgate gaol, waiting for Mrs. Cellier to begin "those transactions between them that have lately made so great a noise in the world." More recent events are hinted at in his note to the reader, where the author alludes to Dangerfield's royal pardon and rationalizes that his present "discoveries" are intended to compensate for his "past transgressions." These discoveries—as contemporary readers knew all too well from Dangerfield's courtroom failures in June of 1680—had been "ill-managed." Nevertheless, the show was not over yet: "some of them may yet take effect." The "rambles," spanning the thirty years of Dangerfield's brief life (he died in 1685), are then given to show how the character of the informer was shaped "so proper for the designs for which he was called out" of prison.

The transactions that made the great noise were late developments in the Popish Plot. The true story of Dangerfield's actions and motives in these affairs may perhaps be never known. In the summer of 1679, when he left off a nefarious career of counterfeiting and turned to politics, Catholic persecutions were waxing furiously. In the preceding year, the perverted Titus Oates had made his discoveries of a widespread Catholic plot to burn London, annihilate the Protestants, assassinate the King, and return England to Catholicism. The murder of Sir Edmund Berry Godfrey and the attempt to fix the crime on Catholics had created a condition amounting to panic. It was Mrs. Elizabeth Cellier, friend to Catholic prisoners, who found the handsome Thomas Dangerfield in Newgate—hungry, weighed down with irons, dressed in rags, and desperate. She had him released from gaol by paying his debts, and then utilized his talents in certain counter-operations directed against the Country (or anti-Court) Party. At first he performed minor jobs, but by the fall of 1679 he was ready to make an ambitious move. He wanted to expose Presbyterian plots, which he had heard talked about in his spying for Mrs. Cellier and which actually erupted in the Rye House Plot of 1683. Lacking any real evidence, he proceeded to fake papers containing full details about a general uprising, to take place after the death of the King. In October, armed with this evidence, he brought his story to the Earl of Peterborough, then to the Duke of York, and eventually to Charles II. But the King was not impressed by "so incredible a thing." Next, when Dangerfield tried to plant the telltale papers in Colonel Mansell's rooms, he was detected in his ruse, arrested, and released on bail. Meanwhile, Mrs. Cellier—the Popish Midwife, as her enemies called her—became more deeply implicated in the Catholic conspiracy, when copies of the treasonable papers were found at the bottom of a meal tub in her house. Since the evidence was known to be concocted, it could be used to incriminate the Catholics, as the diarist Narcissus Luttrell states, of "forging a Protestant plot." Now Dangerfield's betrayal of Mrs. Cellier and his friends the Countess of Powis, the Earl of Castlemaine, and the Earl of Peterborough was inevitable. At the end of November, to enable him to perform as a plot witness, he was granted a royal pardon and placed on the secret-service payroll. Ironically, in the two major treason trials that followed in June, 1680, it was the star witness who was dramatically revealed as the blackest of villains.

The real Thomas Dangerfield, as described in the printed reports of these trials in the King's Bench Court, is like Don Tomazo: burglar, padder, counterfeiter, pickpocket, espionage agent, swindler, all-around rascal. A crisis in Mrs. Cellier's trial for high treason, on June 11th, was her determined stand against Dangerfield as a witness. "If I can prove he was whipped and transported, pilloried, perjured," she declared, "he is no witness." And the shrewd Lady Errant did prove burglary against him, with the help of Ralph Briscoe, who testified that he saw "one Thomas Dangerfield . . . burnt in the hand at the Old Bailey." She then offered evidence for his having counterfeited guineas, and produced a record "wherein it did appear he was outlawed upon a felony." Later she had the court listen to a report from Salisbury—a place mentioned in *Don Tomazo* —about "his standing in the pillory for uttering counterfeit guineas." The person most impressed by this display of a "vicious profligate life" was the Lord Chief Justice, Sir William Scroggs, who finally exploded against Dangerfield: "What? Do you, with all mischief that hell hath in you, think to brave it in a court of justice? I wonder at your impudence, that you dare look a court of justice in the face, after having been made appear so notorious a villain." During the trial, according to Roger North, Mrs. Cellier also testified that Dangerfield once bragged that he had padded and that "he cared for neither fire, sword, nor hell, nor what he said, or swore, for he had studied to be a rogue ever since he was ten years old." Needless to say, the lady was acquitted, and the gentleman committed to Newgate.

Dangerfield's criminal record became the center of attention, again, in the treason trial of Roger Palmer, the Earl of Castlemaine, on June 23rd. But now there was one startlingly new issue. Could a man who had been "burnt in the hand" be sworn before a jury? The question was loaded with many legal niceties that had to be explored by the justices. From the Court of Common Pleas came the opinion "that a man attainted upon an outlawry for felony could not be a witness, though pardoned, but if attainted and burnt in the hand he might." Dangerfield was thereby permitted to testify, but subject to correction from other invalidating evidence. Thus, the exposé of Dangerfield as a criminal left him vulnerable as a plot witness. In spite of this second major defeat, he continued to give false witness. In October, he brought charges before the House of Commons that the Duke of York had given him money toward "the sham plot" and had blamed him for not killing the King. So completely had Dangerfield's authority been undermined that, according to Sir Leoline Jenkins, no one believed a single word he said. Around November 13th, the informer was accusing the Countess of Powis and the Earl of Peterborough, and in February of the following year, he was still hard at work. At the very time when Dangerfield was making these charges and was being repeatedly defeated by the clever revelations of his bad character, *Don Tomazo* made its appearance. It seems unlikely that, under these circumstances, Thomas Dangerfield wrote and published so complete a narrative of those same crimes that were bringing him into disrepute.

Mrs. Cellier's vengeance did not stop with her June triumph. Not a woman scorned (although Gilbert Burnet and others hint slyly at her lewdness), she was still a woman tricked. After her acquittal she engaged Dangerfield in a duel of pamphlets, one of which, *Malice Defeated*, is significantly connected with *Don Tomazo*. Although seized in the presses as a libel on the government, *Malice Defeated* somehow got into circulation on September 1st. In the last chapter of her book, Mrs. Cellier now had her revenge. Entitled "The Matchless Picaro," the chapter gave an authentic summary of Thomas Dangerfield's crimes. This was reprinted as *The Matchless Picaro; or A Short Essay of the Fortune and Virtues of Seignior Don Tomaso Ganderfieldo, alias Francisco de Corombona*. Mrs. Cellier next renewed the attack, around September 9th according to Luttrell, with a recital of more crimes in *The Matchless Rogue; or, A Brief Account of the Life of Don Tomazo, the Unfortunate Son*. Incidents that were here only factually noted were later expanded into the longer fictions of *Don Tomazo*. The two "rogue" pamphlets also provided the view of Dangerfield as a picaro and even the hint for a minor theme in *Don Tomazo*; namely, that parental severity produces dangerous revolt in the child.

The major theme of *Don Tomazo* is Guzmanry—a term derived from Mateo Alemán's *Guzmán de Alfarache* (1599). Through the many editions of this Spanish picaresque novel and James Mabbe's English translation, *The Rogue* (1623), the term "Guzmanry" had been absorbed into English and Continental literature as a synonym for "roguery." But the English Guzman of Restoration criminal fiction is not to be mistaken for the Spanish picaro. The English Guzman callously pursues a naturalistic code in preying upon society. Not until he faces the gallows does he develop a conscience. In contrast, picaros like Lazarillo de Tormes and Guzmán de Alfarache are society's victims. In the Spanish picaresque novel, by definition, the protagonist travels from one society to another, suffering from the "acrid comedy" of human existence, but his main drive is desperately to keep alive. The Spanish picaresque novel, as James Fitzmaurice-Kelly once wrote, is "the epic of hunger."

Don Tomazo brings this distinction between Spanish and English rogues into sharp focus. As the author describes his scoundrel's intention of wrecking "the whole Guinea trade," he comments, "See here the difference between a Spanish and an English Guzman, the one pursuing a poor hungry plot upon his penurious master's bread and cheese, the other designing to grasp the riches of the fourth part of the world by the ruin of a national commerce." Don Tomazo rarely has to fend off starvation. Practically without motive, the English Guzman combats social order. He delights in large-scale operations. The "melting trade" he establishes in various cities of the Netherlands. To provide badly needed "intelligence" for the Prince of Orange, he organizes a gang of spies within the French Army. The English Guzman usually integrates his criminal talents. For instance, at Lyme he masquerades as a Spanish count and executes horse-selling swindles. At Penzance, he robs the justice's wife of her jewels, and at the same time tricks the justice into swapping good money for bad. He gambles, bets recklessly at the Newmarket races, buys cattle to sell at a lower market price—all with counterfeit money ("the readiest way to have money was to make it").

Don Tomazo has the cynicism, as well as the craft, of the English Guzman. In place of Alemán's satire and frequent moralizing, the author of *Don Tomazo* bluntly delivers the criminal's ethic. In the Scottish adventure, the reader looks in vain for the social satire he expects to find in a picaresque novel. Scotland, to be sure, is ridiculed as "the worst of countries" and "as barren of riches as the mountains that disfigure it." The author's obiter dicta are also apt to be ironic: "Guzmans being the only relict of the Golden Age that have all things in common" or "true Guzmans never mind morality." His true attitude he reveals, perhaps, in his remark that "Guzmans call that necessity, when they want fuel to feed the heat of their prodigality." Whether it is provincial mockery of Scotland or ironic thrusts at the English criminal's pretenses, *Don Tomazo* does not evoke the broadly human satire of *Lazarillo de Tormes, Guzmán de Alfarache,* or *Don Quixote.* The criminal biography of a Restoration Guzman is nevertheless immensely valuable for a comparative study of the picaresque tradition in English and Spanish literature.

ABOUT DANGERFIELD: *A Complete Collection of State Trials,* comp. by T. B. Howell, 1816, VII, 1043–67, 1067–1111; Maurice Petherick, "Handsome Thomas and the Popish Midwife," *Restoration Rogues,* Hollis & Carter, 1951; Philip W. Sergeant, "Duke Dangerfield," *Liars and Fakers,* Hutchinson & Co., 1925.

DON TOMAZO, OR THE JUVENILE RAMBLES OF
THOMAS DANGERFIELD

TO THE READER

Youth has generally its extravagancies, and they that are seduced by the temptations of pleasures and bad company in great cities will have their times to sow their wild oats. For Don Tomazo's part he has sowed his already, and finding it such ill husbandry to deal in that sort of grain, has resolved to give over. And now I have thought it convenient to give the world an account of his transgressions, to the end that people, as many have done, may not think him worse than he was, whatever self-interest would have made him. Nor does he expect that any man will henceforth upbraid him for what is past, as being under the protection of his sovereign's pardon, to which all true subjects ought to give an awful respect and obedience.

Had it not been for the high misdemeanours of Clavel we had missed a neat and excellent poem,[1] and the discovery of a great mystery of iniquity. The cheats and cunning contrivances of Guzman[2] and Lazarillo de Tormes[3] have been made English out of the Spanish language, as well to instruct as to delight. And the greatest historians have taken as much pains to recount the lives of bad men as of the most deserving subjects of their pens. Mirrors that do not show the deformities, as well as beauties, of a face are of little use. In short, all sorts of men may gather hence how vain a thing it is to contend with the law, and that they must inevitably incur the misfortune of the pitcher by going often to the well. But the way to amendment is never out of date. St. Austin himself had occasion enough to repent the follies of his youth. Not that he [Don Tomazo] goes about to excuse his offenses, but this he hopes he may presume to say, that it was not his custom to put any man in danger of his life, but himself. He only imposed upon the belief and understandings of others which, being deluded, misguided their wills. And it is no small argument that his being so proper for the designs for which he was called out was half a proof that his discoveries[4] were true; which perhaps, had they not been ill-managed, might in some measure have made satisfaction for his past transgressions. Nor does he despair, but that some of them may yet take effect. In the meantime, while he lives to show that Horace's *"Quo semel . . ."*[5] is not always true, let

the virtuous hence observe how laborious a thing it is to be
wicked, and the vicious learn by his example to amend.

DON TOMAZO

The first corrupters and seducers of youth, especially if
active and sprightly, are the whispers and temptations of
pleasure, and that which boys call "freedom," men "extravagant looseness": which inclination in forward striplings,
being once inflamed by the inconsiderate severity of parents, labours with more violence to cast off the yoke of
bondage, so that unwilling to be under the continual awe
and terror of the lash, they rather choose to stand to the
favour of Fortune and the compassion of the wide world
than the cruel mercy of them that begat 'em. A cynical
way of education, which perhaps many may have learnt
from the morose documents of Solomon's whipping Proverbs, and still as eagerly prosecute, not observing the ill
success it met with in his own son. Upon which instiga-
tions, no sooner has incensed extravagancy resolved to take
its flight, but immediately vice appears in all her harlotry
attire, and exposing all the splendour of her gaudy allurements, so hampers unwary innocence in the nooses of necessity that not knowing which way to disengage itself, the
scene quite alters; so that of a sudden, innocence becomes
criminal before it knows what a crime is, and young offenders incur the displeasure of the law ere they hardly understand what the law forbids, till at length perceiving what
they have done and not believing themselves safe from the
punishment of lesser facts but by committing greater,
they abandon themselves to those unhappy stratagems
which, because they relieve at present, are by them looked
upon as the effect of Fortune's favour and their own prudence; so that encouraged by success, they cannot forsake
the delightful practice of those enormities which maintain
the sweet and tickling pleasures of riot and debauchery. So

easy a thing it is for parents to beget, so difficult a task to
hit the true method of education; for want of which so
many lofty geniuses, so many active courages, so many
soaring and refined wits, all tender pieces, ready for all the
fair impressions of virtue, have quite altered their bias; so
many blooming "expectations" have perished in the deep
abysses of mistaken conduct and irregular severity. How
near the subject of this story was to falling from this fatal
precipice, the ensuing relation will declare, which, it may
be well believed, will prove neither unpleasing nor unprof-
itable to the reader, or rather an incitement to acts of virtue, when he shall observe the pains and labours which
extravagance undergoes to support itself in profuse and
guilty luxury.

Don Tomazo (for so he must be called, as having put his
name into the Spanish garb, to which he was most accustomed in his travels) was by birth of English parents, born
in Essex, no less famous for pleasure than plenty. His tender years were under the eye and government of his father,
a person of a severe and disobliging austerity. In him perhaps it might be thought paternal "care," who observing
which way the current of his son's inclinations ran, deemed
it the fastest course by violence to stop the stream of his
unruly passions. And indeed there was sufficient cause of
suspicion, & the father had a fair prospect of what the
future would produce by the early exercises of his son's
childish talents, for which reason poor Don Tomazo was
not only daily rated and rebuked, but frequently and vigorously chastised, and exposed to the rigid lash for every
trivial misdemeanour. This surly usage so disengaged the
frank and generous humour of Don Tomazo, which was to
have been corrected rather by lenitives than corrosives, that
he looked upon his father as a master rather than a parent,
and himself to be a slave rather than a son. So then for
redress of these grievances there must be a speedy remedy
provided, for finding out of which his tender wits were
soon employed. They argued in his brain that there was
no living at home, therefore he must venture abroad, and

that if a servitude must be endured, it was more easy to be borne under the frowns and spurns of strangers than of near relations, where extravagance had nobody to thank but itself for the hardship it suffered.

In the midst of these serious consultations, the Devil and ill luck soon found him out a helpmeet for his purpose, a pure satanical privy councilor, even a servant of his own father. He was called by the name of Jemmy, a Scot by nation, nature and conditions, indigent, cunning and perfidious, true only to the son to cheat the father, perhaps out of a desire to revisit his household gods, at the expenses of a defrauded master. To this instrument of Beelzebub, the young disgusted squire discloses all the secrets of his heart, tells him the occasion of his discontents, and his design to throw off the yoke of paternal severity, which since there was no way to do but by traveling, he was resolved to take that course and therefore requested both his advice and assistance. Jemmy listened to this discourse like a sow i'th' beans; he applauded his design, magnified his youthful courage, and by a large encomium upon the worst of countries, persuaded the credulous stripling to steer toward the North Pole, to the land of his nativity, whither he might be sure of a faithful guide and, when there, of an assistant in the midst of wealthy and generous relations. This being concluded, they were both sensible that it would be very uneasy traveling without horses; but that care was soon over, when Don Tomazo called to mind that his father was well stored with that sort of cattle, and being their own casuists, they easily overcame all scruples of conscience upon a supposition that an heir in a case of necessity might anticipate a small pittance of his inheritance and that the so doing was positively no theft. But then again, well knowing that neither horse nor man could travel upon the road without corporal food and that it was in vain to swear at an hostler or to kick a chamberlain without money in breeches, it was farther agreed that the young squire should fly to London, there to take up what money he could among his father's correspondents, and

that trusty Jemmy, upon notice given of his success, should
precisely meet him at the rendezvous which was before
appointed at St. Albans. These blessed beginnings were so
fortunately favoured by the assistance of their friend Monsieur Satan, who was loth to lose two such fair gamesters,
that all things being accomplished according to their hearts'
desire, away hastens Don Tomazo to St. Albans, and there
meets his punctual companion with his father's two horses.
And so well-mounted, the young master and the young
man, knight-errant-like, set forward upon their northern
progress. By the way, to make the journey the more pleasant, Jemmy, who was endued with a nimble utterance and
the true faculty of Scotch lying, entertained his master with
several discourses, and among the rest told him such extravagant stories of the sweet pleasures, the contentment
and plenty which he should meet with at his father's
stately mansion, that he had raised Don Tomazo's expectations steeple high. But after some days' travel, there befell
them a small occasion of delay, which somewhat abated
the squire's jollity. For it so happened that Jemmy, already
possessed with one devil, was seized with another devil of
an ague which entered him with that violence, that to ex-
orcise the robustious spirit they were forced to lie still for
four or five whole days and nights, in which time Don
Tomazo's father had been amply informed which way the
two Edomites were marched with the spoils of his purse
and stable. How fatal this discovery might have proved to
these young practitioners in iniquity may be easily conjectured, had the father been eager to follow them. But he,
being more tender of his credit, as disdaining the world
should know how his grave experience had been overreached by two raw whipsters, than to make a noise of his
losses, neglected the pursuit, so that upon Jemmy's recovery the two knight-errants set forward again without any
disturbance. But Jemmy, as unsound in body as in mind,
having ventured too soon into the sharp winter air (for
such was the season of the year which they chose for their
journey of pleasure), before they could accomplish four

days' travel more, fell into a new distemper, to the great
grief and sorrow of Don Tomazo who had then no small
reason to doubt the loss of his guide and pillar of his hopes,
as finding himself, for the love and friendship which he
bore to Jemmy, now more likely to be exposed than ever
to the misfortunes of unhappy undertakers, easily foreseen, but so not easy to be prevented, especially considering the great expense he then and still was like to be at.
These reflections and the thoughts of being a stranger—
without having any bills of exchange for future supply,
among a rude sort of people that would no longer respect
him than his money lasted, which was not likely to be long
at the rate of nurses' and pothecaries' bills—were sufficient
to have confounded all the cogitations that an unexperi-
enced stripling could muster together. But Fortune and
good husbandry so well agreed to encourage Don Tomazo
in his first essays of Guzmanry that in three weeks' time
Jemmy, not yet mellow enough for the Devil's palate, was
well recovered and able to undertake the remaining part
of the journey. And indeed he had then more reason than
ever to promise a retaliation of that care and kindness
which his master had shown him in his sickness. Nor, to
say truth, could Don Tomazo accuse him in the least while
he was yet in England, where he was as lavish of his ac-
knowledgements as could be expected, and protested such
works of supererogation at home as if his father's opulent
seat had been the mansion of gratitude itself. But the
reader shall soon find the vast difference between Scotch
promises and Scotch performances.

Well—after a cold and tedious journey, all weather-
beaten as we were, at length we arrived at Jemmy's father's
palace lying in the county of Annandale near a town called
Moffat. When Don Tomazo beheld it, he was so far from
being overravished with joy at the sight that he took it for
some enchanted castle, in regard he could not see so much
as one stone of all that magnificent pile which Jemmy all
the way upon the road had been building in his fancy.
Rather he was more than usually surprised at the humility

of the structure and the lowliness of the owner. Had he
not been a Scot, you would have sworn him a Turk, re-
gardless of his habitation in this world, in expectation of
fool's paradise in the next. It was a hovel or rather sty, in
length about six and thirty foot, not covered cathedral-like
with lead nor yet with glittering copper after the Swedish
manner, but according to the Scotch custom very meanly
thatched with oaten reeds, not such as the Arcadian shep-
herds piped withal, but plain downright illiterate straw.
The fire was made near the bedside, at one end, which for
want of a chimney wrapped the whole family, guests and
all, like so many Ixions, in a continual cloud of eye-
tormenting smoke. Near to the bedside lay the corn and
hay, which you may be sure was not worth its weight in
gold; and at the other end, without the distinction of parti-
tions, stood two sheep, a cow, and the squire's horses, so
that it may be verily believed that Virtue herself in all her
exiles and persecutions never lived in such a "Homely Her-
mitage," and Marius, when he lay hid among the bulrushes
in the fens of Minturnus,[6] might be thought to have
lodged in a palace to this ill-favoured resemblance of
Noah's Ark.

So soon as we came to this unfortunate apartment, the
old man, overtaken with joy not only to see his son who
had been absent from him several years, but to behold him
in an equipage so genteel, after the English mode, could
not forbear bedewing his cheeks; but when Jemmy fell on
his knee to crave his father's blessing, the old man, who
well knew he had none to give, stood amazed. "What a
mickle De'il," quoth he. "Is the carl wood?"[7] Whereupon
Tomazo, observing his astonishment, acquainted the old
bacon-faced lown that it was the only customary way for
children in England to acknowledge their respect and duty
to their parents, and that Jemmy had done it purely out
of natural affection, and to show his improvement in English behaviour and education. Thereupon the old man,
seeming to be better satisfied, condescended to the breeding of his son and embraced him; which ceremony being

soon over, he requested the squire to enter his Polyphemus' den. But Don Tomazo, being very hungry and not finding the place proper for many compliments, came close to the point and demanded what provision they had in the house; to which they made answer that they had good store of oatmeal and water, but neither flesh nor fowl, milk nor butter, bread nor drink, and which was worse, that none of these creature comforts were to be had for money within six miles of the place, so that poor Don Tomazo, who had always fared well at a plentiful table, began to curse his man Jemmy who after such mountainous promises of a splendid entertainment and princely viands had betrayed his longing appetite to such miserable commons, hardly worth the acceptance of a country mouse. But Jemmy's mother, discovering discontent in Don Tomazo's face and taking pity of his youth, or rather for joy of her dear darling's return, began to comfort up our desponding stomachs with the hopes of a notable banquet. This, after the expense of all her huswifery, proved to be that sumptuous Scotch dish called a steane-bannock, which was a certain composition of bean, peasen, barley, and oatenmeal, mixed together with water and made into the form of a large cake, and being set to the fire against a stone and so baked, was to be eaten with water; and this without first or second course was the cream of their entertainment: a strange sort of philosophical diet that no way answered Don Tomazo's pampered expectations. Supper, if so it might be called, being thus soberly dispatched at the mere instance of craving hunger, the weary guests were no less desirous of repose than they were before of food; to which the old man replied that 'twas the fashion in that country for the family to go to bed altogether, and not one before another, and therefore in regard that Don Tomazo and his son had prevailed with him to be conformable to an English ceremony, he would constrain them to be conformable to one of his country customs. Don Tomazo, not a little disgusted at his diet and like to be worse pleased with his lodging, began to enter into a serious consideration of his forlorn condi-

tion. He found, on the one side, how miserably he had
been frustrated by his man Jemmy whose fause tongue he
now began too late to curse; he saw himself in a wild desert
among a sort of savages more prone to make him a prey
to their cruelty than afford him relief: which, on the other
side, filled his head full of jealousies and fears, as now mis-
doubting that his trusty man Jemmy had some further designs rather of mischief than of kindness, as being privy
to the small treasure he had about him. To repent was irk-
some, to fear, below him. There were no shady woods for
nightingales to lull him into soft slumbers, no murmuring
rills to which he might make his sorrowful complaints, no
kind hermits to invite him to their cells. All his comfort
was in hope and the compassion of his guardian angel.

In the midst of these distractions Don Tomazo perceived
through the thick smoke, which forced those tears from his
eyes that he ought more willingly to have shed, the two
aged parents and five children, of which Jemmy was one,
preparing for bed, which made him desire leave that he
might sit up by the fire all night. But that request would
by no means be granted him so that poor Don Tomazo
was constrained to unclothe and go to bed with the rest.
But in that comfortless place he was so far from finding
any sheets that he scarce found woolen enough to cover
him from the nipping cold. However, all things considered,
the old man was very friendly, for he laid the distressed
Don Tomazo by one of his brawny sides that smelt like
hung beef, a kindness more than ordinary, though it fell
out to the unspeakable detriment of the sadly tormented
squire; for the warmth of his body had soon summoned
together multitudes of that creeping vermin, lice, the common curse of the country, which finding the easy penetra-
bleness of the young squire's tender skin and the sweetness
of his well-nourished blood, fell to their fresh viands with
such an eager appetite that the unhappy Don Tomazo, incessantly tormented with the continual nippings of those
hungry animals, would be often starting up in his litter to
throw off his shirt to prevent those villainous insects from

taking possession of the folds of his underlinen; for which the old man as often rebuked him. But alas! It was impossible for the suffering Don Tomazo to obey the checks of his surly moroseness, while the sharp-set vermin were so busily employed upon his carcass, which it was as natural for the rest to endure as it was to sleep. This restlessness of Don Tomazo at length made the peevish cinque and quatre[8] angry so that at last he began to cry Don Tomazo was a subtle carl and intended to be immodest with his daughter. Whereupon in a grumbling tone he commanded him to surcease his cunning excuses and lie still, insomuch that the afflicted squire was compelled to comply with his austere governor and to spend the rest of the night in wishes for the slow-paced morning. Which had no sooner displayed her comfortable light, but up he rises, leaving the whole family asleep, designing to be gone forthwith and rather to expose himself to the mercy of the cold winds, the severe weather, and the unknown passages of the rugged mountains than to the barbarous kindness of such a savage entertainment for another night. Thereupon, in order to his farther progress, he puts on his boots and leads forth his horse, but going behind the house with his steed in his hand (for to avoid the trouble of leading, he had left his other courser at Jemmy's disposal as the reward of his father's obligations), here Fortune showed him one of her cursed slippery tricks which had like to have cost him his sweet life and put an end to all his disconsolations. For stepping by chance upon certain rotten boards covered with snow, that lay over a deep well, the treacherous boards giving way, in dropt Don Tomazo, who had like to have drawn his horse also after him, had not the bridle broke. Well, it happened for the unfortunate squire that the water in the well was frozen to a considerable thickness, else you might have bid Don Tomazo good night by the name of Nich'las. But the ice putting a stop to his farther descent, he received no more hurt than a slight bruise by the fall. So oddly sometimes bad and good luck conjobble together. However, there he was forced to stand in a kind of cold

little-ease or lob's pound, being fallen much lower than
was within his reach to get out again. Now by that he had
remained there for some time meditating upon his misfortune in chill-blood, Jemmy gets up and, perceiving his
master gone, runs into the back side where he finds the
horse in a cold trance, wondering what was become of the
grass that used to grow in England, but could not imagine
where Tomazo should be. In that amaze he flies about to
seek him, but not succeeding in his search, away he posts
to Moffat. In the meanwhile the old man rises, who finding both his son and Don Tomazo absent, yet seeing their
horses, could not conjecture what the De'il should be become of 'em. He waited for some hours with patience, expecting their return, but neither appearing, away goes he
also to draw dryfoot after both. The old man proved a cun-
ninger huntsman than the son, for he tracing the footsteps
which he observed in the snow, came directly to the well
where he found the unfortunate Don Tomazo, who espying
the countenance of his supposed deliverer, invokes his aid
and begs his assistance to help him out of his winter
sweating-tub. But Don Tomazo was extremely deceived in
the humour of the churlish chuff, for he perceiving his prey
in the snare, told the shivering squire that there were more
words went to a bargain. "You," quo he, "would have de-
flowered my dear Moggee, and therefore you shall stay
there a while to cool your courage. Nay, farther," quo he,
"I am apt to believe that because I spoiled your sport, you
have taken your revenge upon my son and made him away
so that until he be found, you are not like to stir." This
was a sad morning lecture to poor Don Tomazo who would
have given all the shoes in his shop for a warm chimney
corner; but there was no help for no remedy. For the old
villain, full of mischief, leaving him to his soliloquies, returns to the house, and there consults the hag his wife and
his daughters, as ready as himself to exercise their cruelty
upon poor Tomazo, well understanding by Jemmy's information that he had, what they had been but little acquainted with, both silver and gold about him. And there-

fore, having framed their design, they came to the well, let down a rope, and bid Tomazo to fasten it about him. To these glad tidings as to a voice from Heaven, Don Tomazo cheerfully condescended, so that obeying such welcome orders, they presently drew him up. But he was no sooner come forth, but the old caitiff was as yare for his cash, who with a grim aspect threatened to stab him with his dirk, a doleful sight, God wot, if he did not fairly deliver all he had. Thereupon Don Tomazo, finding himself under the paws of an unavoidable violence, put his hands into a pocket that contained about 3 pound in silver, which the false old miscreant took. But not so contented, he further told Tomazo of the concealment of his gold, which he must either part with or with his life; and with that pulled him down by main force i'th' snow, menacing nothing less than downright murder if he did not speedily give it him. Don Tomazo did by no means like this bitter breakfast. Loth he was to part with the life of his enterprise, and it was as sad a thing to think that he should take so much pains to travel into Scotland to be buried in a well. While he was in this peck of troubles, the wife and children, more merciful, prevailed with the old tyrant to spare his life, but to examine his clothes for the gold, which he soon found; and then fetching forth the despoiled Tomazo's horse, bid him be gone, hoping, in regard the ground was thick covered with snow, and Don Tomazo an absolute stranger in the country, that either he might fall into some hole and be starved, or else never be able to give any account of the place where he had been so courteously entertained. But Don Tomazo's better fortune so guided the horse, and the barbarism of the old ragamuffin had so imprinted all imaginable observations in Tomazo's memory, that they were never to be forgotten.

In this forlorn condition Don Tomazo, having wandered till some time before the next night and about ten miles from the den of his grisly robber, happened to espy a small village, to which he rode with great joy. There the scene altered, and he found something of generosity in an ancient gentleman who was called the Laird of Corheid and owner of the village, to whom Don Tomazo, after he had made an apology for himself, gave an account of the old man's entertainment. Which being delivered by the dismantled squire in English, the laird could scarce understand the meaning of his story, till by frequent repetition he better apprehended the matter and then gave credit to the relation, promising Don Tomazo withal that he would use him more kindly. Upon which he bid the empty young gentleman welcome and commanded him to be as free as if he were at his father's house. Moreover he assured the poor disconsolate traveler that the next day he would send his warrant (for he was in commission of the peace) for the whole family which had been so barbarous to a stranger, which he performed accordingly, so that both the parents and all the children, together with Jemmy himself, were brought before him. There they met, to their sorrow, their injured guest who charged the old man so home that he could not deny the fact, especially when being searched, the joyful Don Tomazo's gold was found about him. Thereupon the old rogue, his son Jemmy, and the daughters were all packed away to gaol.

By this time the good Laird of Corheid, being truly sensible of the heinous abuses that had been put upon the succourless Don Tomazo by this same crew of Scotch monsters, and also possessing a natural tenderness of heart, took such an affection to Don Tomazo that he requested him to remain in his house till he could more opportunely dispose of himself. Which kind and seasonable offer Don Tomazo was unwilling to refuse, especially finding the temper of that whole family so truly generous, so that he took the boldness to continue there near upon forty days. During which time he had so won the laird's favour that he called Don Tomazo his son and was often wont to take him, when he went a-visiting, to the houses of several persons of quality, by whom he was so nobly and familiarly treated that it would be a foul ingratitude not to acknowledge their most obliging generosity.

Now was Don Tomazo, as it were, in a serene calm after a violent storm, living at ease and in plenty; he had seen himself revenged upon those violators of the laws of hospitality; he found his money all restored, and his company acceptable to the chiefest in the province: which had inspired so much greatness into Don Tomazo's breast that he, according to the proverb "Taking that for his country where he fared best," did not much care to quit his post. However, considering with himself in the midst of his delights that it would be a rudeness beneath the breeding he had shown, to trespass upon the laird's good nature beyond reason, he bethought himself that it was high time to take his leave, yet with a promise to return (for such was the laird's obligation laid upon him, provided he could find no better quarters). Whereupon he set forwards, being furnished with a letter of recommendation to a person of quality that lived about fifteen Scotch miles from the laird's house, the most part of which way lay over the mountains. But now behold another jade's trick of that fickle whore that men call Fortune. She had for forty days together given the exalted Don Tomazo her sweet milk, but now she resolves to kick down the pail, as if by chequering the accidents of his travels, she intended betimes to teach him what he was to trust to, if he relied upon the mutability of her humour. For by that time Don Tomazo had rode about six of the forementioned miles, from a little cave between two rocks out leaped a brace of St. Nicholas clerks who, violently seizing the person of the squire, took away not only his gold and silver that had already been in so much jeopardy, but also his horse and clothes, stripping him to his very shirt, in lieu of which they gave him a piece of an old plaid, adding withal that that sort of clothing would make him as perfect a Scotchman as either of them; and thus penniless, dismounted and naked they left him to pilgrim it over the snowy mountains, without so much as directing him one step of his way.

You may now easily conjecture that this unfortunate youth had reason sufficient to condole the calamity of his

condition. And indeed there was no person of pity that did
not highly blame these rigorous proceedings of that hare-
brained beldame Fortune, but she made answer for herself
that they could be no true-taught sons of hers that were not
bred up in the school of affliction: experience was not to
be learned by living at a certain rate of content and plenty;
it was the mixture of good and bad luck that was the mistress of knowledge. Quo she, "This young Guzman will be
the better for these two robberies and this damned walk
over the cursed rocks, as long as he lives. This is the way
to try whether he have courage, whether he have patience, whether he have ingenuity." And so indeed it happened; for though at first the stripped and ransacked cavalier could not forbear lamenting the rashness of a journey
that had brought him into so many almost intolerable misfortunes, yet resuming his natural courage, rather than return in that miserable condition to the good laird (who
would most certainly have clothed and entertained him as
before), he resolved to march forward and to try, since
he had no more to lose, how he might revenge himself by
getting something from a people that had taken all from
him, a task very difficult to be performed among the sons
of poverty itself, in a country as barren of riches as the
mountains that disfigure it. Full of these thoughts, Don
Tomazo steers his course by accident to another laird's
house, whose title was the Laird of Creyback Borne; to
whom the rifled squire related his last misfortune only, omitting all the former passages, nor owning that he knew any
person in the country, but only that he was traveling to
Edinburgh where he was in expectation of meeting with
some friends. This laird's compassion was not much inferior
to that of his first acquaintance, for when Don Tomazo had
told him his story, he clad him with a suit of his son's
clothes, civilly entertained him all night, and the next morning, after he had directed him the best way to Edinburgh,
gave him also 3 pounds Scotch, which is 5 shillings sterling,
to bear his charges.

From hence Don Tomazo walked on, till he came to the

old town of Peebles, about ten miles from the last laird's
house and still in the same county, where it fell out that he
met with the very persons that had so lately discharged
him of the burthen of his clothes and money; but though
he kept 'em company and drank with 'em till he had spent
half his small stock, their disguises were such as preserved
them altogether from his knowledge, till it was too late to
prosecute his revenge.

His tutoress Fortune had a mind to keep him fasting, on
purpose to put him upon trials of skill. She knew necessity
and the lowness of his pocket would soon constrain him
to summon his wits to a consultation for replenishment.
Every fool can put the sweat of his tenants in his pocket;
he's the darling of Fortune that carries his estate in his
brains. She never forsakes the bold and daring, O brave
wits! For by their prompt assistance Don Tomazo, now at
a desperate pinch, had called to his remembrance a way
what to do, not to laze under hedges, not to go whining
from door to door to court penurious charity, but to cheat
the crafty, outknave the knave in grain: to whitewash
Boatles,[9] one of which is the sixth part of a penny, so as
to make them pass currently for a certain Scotch piece of
silver called a forty-penny piece, which amounts to twenty
Boatles in copper. Of these pieces Don Tomazo, by the
help of some ingredients which he bought at Peebles, had
got good store, which being by him vended for good, in a
week's time, put about £5 in his pocket. And thus you see
the wide world is no dangerous sea for one that can swim.

With this jolly recruit Don Tomazo, now a Don indeed,
returns to his friend the Laird of Corheid's, to whom he
related the manner of his being robbed the second time,
which the good gentleman could hardly believe till Don
Tomazo had described one of the persons most exactly well
and the other so near as could be possible. The first happened to be one of the laird's tenants, who had often seen
Tomazo and knew of the gold and silver's being restored
to him at the laird's house, the temptation of which booty
prompted him to act a crime which he had never been

guilty of before. But that lame confession served neither
his nor his companion's turn. For being both apprehended,
they were both sent to gaol, companions in their punishment, as they had been associates in the crime. Which put
Don Tomazo into some apprehension of his own danger,
fearing lest his condition might be the same, should he
linger much longer near the places where he had so lately
been sowing his counterfeit pieces. But Fortune that desired
his improvement only, not his ruin, found out a way to
deliver him. For about two nights after, as the laird was
sitting by the fire with his family and Don Tomazo, there
arose a discourse concerning the misfortunes of Don Tomazo, at which the laird fell into a rapture of admiration
how miraculously Heaven had delivered the unfortunate
stranger, saying very devoutly withal that surely Providence
had reserved him to be an instrument of some great work or
other. And therefore, lest the noise of Don Tomazo's gold
and silver might prove a bait for others to destroy this
precious instrument, he resolved the next morning to go
for Edinburgh, to look after the prosecution of the prisoners
and to take Don Tomazo along with him, as indeed the
proceedings of justice required. Now the road to Edinburgh
lay through a village called Perkessen where Don Tomazo
had been very busy in vending his forty-penny pieces, so
that as he passed through the town, the person who had
exchanged the greatest part, espying him, ran to stop his
horse; at which the laird, being surprised, demanded of
the fellow whether he intended to rob him. "No," said he,
"but I want some money which that person," pointing to
Tomazo, "cheated me of about five days since." But the
laird had too good an opinion of his son Don Tomazo to
give credit to his story, but rather believed that the noise
of his gold being spread over the country had set the people
agog to be hanged for it, so that the laird, putting Don
Tomazo before him, without taking any farther notice of
the villager's complaint, rode on. By which means Don
Tomazo scaped a scouring and got clear to Edinburgh with
his true friend, the good laird, who carried him to one of

the judges to give in his testimony against the prisoners; but Don Tomazo, being under age, could not be admitted as evidence against them, and so they were all acquitted.

At Edinburgh Don Tomazo accidentally met with certain English gentlemen whose curiosity had lead them to travel into those parts. These gentlemen knew Don Tomazo, to whom he related the occasion of his coming thither as also how he had been treated, as well by the laird in particular as others. He also gave them an account of his misfortunes and deliverances, which, as they were stories pleasing to the ear, induced them to take Don Tomazo for a companion and to make the same provision for him as for themselves. After which they went with Don Tomazo to wait upon the laird to give him thanks for the great favours he had shown their countryman. Which piece of complaisance was so grateful to the laird that after he had drank a bottle or two in the company, with tears in his eyes (for such was his affection to his new son), he took his leave of Tomazo in particular and then of the rest of the gentlemen: where note that it is not for clowns and men of sullen tempers, but for persons of acute compliance and airy behaviour, to be Guzmans.

With these gentlemen Tomazo traveled through divers parts of Scotland, which proved a very pleasant journey, in regard those gentlemen had letters of credit to most persons of quality in the country, by whom they were for the most part very nobly entertained with good music and other rarities. Nay, in some parts their splendid equipage produced such credit of itself, without their letters, that some gentlemen of the country would stand at the back of a chair, waiting while they sat at dinner, using no less than the title of lord to the meanest of them, though they endeavoured as much as in them lay to persuade them to the contrary. Thus having traveled almost through the whole country and meeting nothing worthy observation, the gentlemen faced about homewards, when coming to a town called Dumfries upon the borders of England, they concluded there to rest for a week or so: in which time they became acquainted with several of the inhabitants of the place, with whom they used to drink smartly. One day among the rest, as they were merry at a tavern, an old woman came into the room to beg a glass of wine, and in particular of Don Tomazo, who for that very reason refused to give her any, unwilling to assume a pre-eminence in the company of friends to whom he was so much beholding. At which the woman went away, refusing to take wine from any other person, but threatening Don Tomazo with most dreadful misfortunes and an immediate curse that should attend him, which the gentlemen, little regarding, drank on to that excess that very few, if one, went home sober.

That night Don Tomazo was not in a condition, but the next morning he went to look after his horse, which he found in such a posture as amazed him; for his body was drawn up in such a strange manner that his head and his four feet were all in a huddle together. Besides this, the colour of his hair was altered, and a thick white foam bedaubed his chaps from one side to the other. This, putting Don Tomazo in mind of the woman's threats the night before, made him suspect her for a witch, which he found upon inquiry had been the hard opinion of her neighbours for many years. Upon which information Don Tomazo, possessed with immediate revenge, or rather to draw blood of her, according as his nurse had taught him, went to the old woman's house where he found her cutting of wood. So soon as she saw him, it seemed to Tomazo that the anticness of her behaviour was such as showed her jealous of Tomazo's design in coming to visit her, who while she discoursed him smoothly and calmly enough, waited for nothing but an opportunity to surprise her. At length, perceiving she had got a great stick in her hand that she could not easily cleave, Don Tomazo very officiously desires her to give him the bill and to hold one end of the stick, to which she readily consenting, Don Tomazo, having by some discourse or other obliged her to look another way, with a home stroke cut off one of her thumbs and so, leaving her to curse and ban him to the Devil, went immediately to the stable where he found his horse upon his legs in decent order and feeding as well as if nothing had ever ailed him.

This accident of the witch, if such she were, exalted Don Tomazo to a very high pitch, as believing he was or should be some great hero. "For," quo he, "Ulysses was beloved by a witch, and Aeneas was beloved by a witch, St. George was charmed by a witch, and Don Tomazo was beloved by a witch, so that had he given her wine and not cut off her thumb, who knows what happinesses had been prepared for him? But having cut off her thumb, she withdrew her affections from him and was so far from advancing his fortunes that she complained to the magistrates of the town of the loss of her joint, for which she accused the "English Lad," as she called him. Whereupon the English Lad was sent for and, upon a full examination of the matter, committed to prison. For, indeed, he owned the fact and upon what occasion he did it, but could not make out by any sort of reason why he should assume the doing of justice to himself. The rest of the gentlemen offered to be his bail, but nothing would serve but one of Tomazo's thumbs, which the magistrate protested should be cut off and given to the old woman to burn before his face, which rigorous sentence you may be sure did not a little trouble Don Tomazo. But Fortune, who knew he had more occasion for his thumb than the old woman, was for none of those Mosaical executions, so that what by her assistance and the gentlemen's industry a rope was conveyed to Don Tomazo, by means whereof he made his escape out of the gaol, without paying his fees; and so being privately conveyed out of town to a place where his horse stood ready, he received directions to post with all speed to Carlisle and there to stay at an inn appointed till the company came to him, which by the good conduct of Fortune and with no small hazard he accomplished, being pursued almost to the walls of the city. About a week after, arrived his companions who, being suspected to have been privy to Tomazo's escape, were detained by the magistrate till they had paid their ten crowns apiece to the poor of the town, which amounted to a considerable sum, there being five in number.

These gentlemen, being come to Carlisle, found there their beloved Tomazo, for which they were not a little joyful, their kindness to him being nothing inferior to the Laird of Corheid's.

From Carlisle they set forward for London with all speed; where in a little time being safely arrived, the company separated, and Don Tomazo was left to himself, who though so near his parents was almost in as bad a condition as at his first entrance into Scotland. But necessity prompting him to some serious resolution, the story of the Prodigal Son took possession of his pate, and he began to study how to be reconciled to his father. A kind office which was soon accomplished by the intercession of a particular favourite of his father's who so far prevailed that Tomazo, after a hearty sorrow and deep contrition for his crime, was again admitted into his father's favour, both expecting various effects of the past ramble: the father believing that the son, now well read in the lectures of necessity, would be more careful how he plunged himself into the same exigencies again; and the son presuming that the father, now knowing what it was to want a living child, would be more tender of provoking him for the future. In both which conjectures both were mistaken.

As for Tomazo (for while he is under his father's roof we must un-Don him), for about half a year he continued very patiently within the bounds of modesty. But the continued austerity of his father, together with certain impressions that love had made in his heart, soon put his discontents into an uproar and quite altered that composure of mind which had given such life to their hopes of his becoming a new creature. The Don began to close again with Tomazo, and all his passions being in a ferment, so alarumed his father that he was forced to double his guards. However, notwithstanding all the father's diligence and correction, the son, having laid aside all thoughts of reformation and forgotten all his vows and protestations of penitence, betook himself so far to his former more natural and consequently more pleasing extravagancies, so that the old man, no longer able to endure the bad examples which he gave in his family, one day in the garden took an occasion to acquaint Tomazo that he must depart those walls. This sentence sounded very harshly in Tomazo's ears; and therefore duly weighing the misery of an eloignment from his beloved mistress, a near neighbour, the great dangers he had escaped in Scotland, his present ease, and the apparent extremities he should be exposed to by the casualty of new travels, he began to intercede with his father, whose good nature at that time was easily prevailed with, to have some farther patience, provided his son would keep up to his promises of mortification. But Tomazo, being engaged in an amour with a loving female that was the sole and first mistress of his affections, had not the power to perform his engagements and therefore found out a ready way to unravel all his father's hopes.

This mistress of his was daughter to a neighbouring gentleman, in her thirteenth year, of no great fortune more than what nature and art in point of education had accomplished her withal, which for the most part are the chief allurements of youth, especially such as are not capable of taking a prospect of their future well-being. Between these two children, as I may safely say, for Tomazo was not then above fourteen years of age, there was an amorous intrigue so cunningly managed as could hardly be expected from such early lovers, to which purpose the damsel, who had a father as severe in all particulars as Tomazo's, had ordered our meetings in the night, to the end she might steal her enjoyments when the old gentleman thought her most secure, that is, in English, fast asleep. Tomazo's condition was the same so that for several nights they entertained each other with all the amorous caresses that an innocent and harmless converse could afford. But it so fell out that Tomazo was unfortunately suspected by his father whose

Argus eyes kept a continual watch upon him, even to that degree of strictness that nothing would serve but that Tomazo's quarters must be removed to a chamber, the passage to which lay through his father's, so that it was almost impossible for Tomazo to meet his mistress that night, as by solemn promise, sacred among lovers, he had engaged himself to do.

But love, that has more ways to the wood than one, furnished him with an expedient. For Tomazo, considering the vast damage it might be to him to disappoint a lady that ventured all for his sake, resolved to make the attempt, though it were through his father's chamber. With this resolution of a deeply smitten gallant, up he rises, puts on his clothes; and laying in his place a periwig and a block with the face of the block turned to the wall and carefully healed up[10] for fear of catching cold, he takes a sheet along with him and adventures 'cross the old gentleman's chamber who, being more wakeful than Tomazo expected, overheard him, but yet let him alone, well knowing the door to be fast and the keys of all the house to be safe by his bedside. Tomazo understood all that before, and therefore not to put himself upon vain and fruitless delays, he takes his napkin and his short stick, utensils that he had ready fixed, goes to the window; and having with much art, but no noise, drawn the bar, he fastens his sheet, lets himself down into the garden, and thence with no less speed than joy repairs to his mistress whose patience was almost tired with waiting for his company, which she had scarce enjoyed above two hours, but break of daylight forced them to retire. But before that time, Tomazo's father, having heard something trip through his chamber, concluded that it was his gracious son; but because he was almost assured that he could find no way out of the house, he therefore expected his immediate return, which not being made, the old gentleman, mistrusting some treachery in his own sense of hearing, consulted his wife. She was of the same opinion, that it was impossible for Tomazo to get out of the house, and therefore undertook to persuade her husband that Tomazo was returned to his chamber. However, the old gentleman, not being satisfied, gets up, and taking a candle, examines the bed, where finding a head with hair that lay very snug and quiet in a true sleeping posture, he could not imagine but that Slipstring was fast in Morpheus' chains, who was then indeed in the fetters of his mistress's arms. But jealousy and age being generally such inseparable companions, it would not out of the old gentleman's pericranium, but that either some hobgoblin or some thief had been visiting the secrets of his house; and therefore resolving to be farther satisfied, once more up he takes the candle, downstairs he rumbles and examines all the doors; but finding all fast, in a pelting chafe to be put thus to dance about i'th' cold in his shirt, up he comes again, when, lo, as he ascends, he spies a pittance of the sheet hanging within the window, whither he marches immediately and observing the posture of the contrivance, concludes there was a robbery in the case. Thereupon the old gentleman calls up his servants and bids 'em search the house who, finding all things in due decorum, bring in an absolute "ignoramus," to the great amazement of the master and themselves, in which astonishment he returns to his warm wife and relates the story to her.

She presently called 'em all fools and bid 'em call up Tomazo, who there was no question to be made would soon unfold the mystery. Thereupon one of the maids was sent to wake him, who receiving no answer, began to jog the block, believing it to have been the drowsy body of her master's son, which she did so rudely that the block, turning, the black physiognomy of the graven image stared her full i'th' countenance. Which so terrified the maid that she ran to her master, crying out that Tomazo was murdered, for he looked black i'th' face. Upon which the master and mistress both rose and went into Tomazo's chamber where, upon a true examination of the whole matter, they discovered the plot, and so leaving the wooden idol in the same posture as it lay when the maid first found it, they went to bed in expectation of Tomazo's return, who soon

after made his silent entry, and having rectified the disorders
of the window, stole barefoot through his father's chamber,
who heard him well enough, into his own, and with much
inward satisfaction for the purloined pleasures he had had,
went to supply his broken rest, not dreaming he was discovered, in regard he found all things as he left them. But
woe is me, before Tomazo was well settled in his repose,
the father, no longer able to conceal his passion, came to
correct the amorous nightwalker. Tomazo, by the cloud
upon his father's brows perceiving the storm coming,
pleaded hard for mercy, beseeching his father to consider
that the innocency of his years could not draw him forth
to any more than only a merrymaking with honest and civil
persons, some of whom he well knew. But that would not
qualify the incensed old gentleman who at first laid on very
smartly; but observing no returns of childish howling, but
rather a manly suffering and passive submission to paternal
authority, he forbore any farther schoolboy's chastisement,
which he saw was but thrown away upon one that so little
regarded it, and upon Tomazo's further entreaty came to a
capitulation which produced these articles of agreement
that the next fault that Tomazo did commit, he should be
thrust out of doors, never more to see his father's face
again. This was a doleful sentence, yet but a fleabite to the
irresistible commands of love. An article with a father was
not to stand in competition with a promise made to a mistress. And the Devil would have it that he had made one
to meet her again the night following in the same place,
so that after the mode of princes Tomazo soon found a flaw
i'th' treaty and was resolved to venture a breach, though he
lost the reversion of all his father's dominions. Thereupon,
being informed that his father, who looked upon him as a
Carthaginian of no faith, was resolved to lock him into his
chamber the next night by way of prevention, love inspired
Tomazo to go in the daytime and pluck up one of the
boards under his own bed, which gave him free passage into
a cellar and so through a window as before.

That done, the hopes of enjoying his mistress made Don

Tomazo very pleasant the rest of the day, having made so fair a progress already, which gave his father no less cause to suspect that he had some notable stratagem in his pate that made his heart so light, and therefore that night he resolved to watch Tomazo's motion himself. Which being come, and the usual hour having summoned the family to bed, Tomazo was locked into his room where, after he had made a seeming preparation to go to bed, he fell to work, and first having removed the board, he let down his clothes with a line, the passage not being otherwise wide enough for his body. Then he descended himself, like an angel from the roof of a playhouse, and thinking himself as secure as a thief in a mill; but no sooner was he in the cellar, but at the same moment his father was in the room, who immediately seizing the line drew back all Tomazo's clothes and left him to meditate i'th' cold cellar all night in his shirt, having nothing to keep him warm but the heat of his desire, a sort of practice of piety which no way agreed with Tomazo's temper. These disappointments did but serve to heighten Tomazo's resolutions whose fires, meeting with reciprocal and equal flames, burnt with that ardent heat, that the least separation from the object of his love was a gash that wounded to the heart, not to be endured. Love, of itself crafty and subtle enough, is a mere Devil in a young Guzman, lawless as an Irish Tory, as impatient as Ajax, and as choleric as Hector, so that had not his modesty argued hard against it, he had ventured as he was in his shirt to show himself a punctual lover to a most faithful Hero who had spent all the night in waiting and moaning, and moaning and waiting for her dear Leander, till the telltale sun began to peep into her amorous sanctuary. At what time, despairing, sighing, and accusing the infidelity of her young gallant, she retired to her broken rest; while, on the other side, the old gentleman came not only to release his languishing prisoner, but also to discharge him without fees out of his house, according to the conditions of the treaty so lately concluded. Which as soon as he was appareled was absolutely performed, and poor peel-garlic[11] turned adrift into the wide world in a worse condition than when he traveled for Scotland, for then he had the blessings of money, now not a Boatle in his pocket.

It was now high time to consider what course to steer. The last disappointment of his mistress had so confounded him in his amours that he had not the face to appear in his mistress's sight. He thought it a crime so far beyond forgiveness that he durst not crave it. And therefore giving her over for lost (for he was yet but in his love-primer and had not learned those lessons of cajoling tender damsels, which afterwards he became a doctor in), he abandoned all his amorous thoughts and rather chose the retirement of a haycock the remaining part of that day, there to condole his destiny. So soon as it was night, with the beasts of prey, to avoid his discovery, he began his rambles, steering directly for London once more to try his father's credit, which proved not so hidebound as the old gentleman intended, who suspecting that Tomazo would make bold with it, as he had formerly done, had by way of prevention fairly warned all his correspondents not to pay any money upon his account without a warrant under his own hand.

Now was Tomazo, with a slender stock of ninepence, arrived at England's metropolis, where he was hard put to it to find a lodging. However, he ventured courageously into a public house, and having refreshed himself with a moderate supper, he calls for pen, ink and paper, and then drawing a letter of his father's out of his pocket, he did most exactly counterfeit the old gentleman's hand to a person of his acquaintance for £30, who not at all suspecting the note but extremely jealous of the messenger, of whom he had had some former experience, was at a wicked nonplus what to do about the delivery of the money. At length, rather than run the risco of disobliging Tomazo's father, the politic citizen found out an expedient, which was that he would send his servant and the money with Tomazo to his father, to which Tomazo cheerfully agreed. So the money was immediately delivered to the servant with positive orders not to part with his treasure to any person living but

Tomazo's father. With these cautions the knight of the burning pestle and Tomazo set forward toward his father's forbidden gates. Upon the way Tomazo, full of invention, often courted his companion with the temptation of drink, a bait that would not take with a zealous writer of shorthand, so jealous-pated that when he came to a house upon the road where he had a mind to rest himself, he delivered his charge to the master of the house to secure it, while he took a nap. Tomazo, wholly intent upon his prey and watching all opportunities with the vigilance of a tiger, was not a little troubled at this reserved wariness of the coy purse bearer. But such was Tomazo's patience that he stifled all his discontents and still beheld his companion with the careless glances of a merry countenance.

After some hours of slumber and repose, Tomazo and his cautious fellow traveler set forward again; but going over a heath, they met with several persons that informed them that if they went such a road, they would be certainly robbed, as they themselves had been but just before. Which so alarumed the cuckoo-brained prentice, who was ordered to deliver his money to none but Tomazo's father, that to prevent a compulsion to breach of trust, he examined Tomazo what private ways there were that led to his father's house. Blessed Mercury soon inspired Tomazo so that he presently called to mind a solitary byway through long grass and corn, which proved so tiresome that the careful Londoner, to ease himself in some measure of his burthen, believing he could deal well enough with Tomazo, most inauspiciously desired Tomazo to relieve his weary arms. Tomazo most affectionately embraced both the opportunity and the bag, so that from that time they carried it by turns, to the great but different comfort of each other. About eleven o'clock at night (for so eager was the faithful trustee to be at his journey's end) it came to young Iscariot's turn to bear the sacred load, who had no sooner lodged it next his heart but Judas's own Devil possessed him and presently taught him a trick, that Monsieur Blunderbuss should be no more troubled with his burthen. For Tomazo, passing by a heap of stones, privately but with a dexterous sleight of hand, takes up a good big brickbat and lays the adored Mammon in its place. Soon after, Tomazo, being to go over a bridge, makes a false step as if he had been near a fall and drops the stone into the river, which the city-dromedary hearing, demanded what it was. " 'Tis the money," replied Tomazo. "Pox take it," quo he, "let it go and be hanged—better let the money fall than suffer myself to be soused at this time a night." The poor sea gull was in such a dismal consternation at the news, so that his senses were just packing up their awls to be gone from a place where they prophesied that they should be but very rudely entertained by the passion of the master upon his booby's return, in so much that Tomazo, who all the while laughed in his sleeve, would have given something to have had his picture as he then looked. In this amazement trusty Tom Fool would have persuaded Tomazo to have put off his clothes and to have gone into the water to make search for the money, which Tomazo, to avoid all suspicion, willingly offered to do, but withal told Nickapoop that it would be but a vain attempt without the help of a candle, so that he easily persuaded the tame dottrel, now as submissive as a pumped bailiff, to stay by the bridge while he went back to certain houses about half a mile off to get a light. In his way, Tomazo had recovered and secured his money and so, making forward to the houses, called up the people, told them the misfortune of young Nicodemus, desired their assistance, and sent them all for a company of fools to the bridge, where while they were poking, and groping, and treading a mortar i'th' water with their bare feet, Tomazo having traversed his ground and taken another road had made a fair step in his way back to London, leaving Tom Tottie[12] to con the short lesson of experience which he had set him. So far Tomazo had reason to applaud his own ingenuity. But Fortune would have her turns and her changes to show him he was yet but a young Guzman and that there were others superior to him, whose art was not to be learnt by rules of accidence or grammar, but by a suffering experience. For he had no sooner secured himself in the City, but he fell into the company of certain town bullies who carried Tomazo to Speiring's Ordinary where, having easily allured the young squire into play, they soon reduced the £30, for which he had taken so much pains and which he looked upon as one of the trophies of his mercurial stratagems, to 20 shillings, to the great grief of Tomazo who, to add to his afflictions, had received information that his father was also in pursuit of him. For the dejected counter-scrubber, perceiving as well by the vain search that the people had made, as by the not returning of Tomazo, that the serpent had been too crafty for him, with a heavy heart jogged on to the old gentleman's house and there told the uncomfortable story, not daring to venture his master's displeasure, though there were not above two inches difference in the depth of their understanding—only the master trusted the man, and the man trusted Tomazo.

Upon this alarum Tomazo makes down for Gravesend with all speed, where he was informed that several ships lay bound for the Straits, whither Tomazo resolved to venture rather than fall again under the jurisdiction of his father. There it was that Tomazo, to whom Fortune was never more kind than when she had emptied his pocket, while he was treating with one of the captains for his passage to Cadiz, met with two of the gentlemen with whom he had traveled in Scotland, bound in the same ship for the same place. To those gentlemen, as to his confidants, he made known his condition and related all that had befallen him since the time that they parted at London. True it is that the stories of his extravagance were not so pleasing to their more serious humours; however, for old acquaintance sake, they promised to take such care of Tomazo, provided he would be governed, that while he continued with them, he should want nothing that was convenient for him (a kindness easily within their power, as being the sons of persons of quality and heirs to fair estates), and thus far Tomazo had Grimalkin's luck, still to fall upon his legs.

While the ship was under sail, the two gentlemen and
Tomazo had several consultations how to shape their travels after they came ashore, in order whereunto it was agreed
that they should travel all Spain first and, after that, set
sail for Egypt, from whence they would visit India, China,
Tartary, and so through Muscovy and Germany, home into
England again. Full of these designed rambles, they arrived at Cadiz, from whence they made haste to Madrid,
where they had not been above four days but one of the
gentlemen happened to kill a Spanish count, which occasioned an immediate and diligent inquiry after all persons
that had been in his company. Thereupon the gentlemen,
upon notice of the search given them by a blackamoor
maid that served in the house where they lodged, stole
away afoot through all the byways of the country, shaping
their course for Leghorn and leaving miserable Tomazo
behind, without either money or credit, who in two days
after was apprehended and in that blessed condition committed to gaol. There he found several other English people whose crimes were only their acquaintance with the
gentleman that had killed the count, which gentleman's
name (the sequel of the story so requiring) is to be henceforward Don Pedro Perguelio. But such was the kindness
of the Spanish justice that when the search was over, all
the prisoners were brought before the court, where nothing appearing against them, they were all discharged. Had
not Tomazo had a wonderful love for the light of the sun,
it had been all one for him to have confessed the fact and
been hanged as to starve for want of mouldy crusts: such
were the violent persecutions of a hungry stomach, under
which Tomazo pined and wasted at that time. But if it
had not been for these blessed butts, of which you shall
meet with enow before the story concludes, poor Tomazo
had been half worm-eaten by this; but then I say, it so
fell out one day, as Tomazo was walking upon the parade
among the soldiers, for his inclinations were always martial,
a certain captain, whose name was Don Pedro del Viejo
Castello, perceiving Tomazo by his habit to be a foreigner,

asked him his country; to which Tomazo replied, of England; for which the Captain, liking him much the better, persuaded him to list himself in his company which lay then at Puerto Ferrara, promising him due payment of his wages, which came to three halfpence a day, but withal by his deportment giving Tomazo to understand that there might be some hopes of advance and better usage for an Englishman than for the riffraff of the country. The offer, considering the nick of time, was as welcome to Tomazo as rain to the parched earth, he having been a stranger to all sort of sustenance for some time, so that now being advanced on a sudden from the grave to be a gentleman soldier, he again resumes his forsaken title of "Don" and marches away in state to his new quarters at Puerto Ferrara.

There he lived about three quarters of a year upon his forementioned allowance and the augmentation of a pound of bread a day, at the end of which term the garrison was in a most violent manner besieged by the Portuguese, with whom the besieged had many encounters; in one of which the colonel of Tomazo's regiment being killed, Don Pedro del Viejo Castello succeeded him in the employment, who not forgetting Don Tomazo in his advancement, whose courage and behaviour had very much won his heart, took such a special care of him that he raised his pay from three halfpence to fourpence, and after that, for some works of supererogation that Don Tomazo performed, from fourpence to eightpence a day. About which time the besiegers drew off, leaving all their trenches in good order, and retreated home for some time, which gave the town both leisure and opportunity to recruit. During this calm, the rest of the soldiers, who had recovered their spirits, envying Don Tomazo's prosperity and the great esteem which his colonel had for him, entered into cabals and consultations among themselves to contrive his ruin; but finding no success in their Spanish plots, a brace of the conspirators undertook to attack him by main force and in pursuance of their design, one evening, at the turning of a corner, set upon him with that violence that Don Tomazo was very severely wounded; but having recovered himself, he drew forth a pistol and shot one of his assailers who soon after died of his hurts; and while he was in pursuit of the other, a corporal came in to his assistance who took the other and secured him upon the guard. Nevertheless, upon the death of the first aggressor, Don Tomazo was tried by a council of war, where upon a full examination of the fact Don Tomazo was acquitted with great applause, and the other assailant that was taken both degraded and cashiered.

This exploit made Don Tomazo more famous than before and more esteemed and redoubted in the garrison, so that when the enemies returned again and renewed their attacks upon the town with that fury that the inhabitants began to be apprehensive of the loss of the place, several of the better sort delivered their jewels to a very considerable value to the custody of Don Tomazo, the better to secure 'em upon the surrender of the town. Which being no longer, after several rude assaults, able to hold out, yielded upon honourable conditions, and so the Spanish garrison marched forth, and as one of the number, Don Tomazo, who now, possessed of so fair a booty and knowing the danger of delays, went to his colonel for a passport. The colonel, unwilling to part with Tomazo, promised to advance him to a commission and to make his fortune, provided he would stay in his service. But Tomazo, who had an unknown fortune within the compass of his breeches, gave those pressing arguments for his departure to his colonel and pressed him so home that at length, vanquished by importunity, the colonel granted him his pass; by virtue of which Don Tomazo posted away for Leghorn as fast as his legs would carry him and there embarked for Scanderoon[13] whither, he was informed, some English gentlemen had taken shipping about fourteen days before, with a resolution to visit Grand Cairo. When he came to Scanderoon, upon inquiry, by all descriptions he guessed them to be the persons that had left him to his shifts at Madrid, which was the reason he was not very solicitous to follow them. At Scanderoon therefore he stayed, till upon the sale of some of his jewels to a Jew that was bound for Leghorn, he was informed by his landlady, an English-woman, that there was an express come with orders to apprehend him. For the Jew, coming to Leghorn, presently offers his new purchase to sale and, as the Devil and ill luck would have it, to a merchant nearly related to the very person from whom Don Tomazo had received them, who had also particular order from his relation to seize all such persons as should expose any such sort of jewels to sale, of which he had sent a particular description, so that the Jew being questioned about the jewels, informs against his chapman and discovers where he was. Thereupon Don Tomazo thought it high time to shift his quarters and posts away with all imaginable speed for Grand Cairo, where if a man do but alter his habit 'tis impossible to find him out. To which purpose he puts on the disguise of a Turk, and in that dress one day met with his old fellow traveler, Don Pedro Perguelio, who admired to find Don Tomazo in such a Mahometan garb; but being acquainted in a few words with the occasion, he received ample satisfaction, more especially when Don Tomazo farther told him that at that distance from his country he could in that heathenish city command a thousand pound, which was at that time no rodomontado in regard the jewels were worth above four times the value.

Certainly there can be no greater pleasure in this world than for one distressed Guzman to meet another of the same order flush in the trophies of successful project, Guzmans being the only relict of the Golden Age that have all things in common, so that if one has it, the rest never want, so that it is but reason that the purses of fools should pay tribute for the maintenance of such a noble generosity. Don Pedro was upon his last legs, when the happy accident to meet a member of the fraternity, so richly laden, made his heart dance in his breast without a violin. On the other side, Don Tomazo understood that it had not been so much the ill husbandry of Don Pedro which had brought him so low, but a generous charity to two English gentlemen, his comrades, who died there of the plague, the expenses of whose sickness together with their funeral charges had exhausted him to a very small remainder, so that as if the two deceased gentlemen had left Don Pedro the executor of their gratitude, from thence forward Don Pedro and Don Tomazo entered into an inviolable league, as well offensive as defensive, insomuch that though they were two bodies, there were the same thoughts and the same mind in both, and an united force now managed all their intrigues.

Grand Cairo is a city famous for its situation and the variety of pleasures it affords all persons so well able to purchase 'em, as then Don Tomazo was, who resolving to know the difference between three halfpence a day and the splendor of unlimited plenty, concluded with his friend to debar themselves of no freedom or recreation which money could command in the greatest mart of the world. But as the sea itself would dry up without the continual supply of swelling rivers, so it was impossible for Tomazo's unreplenished bag, had it been as deep as Virgil's passage to Hell, to answer the expectations of a brace of scattergoods that thought it would never be evening, till at length their inconsiderate profuseness having reduced their lean bank to the low ebb of not above a £150, repentance stept in and put them in mind of the calamities of poverty, a very unsuccessful remedy to cure the surfeits of excess, among the pitiless adorers of Mahomet. Thereupon they began to think of a new ramble; and understanding that there was a caravan of 800 passengers ready to depart for India, both the Dons agreed to make a part of the company. But the season of the year for passing the sandy deserts proving more tempestuous than usually, gave them leisure enough to spend £120 out of their low stock (for the curses of the credulous Portuguese had by this time taken their desired effect), so that they perceiving no more than £30 remaining, altered both their resolutions and their habits, and embarked from Scanderoon for Genoa, where they continued fourteen months to the total consumption of all the

Portugal booty. Then it was that necessity put Don Tomazo to employ the talents of his youth, to which purpose he made love to a Genoese widow, over whose affections in a short time he had obtained a conquest that very fairly answered both his own and his friend's expectations. But having made that post too warm by debauching the woman, getting her with child, and wasting her fortunes, they departed incognito in an English man-of-war that brought them safe to Cadiz, where they behaved themselves so well that the merchants gave them daily invitations and were very free in all manner of accommodations. But one day among the rest, Don Tomazo, to retaliate the kindnesses they had both received (for true Guzmans never mind morality), proposed to his friend Don Pedro a design which, had it taken effect, would have made them masters of a new fortune to the value of above £500. But it so happened that as they were walking upon the beach, in a deep consultation about the most compendious and effectual way to proceed in their attempt, not minding their way, they were rambled about a league from the town, where they were overtaken by three English gentlemen who were in pursuit of eight land pirates for a robbery and murder they had committed the night before upon the person of Thomas Lucie, Esq. These gentlemen requested their assistance, which they readily promised and joined in the pursuit.

After a chase of four hours they found one of the criminals sitting upon a sandhill who pretended himself half dead. This crafty devil sat there as a decoy, having planted his other seven confederates under the sand, whence they were all ready to rise with pistols and stilettos if occasion required, as indeed it most unfortunately fell out. For the gentlemen eagerly falling to search and examine the single picaroon, he presently gave the watchword to the rest who, presently rising from their ambuscado, fell upon the gentlemen, not a little surprised at their number and their instruments of death, with that violent fury that one of them was killed outright, having received near twenty stabs with

a stiletto, and the other two so wounded that they were
left for dead. Tomazo was shot in the back and shoulder,
and Don Pedro pricked in five or six places with a Spanish
tuck, and both conveyed by the victors among the great
sandhills. The other two, who were left for dead, made
such hideous outcries through the extremity of their pain
that a Spaniard fishing not far from the shore, came and
took them into his boat. Don Tomazo and Don Pedro had
the good luck to taste of the freebooters' mercy, who very
carefully dressed their wounds, as if natural instinct had
prompted them to be kind to persons that lived upon the
spoil as they did, and when they were in a hopeful way of
recovery, persuaded them to enter in their society and to
run the risco of their fortune: which there was a necessity
for the two Dons seemingly to condescend to. Nor was it
long after the completing of their cures before those sons of
rapine had cut them out an employment. For those miscreants, hearing of a parcel of merchants that were to pass
by their territories, set the two Dons to guard a pass upon
the road to Madrid, which was convenient for an escape if
need required, while the master rogues, having met with
the unfortunate merchants, robbed them of their goods and
money to the value of £6,000 sterling, of which they gave
a reasonable proportion according to the justice of thieves
one among another, promising that the next time they
should be both equally concerned. From thence they made
to their sanctuary among the sandhills, a place which did
not afford those delights to the English gallants that their
hearts panted after when their pockets were full. Whereupon Don Tomazo and Don Pedro agreed to make their
escape in the night, which an odd accident much facilitated
to their advantage. For one night among the rest, which
proved darker than ordinary, one of the picaroons being
upon the watch, certain flashes of combustible meteors appearing among the sandhills, so terrified the guilty sentinel
that he awaked his companions, who believing the country
was risen upon 'em and hearing Don Tomazo and Don
Pedro affirm withal that they had heard the voices of

strange people, put the villainous crew into such a consternation that for their better security they concluded to march off several ways by couples, having appointed a rendezvous when the danger was over. The two Dons, keeping together, steered directly for Cadiz, being followed by two more of the gang aloof off. Upon the way they met with two of their old acquaintance in the town, with whom they presently agreed to pillage the two picaroons that came behind, which they did, leaving them sorely maimed and beaten upon the place, and so with light hearts and heavy purses continued their journey to Cadiz, where being arrived they were entertained with great joy by their former correspondents. Being thus got together among their friends, the main discourse of the company was about two English gentlemen that had been most barbarously used by eight thieves, and of two other English gentlemen that were gone away with the robbers. Thereupon Don Tomazo, having first made inquiry how the gentlemen did and understanding they were safe and well, began to relate the whole story, confessing himself and Don Pedro to be the two lost sheep, and after that gave them an account of the last robbery. Which happened not a little to their disadvantage, for one of the merchants that had been robbed, being then in company, spared not to bellow forth his losses and his usage; insomuch that the two Dons, being conscious that they had about them some of the goods which the merchant had described and unwilling to run the risco of a discovery, thought it very conducing to their future safety to refund what the merchant laid claim to and to put the rest into the hands of the magistrates, who promised them an ample recompense for their fidelity, but were never so good as their words. Which cost one of the Spanish merchants, by way of revenge, a cornuting, Don Tomazo having entered into a league of familiarity with his wife, to the production of a very comfortable subsistence for himself and his friend while they continued in the town.

At length, perceiving no more good to be done there and

finding several ships bound for England, they embarked for
the land of their nativity in one, which by the master's
ill conduct had the ill fortune to be cast away, so that
there had been an end of all the ship's company, and the
two young Guzmans had been coffined in some sea-mon-
ster's belly, had not a Dutch vessel been so kind as to send
out their boat and save all the men, whom they carried
along with them to Amsterdam, a place to which Don
Tomazo and Don Pedro were both absolute strangers. But
finding several English there, they told their tale so
smoothly that they found very compassionate entertainment among their countrymen. During which leisure time,
Don Tomazo, having made his interest with a burger's
wife, had soon wheedled the loving soul out of 300 guil-
ders, which amount to near £30 English. With this money
the two Dons, having picked up and joined in confederacy
with two more Spaniards of the same order, Philip de Mexico and Gulielmo Porfeire, fell to the national cheat of
coining; wherein after they had cut their own stamps, they
were so successful that in two months' time they had filled
all Amsterdam so full of double stivers, composed of three
parts copper blanched with arsenic and one third silver,
that there was hardly any other money stirring among the
butter-boxes. By which piece of dangerous industry, they
advanced their stock to £1,200 sterling. All which being
rightly considered by the four engineers, they forsook
Amsterdam and retired with their bank into Zealand.
Where they were no sooner arrived, but the £1,200 had
so inspired them with high thoughts that then little gains
were looked upon as ridiculous, and nothing would serve
less than £10,000 apiece. For the raising of which princely
sum there was a general consultation of all four heads,
wherein it was concluded that doubloon stamps, ducatoon
stamps, and all sorts of stamps for Spanish gold should be
forthwith prepared, but the metal could not be fixed till
near £400 of the main stock was embezzled in experiments
and necessary expenses. But then Fortune, loth such men
of art and industry should lie any longer idle, found them

out a composition to their hearts' desire, consisting of one third copper artificially tinctured with yellow, one half third gold, and half third emery, and one third superfine silver—of which metal they made about £2,000, according to their modest computation and the conscience they used in putting them off. Which that they might do with the more facility and speed, they dealt with all persons, bought the best commodities, and gave the largest rates. And for the better management of the affair, every confederate had his particular employment assigned him. Philip de Mexico and Gulielmo Porfeire were to reside at Middelburg and prepare the coin; Don Pedro was the merchant that bought the goods; and Don Tomazo, the factor, who resided at Ghent, whither all commodities were sent and immediately exposed to sale or transported to places more secure. But this trade lasted not long. For Philip de Mexico, being a person inclined to all sorts of debauchery, one day gave a certain female that had caressed him with more than ordinary civilities, one of his counterfeit pieces, who having a sudden occasion for money, as women of that profession are seldom hoarders, carried the piece to exchange for silver with a goldsmith who had forfeited his judgment by being bitten with about thirty pieces of the same nature before. Whose revenge exasperating him to a strict examination of the woman, she was constrained to discover where she had it and then to go along with the officers of the city and show them Philip's lodging, who was immediately surprised and apprehended with all his materials and instruments about him and, without inquiry after farther proof, committed to prison.

This apparent discovery, and the great alarum it gave the whole city, was notice sufficient for Don Pedro and Gulielmo to shift for themselves, who made all imaginable haste to Don Tomazo, to whom they related the doleful disaster and the sad tidings of their interrupted commerce. Thereupon Don Tomazo sold off all his merchandise, and having quartered his companions in a village near to Ghent, he went himself to Middelburg with an intention to use all his endeavours to help Philip out of the briars. But by that time he had been twice with Philip in the prison and had ordered all things ready for his escape, there came in the middle of the night several of the officers of the town to seize Tomazo upon information given to the *heers* against him by Philip himself who, not believing it was in Don Tomazo's power to bring him off, was in hopes, by an ingenious confession and the conviction of Don Tomazo, to save his own bacon. But his treachery did him no kindness. For he wanted money, without which there is nothing to be done in that nor in any other part of the world. On the other side, Tomazo had plenty and with his golden showers so mollified the gaoler's daughter that she not only brought him an iron instrument to dig his way through the wall, and rope to let himself down, and a boat to receive him, but accompanied him, her none tender self, leaving father and mother for the sweet satisfaction of her fleshly appetite. Being both safe in the boat, away sailed Feliciano and his Feliciana to Flushing, and from thence, without any provision, put to sea, where they drave almost starved to death upon the wide ocean, till Fortune threw them at length upon the coast of Flanders, at what time they quitted the boat and traveled the country by land, like a tinker and his doxy, till they came to Don Pedro and Gulielmo, to whom Don Tomazo gave an account of the kindness Philip would have done him in requital of his pains and friendly intentions. Nor was it long after, that we heard of poor Philip's being transported to the other world in a caldron of boiling oil, according to the sentence of his judges, which sort of terrible execution did not little startle the rest of the confederates, yet not so as altogether to daunt 'em in the progress of their profession. For Don Tomazo, Don Pedro, Gulielmo, and the gaoler's kind daughter, whose name was Mariana, removing to Brussels, they fell again in that place to their Zealand sport, resolving to hazard t'other caldron; where after they had made a considerable quantity of coin, they took their several stations and employments of merchandising till all their pieces were gone, which good success encouraged them to go on afresh. But so it fell out that Mariana, who had altered her habit and went for a Dutch mynheer, and Gulielmo, going one day to court to buy horses of Count Monterey's servants, were spied by a person of quality, of whom they had purchased other horses before and paid him 200 pistols of coin out of their own mint. This same person was a certain count, who made such a noise that the whole court was alarumed; the parties accused were both apprehended and sent to eat the bread of affliction in lob's pound where they endured no small torment both of body and mind, especially Mariana whose misfortune was the greater for want of her dear Don Tomazo. But neither were his love nor his jealousy so importunate nor so vehement at that time, but that he was content rather to trust the Spaniard with his mistress than venture his carcass for them, as he had done for Philip. A piece of ingratitude which his conscience and self-preservation were forced to dispense with at that time, in regard he was too well known to be their solicitor. Which was the reason that both the wary Dons stole privately away for Dunkirk, there to attend the issue of Gulielmo's and Mariana's imprisonment, who in a short time after were both convicted by their own confessions and forced to evaporate their souls in boiling oil, as Philip had done, by an infernal torment in this, the better to prepare them for the bituminous tar-pits of the other world.

The news of which hellish execution reaching the ears of the two Dons at Dunkirk, the very thoughts of Dutch and Flemish crucibles so cooled their courages that for the future they resolved utterly to abandon the "Molting Trade." And believing that time would obliterate the memory of these extravagancies, they resolved to employ themselves in travel, as they did through most parts of France. But returning for Calais with an intention to embark for England, the boiling oil had so perfumed those parts that not able to endure the scent they retreated to Dieppe, from whence they arrived safe and sound at Rye in Sussex, where

when they came to cast up their accounts, they found themselves reduced to £500 apiece, a sound foundation, could
they have had the patience to build upon it like either
Suttons or old Audleys.[14]

But they had no skill in grazing, or malting, or setting
up of brewhouses, by which they had known as many
ruined as raised. They were for the quick dispatch. They
were for drink and be rich. They looked upon themselves
like two children of Israel, and all the world beside as
Egyptians, from whom they thought it no crime to borrow
in their necessity. And Guzmans call that necessity, when
they want fuel to feed the heat of their prodigality.

The inseparable Don Tomazo and Don Pedro, being
thus returned into their native country like two sons of
Priam, *Per varios casus, per tot discrimina rerum,* made
haste to London, the grand receptacle of all the most refined virtuosos in Guzmanry, where they made it their business to repair the loss they had sustained by the parboil-
ing of their Spanish companions. Nor was it long before
they had found out a parcel of projectors as fit for intrigue
as themselves, to whom they communicated a certain co-
nundrum, which they had just coddled in their continually
working brains; the sum and shape of which piece of midwifery was this: that six persons should lay down £300
apiece to fit out a privateer to sea, a gudgeon quickly swallowed among persons that took all for fish that came to
net. Thereupon there was a person employed to go to Dunkirk to buy a vessel and to fit and victual her out to sea.
They that made the grand council at London were to pick
up men and to have them ready to go aboard when the
vessel should arrive upon the coast of England, wherein
the concording Guzmans were so punctual (for the sinews
of their war began to waste) that the men being conveyed
away in boats, the little dreadnought set forward in pursuit
of her design which was no less than the intended destruction of the whole Guinea trade. See here the difference
between a Spanish and an English Guzman, the one pur-

suing a poor hungry plot upon his penurious master's bread and cheese,[15] the other designing to grasp the riches of the fourth part of the world by the ruin of a national commerce.

Thus with a firm belief that they should have ballasted their ship with dust-ore, they hoised their sails; but being driven by most violent storms upon the coasts of Ireland, they lost both their vessel and all their hopes, no other good luck attending that voyage but only that of saving the men, which were in number above three hundred, who dividing into small companies for convenience of travel took several ways to seek for new employment, by which means the coast of Guinea scaped a most desperate scouring, and the African Company had a very great deliverance. Don Tomazo and Don Pedro, so lately men, though now but mice, kept still together companions in misery, and coming to Dublin, by the instigation of pure necessity (a thing which the morose law never considers), fell to their old trade, which was to counterfeit guineas and broad pieces of gold, which after they had done and carried on about two months, some as good and as expert at the sport as themselves, not enduring interlopers to their own prejudice, traced 'em out and found their quarters. Where they gave the Dons very courteously to understand that that small city was already too well stocked with gravers of the King's image, and therefore desired the right worshipful coppersmiths to depart, lest worse befell them. Upon which kind advice the two Dons took shipping for Bristol, a place much more fit for their purpose. There, being loth to draw bills and break the bulk of their London stock, with a poor inconsiderable bank of 30 shillings, of which 15 were milled, they began again. Those 15 milled shillings did the two Dons knight's service, for being double gilt and inlaid with scepters, they marched off currently. Upon which foundation they wrought so long with ease and little expense, till they had well lined their pockets, were well mounted, and in a good condition to ramble.

From thence, well knowing the danger of staying too

long in a place, they rode to Gloucester where after they
had made up near 350 of their own St. Martin's ware,[16]
they were disturbed by an officious rumour and forced to
ride the country. During which journey of pleasure, in exchange either for good money or commodities, they put
out all their illegitimate pieces to nurse. After which, like
a little running pestilence, they went to infect the city of
Worcester. There the two Dons met accidentally with
four other persons of the same profession, who being pursued by the country were apprehended in their company.
At what time one of the strangers, to prevent the fatality
of a search, conveyed under the table into Tomazo's hands
a certain bag both large and weighty. Don Tomazo was
with child to know the contents, and therefore being got
to his lodging, his dear Pylades and he made bold to open
the bag, in which they found six letters to as many gentlemen in the neighbouring counties, a note of considerable
sum of money left with an innkeeper at Bridgnorth, and
220 false guineas most artificially and elaborately ordered.
The letters they opened, took copies, and sealed up again,
having found by the contents how affairs stood with the
gentlemen to whom they were directed. Thus fortunately
provided, Don Tomazo and Don Pedro departed forthwith,
and galloping tantivy to Bridgnorth, they received £337
from the innkeeper. From thence they took their rounds
to visit the six gentlemen, who being all persons of valuable estates and fearing to run the bloody hazard of having
their spotless reputations brought upon so dangerous a
stage, upon the delivery of the letters and a relation of the
misfortune that attended the persons from whom they
came, willingly bled their 50 pound apiece for an obligation of secrecy. The two Dons, having thus made the best
of their market, left the gentlemen for that time and took a
ramble for Stourbridge, where being forced to continue by
reason of an accident that befell Don Tomazo's horse, they
lived to the height of their estates. During which demurrage, Don Tomazo's behaviour (always taking among the
tender sex) had infused such a passion into the heart of a

gentlewoman in the town, who wanted neither wit nor caution to manage her amorous diversions, that partly out of gratitude, partly for profit (for he seldom loved but for his advantage), partly for pleasure, his friend and he were forced to encamp in that place much longer than they intended, Don Tomazo passing for a German and humouring that pretense with broken English. All that while Don Tomazo lost no time in improving the advantage of his amours, nor spared for any sort of caresses which he thought were proper to entertain so kind and bountiful a lady. But that post growing too hot through the jealousies and suspicions conceived of Don Tomazo and Don Pedro, in regard of the high rate they lived at, the two sparks were forced to remove, though not without taking leave of the young lady, who was so concerned for the loss of her dear German's society that the magnetic virtue of his embraces had almost engaged her in a resolution to be the companion of his fortunes. But Don Tomazo, not desiring to travel with the expensive molestations and inconveniences of female luggage, diverted her affectionate humour with such powerful arguments that at length they parted, though not without some briny deluges that overflowed the sorrowful lady's rosy cheeks. Don Tomazo, having thus disengaged himself from the labyrinths of love after a prodigal waste of his venereal ammunition, set forward with his other self, Don Pedro, for London, where they ranted with a profuse pomp and vainglory for about half a year, till finding their exchequer grow low, they began to think it time to recruit. Neither was it for such extraordinary, high-soaring Guzmans as they to play at ordinary games, whose prodigality was not to be supplied by the dipping of country squires or the little cheats of high and low fullums.[17]

At that time the French and Dutch were at daggers drawing, and they understanding that there was a fleet of Holland merchantmen in the River of Thames, very richly laden to the value of £800,000, all outward bound under a convoy of two men-of-war of forty guns apiece and very well manned, concluded upon a design to surprise these

ships and their convoy, and to make them prize by virtue
of a French commission with which they were already furnished. First then in order to this attempt, by their acquaintance with some of those seamen who had been fellow sufferers with them in their intended voyage to the
coast of Guinea, they raised a very considerable number of
men, which by the leave of the captains of the Dutch men-
of-war were to be put aboard their ships under pretense of
being raised as recruits by certain officers employed from
Holland for that purpose. And it so happened that
Tomazo's great diligence had found out a parcel of such
sons of necessity as had not only Dutch commissions, but
as good a will to the design as himself. These persons
treated with the aforesaid captains for the carrying over so
many men for the service of the States, which the captains
were very willing to undertake for the good of their country, so that in two days' time, the whole fleet lying at
Gravesend, the major part of the men were sent aboard in
the habit of new-raised men, but all resolute sea-tories and
privately well-armed with poniards and pistols. These were
to have been the fatal instruments of the grand surprise.
For it being the custom at sea to divide the ship's company into three parts that make three watches, of which
one is to be always upon the deck, it was so laid that the
English, in the dead of the night, after they had secured
the powder rooms, should run upon the decks, shut down
the hatches to keep down those that were below, and cut
the throats of all that made resistance above. By which
means having got the command of the men-of-war, they
might with ease have commanded the merchantmen and
so have made for the French ports where their commissions
would have borne them out.

About two days after the men were thus disposed of, the
pretended Dutch officers sent down about forty large trunks
of a prodigious weight, with particular care to put them
aboard in the night, for fear of meeting with the searchers.
All which trunks were filled only with hay and bricks, to
possess the people with a belief of some considerable

treasure or some great quantity of arms that might be in them, to avoid the suspicion of men whom they saw entrusted with such a ponderous charge.

By this time the wind stood fair, and the English officers were ordered by the Dutch captains to repair aboard with the rest of their men; in order whereunto they went all down to Gravesend, where the officers having sent their men aboard, went themselves ashore and in their company Don Tomazo and Don Pedro, the masterwheels of this confounded piece of mischief, under the notion of servants to one that passed for a lieutenant-colonel. Thus far things went prosperously on, and the gale of Fortune blew as fair as the wind then favourable to the voyage. But the Devil's i' that thing called "fond love," which had made me think that the poets did ill to couple Mars and Venus together, considering how many brave martial designs have proved abortive through the openheartedness of amorous folly. For to the total destruction of this Babel-like structure of two unwearied brains, it happened that one of the men who went last aboard and was to have been a private sentinel was married forsooth to a Dutch woman, who had so ravished or rather infatuated him upon the leave-taking night that like the hairbrained Curius,[18] he could not conceal from his charming Fulvia the great design he was going upon. Whereupon the plaguy Delilah, out of a pure affection for her countrymen, went and discovered the grand plot to the Dutch captains, who were at first struck with a strange kind of terror to see themselves so near the brink of danger; but soon recollecting themselves, they kept their discovery close, not making it known to any but the officers of the ships. After that, having prepared all things for a close fight, they ordered all the English which were above to go under deck upon pain of death, which they did, all but some resolute fellows, who being overpowered were beaten, wounded, and forced down. Which petty conquest being thus obtained and the fatal Sinons secured in the bodies of the two Trojan sea-horses, one of the captains was sent ashore to entreat the English officers to come aboard in regard the fleet was ready to set sail. But those sons of guilt and jealousy reading something more than ordinary in the Dutch captain's face, one of them with a loud oath swore they were all undone, and was making an offer to shift for himself; but the Dutch, having raised the town, had so beset the houses that they were apprehended, every mother's son, and delivered up to the magistrates with a general information against them of the crime and of the design they had in hand, but not a word in the least of the men which they had secured in the two vessels. The Dutch captains, having thus escaped a danger ten times worse than that of Scylla or Charybdis, weigh anchor, and being safe arrived at their intended port, acquaint the great mynheers what a whirlpool they had so narrowly missed, and delivered up all their prisoners to the mercy of the Hogen Mogens,[19] who ordered them to be sent to the Indies for eight years, while they that were seized at Gravesend were discharged for want of farther prosecution and so returned to London. In which wide place, neither Don Tomazo nor Don Pedro durst show their heads, as having not only spent their own ill-got bank, but run in debt to defray the charges, which you may be sure the expenses of such a design would require.

Such is the fate of Guzmanry, sometimes to abound and sometimes to want bread. In which condition the two reduced projectors were forced for a while to sit and bite upon the bridle: till in some short time, having raised so much money as would pay for their passage to Haarlem in the Low Countries, they embarked for that place, where the two Dons prevailed with a certain merchant to furnish them with £30, for the repayment whereof they drew a bill upon another merchant of their own invention and nomination at London. Thus set up again, they departed for Amsterdam, where they possessed the English with so firm a belief of their being young Irish merchants who had suffered shipwreck, that they, compassionating their condition, assisted them with money and credit to the value of a £100. Which good success in those two places made them resolve to try how high they could build upon this same oddly begun foundation of the world's opinion. Which is many times the beginning of a trade that advances several to vast and real fortunes. In order to this design, away they go to Rotterdam, where they found an English merchant who being newly crept into the world, struck in with Don Tomazo and Don Pedro who pretended to be of the same profession and that they would send for goods out of Ireland with the next opportunity. Upon which score the Dutch merchant furnished his two new partners with wines and other commodities to the value of £400 which were presently shipped off for Flanders by the general consent of all the three.

Into that country the inseparable couple followed their game and at Bruges set up their staff. There, for a short apprenticeship served their turn, they fell to trade with the merchants of the city and bartered their commodities very fairly for Irish goods, and with good advantage. And which was more, very honestly from time to time sent the effects to their correspondent at Rotterdam, who by that hocus of just dealing was so satisfied with the reality and good intentions of his two Irish chapmen that they continued trading together for above a year, in which time he had furnished them with goods to the value of £3,457, for which the two Dons returned him still most punctually commodities of equal value, to the great content of the Rotterdammer and the great reputation of the two English Guzmans, who in this time, by virtue of their commerce with the merchants of Bruges and the great entertainment which they gave them, were grown to be as high in the credit of the city-merchants as with their correspondent at Rotterdam, every one courting their custom and expressing how deeply they would trust 'em for their farther encouragement.

One would have thought this genteel and gainful way of living, the kindness of strangers, and their own gratitude should have obliged these two Dons to have kept within the bounds of reason and common honesty. But there is that lechery in some men to triumph in their frauds and to be profuse at the expenses of other people's purses, that they cannot be contented with other gains than those that will satisfy their prodigality, and the toil of keeping accompts was a labour too tedious to their mercurial brains, and therefore they were now for reaping the harvest which they saw ripe for their sickle. The sun shined, and they must make their hay. The merchants had fairly promised, and they resolved to try how far they would be as good as their words. *Volenti non fit injuria*[20] was a Machiavellian maxim that very much prevailed upon their consciences, none of the tenderest at that time. Thereupon they took up several parcels of goods to the value of £2,000 or upwards; which being shipped off for England, away marched they after their prey; and taking Ostend, Newport, Dunkirk, Calais, and indeed all the considerable ports between that and Saint Malo, at the same places, by virtue of several counterfeit bills from several parts but more particularly from Rotterdam and Bruges, they raised (all expenses borne) an additional stock of ready money amounting to £1,507, with which recruit they bore away to the Port of Exeter, where the two Dons thought to have found the ship which carried their goods. But being arrived there, they understood by a merchant concerned in the same ship that the master and some of the company had carried the vessel and goods to Bayonne and had there exposed them to sale. Nor was this all, for the same merchant, keeping a correspondence at Bruges and, by the intelligence he had received from thence, concluding Don Tomazo and Don Pedro to be the two persons complained of for the exploit they had there so lately committed, caused them to be both arrested in the names of his Flemish friends, to whom he sent word of the embargo which he had laid upon their persons. The Bruges merchants had no sooner received the information, but they sent over a person to treat with the two young sparks, who being unwilling to lose time by lying in prison, the worst place in nature for men of their profession, came to a seasonable composition, and having to their great grief refunded £1,360, were presently discharged. Happily for them. For they were no sooner gone, but fresh orders came to the same merchant from several persons out of France to detain them upon their accounts. However, the birds being flown, there was an end of that prosecution. The guilt of the two Dons made them wickedly jealous of the diligence that would be used to entrap them, and therefore they made all the haste they could to London where they lay still a while, till they thought the danger over.

This terror being past, the two Dons fell to new consultations, and finding the ill success of merchandising, they resolved to set up the old trade of coining, wherein they were more expert as being more suitable to their "geniuses." In order to the better management of which affair, like men of gravity and prudence, they consulted the statutes of the kingdom, by which they found the counterfeiting of Spanish gold to be the least dangerous in point of penalty.[21] And therefore, having got their materials and confederates, such as broken goldsmiths and gilders, all in a readiness, they fell so sedulously to their business that in fourteen days' time they had made as many doubloons and double doubloons as amounted to the value of £3,245 according to the price of their mint. Part of these pieces Don Pedro and Tomazo undertook to put off in the West and Northwest parts of England. To which purpose they took their progress, well-mounted, genteelly clad, well-attended with servants, besides the traveling grandeur of led horses. However, they did not always appear in this splendor, but at certain times and for colour of some great designs, having for projects of lesser moment other disguises and pretenses. Among the rest they had an easy excuse for their stay at seaport towns, in expectation of ships from several parts: during which demurrage, it was no difficult thing to put off thirty or forty of their pieces and then remove to another place; neither was Lyme in Dorsetshire the scene of one of their meanest exploits.

In that place lived a merchant nearly related to their

correspondent at Rotterdam, upon whom they had a design
of no less than three or four hundred pound thick. This
man was a wary person and one that, having been often
scalded, dreaded the fire, which made the enterprise much
more difficult; however, the resolution of the two Dons was
such that they resolved to attempt it, as they did in this
manner.

Don Tomazo and Don Pedro, with their servants and
horses, in great splendor, went to Lyme where they took up
all the chiefest inns of the town, Don Tomazo (and Don
Proteus himself could have done no more) having now
metamorphosed himself into the shape of a Spanish count,
to whom he pretended the King of England and several of
the nobility had given several horses and liberty to buy
more and to transport them at his pleasure, for the service
of his own sovereign. In prosecution of which affair, he had
been in the adjacent counties and had made several pur-
chases, which he daily expected in that town, and was
therefore come to make provision of hay, corn and stabling
for their accommodation, till he could have the conveniency
of shipping them off, insomuch that the countrypeople that
came thither to market were forced to set their unregarded
beasts in the streets to make room for the Spanish Count's
horses. During the Spanish Count's continuance at Lyme,
which was about four days, he sends for the merchant upon
whom he had fixed his design and, after he had amused
him with a noble entertainment, entered into a discourse
with him about his horses and how he intended to have
them transported, desiring him either to assist him with his
advice or else himself be pleased to hire him some vessels
for that purpose. An employment which the merchant
readily undertook and, to that purpose, brought four or five
masters of ships to the Count, with whom his Lordship
soon agreed for the passage of his numerous cavalry. The
next day, the merchant being present, the Count received
an account from one of his servants, who pretended he
came from the horses, that they were at such a place, but
that his agents had bought more horses than they had

money to pay for, and therefore desired the money might
be sent them. Presently the Count, calling for his steward,
bid him go and fetch as many pieces of Spanish gold as
would make up the sum. Which being brought as soon, the
Count desired the merchant to exchange them for silver.
Which the merchant undertaking to do, went home, carries the gold along with him; and sending for three more
of his friends, they all laid their heads together to make
trial of the pieces, which they did by all the usual ways
of touching, cutting, weighing, and the like. But the metal
was so superexcellently tempered that they could make no
other discovery but that it was absolutely real, so that the
merchant returned with the full change in silver, which the
Count immediately delivered to one of his grooms, who
carried it away. The next day, the former messenger returns
again to Lyme and tells the Count that all his horses were
seized, in regard the countrypeople had consulted together
and were of opinion that the horses were to be transported
contrary to an act of Parliament and without the King's
leave. At which unexpected news, the Count was seemingly
strangely alarmed and surprised, and in a passion as well
counterfeited as his Spanish gold, commanded his groom
to make ready his horses, pretending to go in person to dispute a business so prejudicial to his grand affairs. On the
other side, for the prevention of all disturbance and delay,
and to show that he came not into England upon a first
of April day's errant, being as it were come to himself, he
desired the favour of the merchant to ride post to London
to give the King an account of the abuse and scandal he
had suffered from the country, and to pray his Majesty's
warrant for the release of his horses; and in consideration
of his trouble, allowed him one of his servants to wait upon
him and ten pistols to bear his charges, with assurance
that at his return he should find the Count at Lyme. The
merchant, as well to oblige a person of so much honour as
the Spanish Count as to serve his neighbours who were not
a little discomposed at the loss they should sustain by the
Count's being so rudely disappointed, set forward with

more than good speed to solicit for the Count. For upon his arrival at London, the Count's gentleman, who had his private instructions to prevent the merchant's going to Court, sent for a confederate that well understood his lord's affairs, who presently entered an action of £4,000 against the Spanish Count's ambassador and arrested him as he was going to Whitehall, with a crew of pretended officers of his own garbling. In this condition they hurried the helpless merchant to prison, as they made him believe, but indeed to one of their own private haunts, a certain dark, diabolical cellar, where they so roughly entertained the terrified stranger that to free himself out of the clutches of such a surly sort of rake-shames, he was forced to draw bills upon his correspondents in several places; which being received and due intelligence given to the Count of all proceedings, the poor merchant of Lyme, who had by this means moulted a good part of his gayest feathers, was discharged out of captivity. As for the Count himself and his retinue, they soon quitted that post and, having altered their habits and changed their horses, ranged farther up into the country, not deeming the seaports proper to be visited while such exploits as these were fresh in memory. So like are these sort of Guzmans to the Tartars who, when they have devoured the products of one place, remove into fresh accommodation.

But though they had changed their horses, they did not alter their pretense of buying horses. To which purpose, Don Tomazo, now acting the part of a jockey rather than a Spanish count, made it his business to ride with a servant up and down to farmers' houses, having first inquired the names of such gentlemen as lived nearest thereabouts and also taken a prospect as far as he could of their qualities, their honours, and their conditions.

'Tis well known to be the custom in many parts of the West of England for many farmers to breed up horses of fifty or sixty pound a pair and sometimes of greater value. Such horses as these, Don Tomazo would often cheapen and sometimes bargain for, but when the seller and the purchaser came to the point, Don Tomazo had no money which was passable; nor was it his intent it should be so, as knowing well the humour of those sort of people, which was to raise the country presently, to make a thousand hubbubs and put all the world into noise and uproar; whereas a gentleman, having been smitten under the fifth rib, will first consider his own reputation and hold a private imparlance with his own reason, of which some are so highly conceited that they would not have the world believe they could be out-noddled, for the half of their estates. They observe themselves to be the great idols of wit and parts, to which the people offer in the high places of the country, but should it once appear that their divinity-ships had once been subject to the frailty of having been cullied and cony-catched by mortal Guzmans, their oracles would be no more frequented among the vulgar, and the smiles of the gentry would expose them to the satirical extension of the forefinger, which was a punishment of their unwary folly that so overawed their considerative prudences that hardly one in twenty ever divulged the tricks that Don Tomazo put upon them. And therefore, because they were best able to bear the loss, most ready to put it up, and most easy to be played upon (as depending upon their own judgments)—in point of morality, in point of policy, and to save trouble, Don Tomazo seldom dealt with any other than those of his own rank, "gentlemen."

Having made this digression for the better instruction of the reader, we shall clear the foregoing axiom by the following demonstration. For as has been already hinted, when Don Tomazo had bargained with any farmers for one or more horses, he still told them he had not current money to pay for his markets and therefore desired them to send one of their servants to such a gentleman's house where he was certain to be furnished with English coin, delivering himself in such a manner as if he were most intimately acquainted there. Thereupon the farmer would presently order a servant to ride along with their genteel chapman who, by the way, never failed to intoxicate the credulous

bumpkin with the promise of some gratuity for his pains
and then to make him perfect in his lesson, which was, to
give such a short account of Don Tomazo, as he himself
directed him. The fellow, being thus prepared and inspired
with expectation, so soon as they came somewhat near the
house was sent before to inquire whether the gentleman
were within. A question which Don Tomazo could have
resolved before, but done on purpose to give the gentleman
opportunity to inquire of the servant, who the person was
that was coming behind. For then it was that the country-
fellow generally gave his worship this answer, that either
he was a person of quality and of his master's acquaintance, who had bought horses of one that lived in such a
place, or else that he was a near relation to his master, who
had bought horses of another of his acquaintance: either
of which pretenses so formal and so probable were enough
to prevail with a gentleman always ready to oblige his
neighbours, so that by these artifices Don Tomazo seldom
failed of having his gold changed or silver lent upon it,
with his promise of sending for it again in such a time. But
the fish being caught, Don Tomazo had no more business
either with that farmer or his servant; and therefore at
parting, he only gave the fellow a small reward and bid
him tell his master that he was gone to such a place, quite
contrary to that corner of the wind whither he was bound,
and would be with him in three or four hours, in which
time he was got out of reach to his next conveniency. For
Don Tomazo and his brethren always so managed their
business that they rode first about the country to inform
themselves of everything material before they made any
attempt, so that when they once began, two or three days
put an end to all such designs as they had in those parts
of the country.

During the time that these pranks were played, the Lyme
merchant, being returned home full of choler and revenge,
had made a strange hurly-burly in the country, but could
hear no tidings of his Count, so that all things being once
more still and quiet, Don Tomazo and Don Pedro resolved

to take the opportunity of the calm and to favour their beloved, the seaports, with a fresh visit. Among the rest, they arrived at length at a place called Kingsbridge in Devonshire. There, coming in upon a market day, Don Tomazo found divers gentlemen, and several of their number, in whose faces he could read a chapter fit for his purpose, better than some astrologers. And indeed the circumstantial accidents fell out so propitiously that they seemed, as it were, to assure him of success. For upon a sudden, not only about the town, but all the country round, there fell so deep a snow that neither horse nor man could travail. By which confederacy of the season, Don Tomazo and Don Pedro came familiarly acquainted with several of the said gentlemen, under the notion of persons that were newly arrived from Spain. This happy time of leisure afforded Don Tomazo a kind opportunity to enter his new acquaintance into play (which is one of the laudable exercises that waste our time in these parts of Europe), at which sport he gave them leave at first to win much of his Spanish gold, which some of the gamesters, having been travelers in that kingdom, pretended to understand as well as the losing stranger, who, to give the better colour to his design, seemed not a little troubled at the loss of his *summum bonum*, the only true friend to a traveler. But the fickle dice, i' faith, soon altered their career and ran so much on Don Tomazo's side that in a short time he had taken captive good store of the gentlemen's coin, who were so fond of the gold that rather than part with it they borrowed money in the town to pay their losses. But this same sport was too hot to hold, so that the gentlemen, weary at length of ill luck and tired with the inconveniencies of losing, as having taken their leaves (besides the satisfaction for Don Tomazo's gold) of near a £100 of their own money, thought it high time to knock off and return to their several habitations.

At their several departures, there was one of the company that prevailed with Don Tomazo and Don Pedro to ride with him home, where they were not only received with a most hospitable accommodation by the gentleman at his own, but by him also carried to a person of quality's house not far off, where they were likewise entertained with no less kindness than plenty. But such is the ill nature of Guzmanry that it spares neither friend nor foe: for of this very person of quality, who had been so civil in his entertainment, did Don Tomazo very gratefully buy two horses, for which he paid 147 pistolets, and sent them away by his servant. This scene being over, they were in haste to be gone; and therefore to avoid the sour sauce that might happen to season the sweet viands of their entertainment, they took their leaves of the civility of those places, and set forward for Plymouth, but giving out that they intended for London.

When the two Dons came to Plymouth, ere they had time to alight, Don Tomazo was spied by a person that knew him, who informed him that his master was in the town. This news was to Don Tomazo like aloes and honey, a strange mixture of sweet and bitter. For the gentleman was his acquaintance, but one of the persons that had won some of his gold at Kingsbridge, so that Don Tomazo, suspecting that the gentleman was come thither to make trial of his gold, thought it not proper to stay there. Thereupon the two Dons turned their horses' heads; but as they rode by a goldsmith's shop, Don Tomazo's counterfeit pieces began to ferment in his pocket, so that at their instigation Don Tomazo, deeming it a foul shame that he should come into such a town as Plymouth and leave no monument of his fame behind him, alights at the goldsmith's shop and desires silver for as much gold as amounted to £14/10s/9d. The goldsmith, satisfied with the trial he made, delivers the silver demanded; and so the two Dons, having given that great town a small taste of their ingenuity, steered directly for the county of Cornwall where they found great opportunities of business, played several pranks, and among the rest, this in particular.

Don Tomazo, having taken up his quarters at a town called Penzance, and Don Pedro at another called Saint

Ives, both seaports, lay there without taking the least cognizance of each other. They had been such strangers one to another for some weeks that the one had not been in the other's company but once, and that, as it were, by an accidental meeting, so that it was impossible for the country to imagine or suspect any such thing as an intimacy between them, which was the foundation upon which many designs were laid and brought to perfection.

One time among the rest, it happened that Don Tomazo, being at church upon a Sunday, paying his devotions to something or other, Cupid finding him at a loss for an object of his zeal, fixed his eyes upon a very pretty lady whose beauty made no slight impression in Tomazo's heart. The inflamed lover, whose business it was always to use the swiftest expedition in his affairs, now more violently hastened by his amorous impatience, returns to his quarters and makes all those diligent inquiries after the lady that lovers are wont to do, which concluding with such a passionate joy that all their answers satisfied his expectations, the people easily from thence drew their wonted conjectures and presently reported that Don Tomazo, who passed for the son of a person of great quality in the North, was deeply in love with such a lady. This report flew like lightning and was presently bandied from one tittle-tattle to another, till it came to the father's ear with all the embellishments of multiplication, in reference to the behaviour and gallantry of the enamoured esquire. The father was tickled at the tidings and, as it is the fashion of the unwary to look upon distant prospects with a magnifying fancy, thought it but an act of paternal affection to advance his daughter's fortune; and the daughter herself, proud of the conquest of her victorious beauty, already imagined herself riding in her coach and six horses, the adored mistress of many tenants and the charming wife of a brisk, bonny, and wealthy heir. Thereupon the Justice comes thundering to Penzance to take view of his son-in-law and, having found him out, took an occasion to fall into a sifting discourse with Don Tomazo, who had all his story so geometrically framed and delivered it with such a careless exactness, without the least hesitation, that the Cornish chough was not only taken with his person and behaviour, but so intoxicated with his narrative that he invited him over to his house. Don Tomazo kindly accepted his invitation and accordingly gave him the honour of his company home, where he had leisure enough to unbosom his affections to the young Isabella, the name by which henceforward she shall be known.

Some time after, the Justice, his wife, and his daughter went to visit a gentleman of their acquaintance that lived not far from Saint Ives, who after dinner informed the Justice of a gentleman that quartered at Saint Ives that was certainly the best company that ever he met with, withal, that he was a Spaniard whose curiosity had brought him thither to view the country. Upon which rare character of an intimate friend, the Justice desired he might be sent for, as he was, with all speed. But when he came, the country gentleman, who only thought to complete his pastime with the mirth of some comical droll, was strangely out of countenance and in a surprise, believing his old acquaintance had put some trick upon him. For such was Don Pedro's air and deportment that the Justice took him for no less than some person of high quality, which was no small trouble to the Justice to be put out of the road of his rural addresses and country compliments, and forced on a sudden to recollect the exercises of his youth at the dancing school for new congees and refined expressions. For, indeed, Don Pedro might well have passed for such a one as the Justice took him to be, in any part of the world. He was a person so comely that few Spaniards were like him, very fair, full eyed, with a lovely head of long hair as black as a raven's wing, and a body most curiously proportioned, to which his graceful carriage, his affable, sweet, and complaisant humour, his fluency of speech, and his noble equipage, were such charming additions that it was no wonder Cupid took his stand in such a face and bent his bow to kiss two birds with one stone. I say "bent" because, at that time, I believe the god of love made use of a crossbow, in regard of the crossness of the shot. In short, the mother and the daughter were both shot plumb dead at the same time, insomuch that there was no peace or quiet in either of their bosoms, till they had prevailed with the Justice (who could hardly think his mansion worthy such a guest) to invite Don Pedro to his house. But at last, overcome by their importunity and his own ambition, he took the confidence to give him a solemn and cardinal-like invitation, which Don Pedro readily accepted. You may be sure, the entertainment could not choose but be splendid, where the master consulted his honour; the mistress, her deep affection; and no question but the daughter sat up late and had a finger in every pie and every tart. Nor was the female diligence of those two love-shot ladies less, to dress, and trim, and trick and adorn themselves, with all the ornaments their trunks and cabinets could afford. What fairs and christenings saw but seldom and in parcels, that Don Pedro saw at once and every day displayed, while the mother strove to renew the youth of her past beauty, the daughter to beautify her present youth.

All this Don Pedro contentedly observed, and as he was extremely acute in his observations, after dinner he gave Madam Isabella an occasion to convey a little billet into his hand; at what time the mother took an opportunity to slip another into his pocket, ignorant of what her rival daughter had done. Neither, indeed, was Don Pedro aware of the mother's contrivance. So ambitious they were, which of the two should make the first and deepest impression in Don Pedro's heart. The two ladies having thus disburthened their affections, the one into his pocket, the other into his hand, Don Pedro, after a power of compliments and kindness, took his leave and, being returned to his quarters, drew forth the billet which he had received from Mrs. Isabella, wherein he read these following lines:

SIR,
 The first time I saw you, the idea of your perfections caused a violent passion in my heart, which having ever since tormented me, pardon the flame that

enforces me to let you know the wound you have given me. I doubt not, but that a person of your quality will be careful to manage this secret with that prudence as shall be no way to the disadvantage of a person so young and tender, that languishes for your sake.

Don Pedro was so startled at the reading these short ejaculations of a wounded heart that he wrote a letter to Don Tomazo and within enclosed the billet, desiring him to consider what design would be most likely to succeed among people that had laid themselves so fairly at the feet of their mercy and, as it were, put their lily-white hands into the lion's mouth. Withal, he cautioned Don Tomazo for the future to avoid suspicion, to write his mind and send his servant with it, to be left in a hole of a certain rock halfway between Penzance and Saint Ives, which was afterwards observed. But when Don Tomazo came to read the billet which Don Pedro had informed him came from the Justice's daughter, he was in a strange quandary, for he loved her himself even beyond the pleasures of his profession. He could not imagine the reason of his misfortune, not dreaming the young lady had been such an early Maycherry, so soon to allure the gatherer's hand, of whom he then himself had no other hopes but as the paternal heat of her father's care mellowed her for his embraces. Of his approbation, good will, and favour, he thought himself cocksure, as well for that they had been more intimate together, as in regard the deportment and natural parts of Don Tomazo were not much inferior to those acquired endowments of Don Pedro. But while Don Tomazo's thoughts were thus tennis-balled between love and Guzmanry, the lady herself sent him a cordial that soon composed this disorder of his senses. For within two days after, Mrs. Isabella, finding a convenient opportunity, and as young and innocent as Don Tomazo thought her, willing to have two strings to her bow, writ Don Tomazo the following letter in answer to one of his:

Sir,

Your immediate passion surprises a person so great
a stranger to things of this nature; and besides, you
men (as I have been informed by my mother) are most
kind things till your ends are accomplished and then
as full of slights. But if I could be satisfied of the
reality of your affection, it would be more serviceable
to your interest. But, alas! How shall I credit anything from a man who burns and dies, swears, vows,
and protests, and all in one single minute, quite contrary to the thoughts of his heart? This from a person
so great a stranger, as well to yourself as to the thing
called love, as I am, you may, if you please, value as a
piece of liberty I allow you, to be what in yours you
express.

This letter from so young and so unexpected a piece of
female treason did not a little damp the amorous Don
Tomazo's flame. He saw how the subtle traitress was only
coaxing poor Tomazo with the shadow, while she was dis-
posing the substance to Don Pedro, cunningly providing
that if Don Pedro should slight her proffered fondness, then
to accept of Don Tomazo's courtship. This double dealing
of Mrs. Isabella, though unlooked for, was upon better consideration the more welcome to Don Tomazo to support
the morality of that injustice which he intended the family:
which while he was meditating how to bring to pass, his
servant brought him a letter from the rock, with another
billet in the belly of it. For by this time Don Pedro's servant,
after his master had shifted his clothes, had found the Justice's, Seignior Cornuto-Elect's, wife's love-letter in one of
the pockets, which Don Tomazo reading, found these violent expressions of an amorous fury:

Most fair and dear to me of all your sex,

Whose charms no creature is able to resist, I that
have lived in the state of marriage this twenty-five
years, a just and dutiful wife and, as I thought, to the
best of your sex, am now so altered in my respect to

that thing called an husband that I hate him for your sake, for which I would quit all my immediate plenty to enjoy your dear company but one hour. Pity the weakness of a woman, and do not slight a passion so great that no breast can conceal; and consider how I break the impalement of a virtuous life forty-three years long to come to the embraces of yourself, whom I love above all the world. Let not my age render me insignificant, but meet me tomorrow at the mount.

Don Tomazo, having read this letter, could not choose but laugh to see the infidelity of the daughter so prettily revenged by the wantonness of the mother who was all this while in a fiery torment, like St. Laurence upon the gridiron, believing that if Don Pedro had not slighted her, he either would have met her, or else she should have heard from him.

It seems Don Pedro knew nothing of this letter before his man had found it; and therefore not to lose his opportunities, having received some private instructions from Don Tomazo, he thought it high time to answer both his clients, beginning first with Madam Isabella, in this language:

Fair Isabella,

When I had perused your little charm, I found myself under a thousand constructions: but by the contents thereof, being truly sensible of your great affections for me, assure yourself, nothing on earth shall labour more to retaliate those your favours, nor manage the whole matter with more safety to yourself than I will. So if you'll but meet me at the Little Rock, I shall there express what is now too much to expose in written lines,

Adieu.

After he had wrote this and was assured of Isabella's coming to the place appointed, Don Pedro, apprehensive that the absence of the daughter might raise jealousies in the mother and put her upon the search, like Ceres after her daughter Proserpine, to prevent her, sent her this julep to qualify the heat of her fever.

Dear Madam,

I curst my ill fate a thousand times for concealing your billet so long from me: for I never knew of it till shifting my apparel, and then my *valet de chambre* found it by accident in the same pocket, which I suppose you put it. But the content thereof has given me such demonstrable satisfaction of your great and good inclination to me, that it puts me under no small surprise to qualify myself for the reception of so much honour, the least grain of which, as coming from you, I shall more esteem than my life and finally make it my study how to embrace you with such a tenderness as may be most proper for a lady under the circumstances of so great a passion. And from hence forward, to prevent the jealousy of a husband, let us only meet and not write. For nothing is of more dangerous consequence than letters of such a nature as this, when once discovered, especially by a man so apt as the Justice. I will meet you tomorrow at the same place you appointed and the same hour,

Adieu.

At the receipt of this letter, the lady was so transported that for that day all the gaiety and pleasure she had ever shown or enjoyed in her whole life seemed to be recollected and rendezvoused in her countenance. She thought of nothing but of reinforcing her amorous heat, that she might be able to meet her dear Don Pedro's fires with equal flames. Her heart danced the "canaries" in her bosom for joy that she should so soon be happy in the embraces of her beloved Spaniard; and the continual meditations of her brain upon these voluptuous felicities did so employ her thoughts that her daughter might have had the opportunity to have lost more maidenheads than Hercules got in one night, for any inquiry her mother made after her. Thus was the mother's security the daughter's safety, who by this time had lost her troublesome virginity in those embraces, to which the other was the next day to resign the matrimonial loyalty of many years. So little does the continual sight of a gold thumb-ring control the temptations of a wanton appetite.

Isabella, having by this means obtained a full satisfaction from Don Pedro and now become as wise in the natural philosophy of love as her mother, left her instructor a thousand sweet kisses in pawn for an assurance of her farther society, and with the modesty of a nun, returned home to laugh in her sleeve at the cheat she had put upon the vigilance of her mother and all her female guardians. But before Don Pedro and she parted, there was an agreement made that whenever Don Pedro came to the Justice's house, it should be under pretense of making love to her who had already given him the surest pledge of her affection. For under that colour Don Pedro, being now to manage the intrigue between the mother and him, where lay the stress both of his and Don Tomazo's design, and the prospect of their gain, it was necessary to uphold the amorous correspondence which he and Isabella had begun.

And now the happy hour was come, Don Pedro and the enamoured mother met; and he that had so deliciously fed the young kitling was now to purr it with grimalkin the elder, whom he entertained with such variety of embraces that she protested all the Justice's "Cornish hugs" were but bavin-bands to 'em. Which gave her such an intrinsic satisfaction that she enjoined Don Pedro to stay in those parts a month longer and, indeed, till those quarters were grown almost too hot to hold either him or his company. In order whereunto, she had contrived a way for his coming to the Justice's house. But Don Pedro, not deeming her way so commodious as his own, acquainted the mother with his affections to her daughter, who thereupon approved of his intentions; and having resolved to act conformably to the design, they parted for that time.

Don Pedro, being returned home, wrote a letter to be left at the rock for Don Tomazo, wherein he gave him an exact account of what had passed between him and the two ladies, and farther desired Don Tomazo with all speed to get himself introduced into Isabella's company and to make his addresses to her, wherein he promised to be assisting, so soon as there appeared any public acquaintance between them.

This letter Don Tomazo read with great regret, cursing Pedro's happiness and his own ill conduct, not so much for the love he bore the dissembling Isabella, as for that he had not made the same improvement of his opportunity that Don Pedro had done; but finding it was now Don Pedro's intention to carry on the common advantage, and that the design began to ripen, he easily rid his head of those impertinent imaginations and, two days after, gave a visit to the Justice who, being at home, entertained him with great respect; and among the rest of the discourse, knowing Don Tomazo was well skilled in the Spanish tongue, informed him of a famous Spanish gentleman that was in those parts, well worth his acquaintance. Of which Don Tomazo seemingly made slight, telling the Justice that he was a young man and did not know what inconveniencies the knowledge of that gentleman might produce. But the more Don Tomazo slighted it, the more earnest the Justice was to send for Don Pedro, so that Don Tomazo, unwilling to disoblige the Justice by his obstinacy, suffered himself to be overruled. So soon as Don Pedro came, Don Tomazo entertained him with all the ceremonies according to the gravity of Spain, and afterwards discoursed him in the Spanish language, which fell out luckily for their business, in regard that none of the Justice's family understood what they said.

This interview between the two pretended strangers, Don Tomazo and Don Pedro, first begat a familiarity, then frequent meetings; and at length, by the Justice's consent, his house became the general rendezvous. During which time, Don Pedro, having had the frequent sight and handling of his enamoured mistress's jewels, had got such a perfect idea of the shape, form, and bigness of the pearls and stones, and afterwards drawn them so exactly in paper, that there was no question of the success of the design. Thereupon

Don Tomazo dispatched away his man to Exeter, who there bought up several pendants of counterfeit pearl and Bristol stones, so well matched that they were hardly to be distinguished from the originals. Which being brought to Don Tomazo, he delivered them to Don Pedro who, watching his opportunity, which the fond dotage of Isabella's mother often gave him by opening her cabinet and displaying her wealth to dazzle his eyes and oblige him to the satisfaction of her desires, took an honest occasion to pay himself for his drudgery by taking out the real substances and conveying the counterfeit shadows in their places. Which being done, for about three days after, Don Tomazo and Don Pedro drank the Justice very hard and, indeed, made it their business to keep him elevated for the most part of their stay, after the moral exchange which Don Pedro had made with his wife. During which time, one evening, the Justice being bousy, they took an occasion to make a repetition of the great favours he had shown them, promising those returns which they neither durst nor ever intended to perform. In the conclusion of which most lofty compliments, some discourse arising about Mrs. Isabella, Don Pedro catched at it and spared not to say that he loved her beyond measure and little less than his life; but he came short of Don Tomazo who swore, by way of reply, that she was more dear to him than life itself, and in pursuit of his zeal for the lady, requested the Justice to declare if it were his intention to dispose of his daughter in marriage, and if it were possible for her to love Tomazo and Pedro both alike, on which of the two he would soonest bestow her. The Justice, being ravished to hear such a brisk contest about his daughter between two such great persons of quality, was at first in a dilemma, but at length, heightened by the t'other round and the more generous protestation of Don Tomazo, frankly declared in favour of him. At which Don Pedro seemed to take snuff, but carried it off for the present, and so they drank on all three till the ladies were gone to bed; but then Don Pedro and Don Tomazo took an occasion to slip out of the room, leaving the Justice alone who, perceiving they did not immediately return, presently began to reflect upon the discourse that had past between 'em. With that he ran to the garden door, at which they went out, where he had not stood long before he heard the clashing of swords. Which so amazed his worship that in a trice the whole family was alarmed, and the Justice with some of his servants came in great haste to part them. In this counterfeit fray, Don Pedro had pricked Don Tomazo in the arm, more like a surgeon than an enemy, which, with another green hurt that Tomazo had received but a little before, past for two great wounds. The Justice caused his servants to take Don Tomazo into the house, while he laboured to appease Don Pedro, who seemingly would fain have had the t'other touch with Don Tomazo. But his violent passion at length submitting to the Justice's mediation, he was prevailed with to go to bed. The scuffle being thus over and the great mischief prevented, the Justice visited Tomazo, who all in a boiling choler lay swearing he would make Don Pedro smoke for the injury he had done him, and what he would make him pay for damages. The old gentleman gave all the sugar words he could think of and sent for a chirurgeon, whose honesty Don Tomazo easily tempted to delay the cure to enhance the bill of costs. After that time, the two rivals never met, Don Tomazo returning to his quarters, and the Justice for his own reputation so ordered it that there was no noise made of the dangerous duel. Nevertheless, Don Pedro, who all this while lay at rack and manger in the Justice's house and took that care of his wife to find her other sport than visiting her cabinets, seemed to be not a little afraid of his rival, and therefore persuaded the Justice to give Don Tomazo a visit and, withal, to pump him in reference to his demands for satisfaction: to whom Don Tomazo protested that £500 should not reconcile 'em. But the cure being over, Don Tomazo was persuaded by the Justice (whom they found very much pleased with his office of mediation) to treat with Don Pedro, who was willing to refer himself to Don Tomazo, as not thinking it convenient to encumber himself

with the laws of the nation to which he was a stranger, so
that at length Don Tomazo was overruled by the Justice to
take £225. Accordingly Don Pedro laid down the money in
Spanish gold, which Don Tomazo refused as not being the
coin of England. Thereupon Don Pedro, mainly desirous to
be rid of trouble, requested the Justice to take the gold and
furnish him with so much money, which he not having in
the house, courteously sent to Penzance for and delivered it
to Pedro, who upon the payment thereof to Don Tomazo
received a full and ample discharge, but refused to have
any more to do with such a litigious gentleman.

By this time having stocked all that country with their
precious metal, by a letter from the rock they agreed to be
gone, as they did in a most slovenly manner. For without
taking leave of the Justice, who was so courteous, or his
wife, who had been so kind, or the daughter, who had
been so tenderly loving, they took horse of a sudden and
vanished out of the country, leaving nothing behind 'em
but the remarks of an old musty proverb, "Happy are they
that beware by other men's harms." Neither were they very
scrutinous to know what curses or lamentations followed
'em from the Justice's house, who they knew had no great
reason to be overzealous in their pursuit.

During this pleasant ramble, the two brethren in evil had
returned several considerable sums to London and disposed
of all their counterfeit Peruvians. And now, coming to a
certain market town beyond Exeter, the little god with a
muffler about his eyes found a way to shoot a new passion
into Don Tomazo's heart. He that had so long defied the
yoke of wedlock was now altogether for the bonds of matrimony. He had met with an object beautiful and rich that
had enslaved him even to a sense of honour, as if the sickness of his love had caused a qualm of honesty in his mind,
so that having succeeded in his courtship, he resolved to be
faithful to one he entirely loved. And now all things being
concluded, and nothing wanting toward consummation but
the ceremony of the church, Don Tomazo rides back to
Exeter to provide the nuptial ornaments. By the way, at

another market town, he met with some gentlemen of the country who persuaded him to dine with 'em at an inn, where after they had drunk pretty hard, one of the company (who was master of the inn where Don Tomazo quartered at Lyme) began to relate the whole story of a certain exploit that was done at his town by a pretended Spanish count, and at the conclusion of his story pointed to Tomazo, saying that the Count was like him as ever he saw any man in his life, only that the Count wore a peruke, and Don Tomazo his own hair. This narrative did not a little disorder Don Tomazo's cogitations, but he who had the confidence to outbrazen the stern looks of so many dangers, scorned to betray his fear of such a scarecrow as this; and so, putting a good face upon the matter with a story of the same nature with his own concern, which led to others quite different, he lulled the Lyme man's relation asleep; and for fear it should wake again, he kept the company so well soldered together with pleasing healths that all manner of stories were forgot, there being not one in the company but what was carried to bed. Only Don Tomazo, having been more careful of himself, rode to Exeter that night to meet a more unlucky misfortune. For early the next morning after he came thither, the ostler of the inn where his horses stood, taking one of them to the farrier's upon some occasion or other, a certain person casting his eye upon the beast demanded of the ostler whose it was, who answered, he knew not. Thereupon the person who asked the question waited till the horse was led back and, following him to the stable, there found the very horse on which Tomazo rode when he changed his Spanish pieces with him at Plymouth for £14 odd money. For so it fell out that this was the very individual goldsmith that had been nicked in that manner, who thereupon went to Don Tomazo's lodging and caused him to be apprehended. A sad catastrophe to a person that dreamt of nothing but epithalamiums and hymeneal flambeaus! Presently he was carried before a magistrate by whom, upon the justice's information, he was committed, but left bailable. Don Tomazo, being thus in the climm

and well knowing that the report of his being in prison
would muster a wicked battalion of the same crimes to his
destruction, to prevent the threats of his hard fate, writes
away a letter to a gentleman who was a justice of the peace
in the county of Devon, whose surname he then assumed
to himself, wherein he gave him to understand his condition, and that he was a person nearly related to him; and
therefore requested his worship (for nothing less than a
justice of peace of the same county would serve) to favour
an innocent stranger so far as to stand for one of his bail,
pretending, as well he might do, that his imprisonment
would be his ruin, as being a person that came not into the
country to utter false money, but to court a young lady
that lived not far from him, of which he would give his
worship a farther account if his request were granted. Don
Tomazo's letter was well considered and scanned by the
justice before he sent an answer, and inquiry was also made
by his order after this new-discovered kinsman, by which
the justice finding many of the circumstances to be true,
as Don Tomazo had expressed, believed the rest and wrote
him word that though he knew him not personally, he was
satisfied that he had such a kinsman in the world and believed him so to be; and therefore rather than suffer a relation to lie under such a scandal, he promised to bail him
off, which was immediately done by himself and another
justice of the peace whom he had engaged to stand with
him. With this new relation Don Tomazo went home,
where he was civilly entertained till the time of his appearance at the sessions. During which interval, being brought
acquainted by his cousin with the justices of the peace of
the county, he had so insinuated himself into their favour
that several of them had obliged themselves by promise to
be his friends, which made him resolved to stand his trial.
When the time came, the goldsmith exhibited his indictment against Don Tomazo, wherein he charged him with
having exchanged at his shop a certain weight of metal for
so much real money, but that when he went to melt it
down in his forge, the whole matter by putting a smart

fire under it evaporated with that violence, that his servant standing on the other side of the forge, having received some of the vapour into his nostrils, to the great wonder of his master. Upon this indictment Don Tomazo was found guilty of a high misdemeanour and fined £45, which was afterwards brought down to 40 shillings, and presently paid with great joy by Don Tomazo. For upon payment of his fine, no other charge coming against him, he was acquitted by proclamation.

Don Tomazo, having thus escaped the goldsmith's tongue, almost as bad as St. Dunstan's, having made all the expedition he could to render his acknowledgments to the gentleman he was so much obliged to, made as much haste out of the country, and with his other self Don Pedro set forward for London, no more regarding his intended marriage, which indeed had been to little purpose: for his mistress's relations, having heard of his misfortunes and that he had been no sufferer for his religion, took that paternal care as to send their daughter far enough out of his reach. When the two travelers arrived at London and had cast up their accounts, it appeared by their books that they and their confederates had uttered in this kingdom 4,050 pieces of their sorts of Spanish gold, amounting to near £5,000 sterling, of which, being divided, £1,700 came to Don Tomazo's and Don Pedro's share; all which, together with the stock they had before and the jewels which they had borrowed of the Justice's lady (clear booty to them, too) rose to a very considerable value—and yet no such vast sum neither, for those that had been sowing and reaping all over England.

Now, you will say, What became of all this money? Oh! never fear it, you shall have a faithful account of it by and by. You'll be impertinently questioning, too, Why did not these two Dons put themselves in "a way"? So they did, and that in as fair a way to be hanged as ever they did in all their progresses through all the ways of Great Britain. Now loosing, and venturing life and limbs to impose upon

princes and generals, as they did before to cozen goldsmiths and country gentlemen. But how you will approve
of their ways is not for them to determine.

For to tell you the truth, the two Dons finding London
the coolest place in England for men of their profession,
now grown by continual persecutions rather like the stoves
i' the new bagnio than like a gentle Egyptian oven to hatch
more mischief in, resolved to pass over into Holland, with
a resolution to serve the Prince of Orange, and so they did
more tricks than ever he thought they deserved thanks for.
To which intent, they took their leaves of their native soil
like two philosophers, carrying all they had along with
them, though it were a hard thing to judge whether their
country were not as glad to be rid of them as they were
to be rid of their country. But let it be as it will, they were
no sooner entered upon the stage of Holland, but they were
admitted to kiss the Prince's hands. Such an ascendant has
the dazzle of garb and behaviour over all mankind, and all
because the body of man is not as transparent as it is brittle.
Soon after they had performed this ceremony, they had
leave to enter themselves as volunteers; for there were no
commissions to be had for money, it being then at the beginning of the "campaign." During all which time of military duty and the winter following, the two English sparks,
not considering that their bank was to be fathomed or
rather building upon the fair promises made them of employments that would soon replenish the vacuums of their
empty bags, what with "item" for excessive expenses, "item"
for gaming, that bane of plethoric pockets, were brought to
sing "Lachrymæ" over the last penny, so that for want of
foresight, seldom regarded by the great masters of art in
Guzmanry, having disposed of all their equipage and bravery, for it came to that at length, they were resolved, however, not to starve. And therefore to prevent that miserable,
pining death, Don Tomazo, who had some knowledge in
the art of fortification, as being one that had often built
sconces, took the boldness to wait upon the Prince, to whom
he expressed the great desire he had to serve his Highness

to the utmost of what he was capable. Then, for Don
Tomazo was always one that kept close to his text, he made
known to the Prince the necessity he was in, not forgetting
to mind him of the good services he and Don Pedro had
done at several places and more particularly the siege of
Grave, which were not unknown to the Prince, who thereupon bid Tomazo look about and find out something within
his Highness's disposal, and that then both he and his
friend should not fail to see the effects of his Highness's
favour answerable to their expectations. But Don Tomazo,
not to be baulked by those plausible evasions of courtship,
came close to the point, for it was money he wanted, and
thereupon he acquainted the Prince that if he would order
him a £100, he would undertake to serve him as a spy in
the French army. This the Prince desired time to consider
of, and in a short time communicated the secret to some of
his council, who being as truly sensible as himself of the
great want of intelligence among the Dutch, persuaded the
Prince to employ Don Tomazo, since 'twas his own volun-
tary offer. In pursuit of this advice, the Prince sent for Don
Tomazo and told him, provided his friend Don Pedro
would condescend to be left as a pledge, he should have a
£100 to put him into an equipage fit for the prosecution of
his proposals. For the Prince had had several tricks put
upon him by the English before, which made him the more
cautious. Upon this, Tomazo advises with his friend Don
Pedro; and as they two were not wont to Spaniolize in
their consultations, the matter was so ordered to the
Prince's satisfaction likewise that Don Tomazo, as much to
his satisfaction likewise, received the £100. Upon the receipt whereof, away went Don Tomazo for Brussels, altered
all his habits, and in the disguise of a boor of that country
trudged to the French army that then lay encamped near
Soignies under the command of the Prince of Conde. There
Don Tomazo got a full view of all their standards, cannon,
and the manner of their encamping, as also a very near
account of the number of their men, both horse and foot.
With this discovery Don Tomazo returned to Brussels

where he put all things into a formal draught, exactly representing the whole camp; which being showed to the Prince of Orange, he compared it with one which he had received before from another person of the same occupation. By which comparison, the Prince found Don Tomazo to be a very fit person for his employment, and therefore encouraged him and promised him that so long as he could furnish them with good intelligence, he should want neither for money nor advance. Thereupon Don Tomazo returns to Brussels, where finding several of the countrypeople whose houses had been plundered and themselves stript by the French, so miserably poor that they wanted bread, Don Tomazo picked up one of these forlorn creatures, which by conversation he found most acute, with whom he prevailed to undertake such enterprises as he should put him upon, and to follow his directions, for which he promised him half a crown English a day. The boor, taking Don Tomazo for an angel sent from Heaven to relieve his misery, embraced his offer with all the readiness imaginable, so that Don Tomazo having given him full instructions, sent him about his business. Upon his return, the boor gave a very good account of things, which being put into form together with such other discoveries which Don Tomazo had made (unknown to the boor), he presented them to the Prince, who still received more and more satisfaction from the labours of his new spy.

Sometime after, Don Tomazo had by the diligence of his new-acquired confederate prevailed with ten or a dozen more of the same stamp and in the same condition to list themselves in his service for the same pay. By this increase of number, his intelligence notably increased, insomuch that his double diligence had highly advanced him in the favour of the Prince, who believed that whatever Tomazo brought him was clearly gotten by his own hazard and industry, as indeed the best part of it was; for you must always allow the master to outdo the servants.

These smaller attempts so well succeeding, Don Tomazo was desired by the Prince of Orange to use all his art to insinuate himself into an acquaintance with some of the Prince of Conde's family or attendants, promising that if it could be accomplished and any service accrue from thence, no sum of money should be wanting for gratification or reward, or remuneration, or whatever ye please to call it. Don Tomazo, thirsting after fame and money and believing that having so many irons in the fire it would not be long ere some of them proved hot enough to strike, readily undertakes the affair; to which purpose he provides a frock of sackcloth, a pair of wooden shoes (for such is the habit of the boors in those parts), a rundlet of brandy, and a parcel of tobacco. This rundlet had two divisions, the one for the soldier's liquor of life and the other for blacklead pencils and parchment, and such other necessary materials. In this garb, who the devil could know so great a person as Don Tomazo? So that under this disguise he walked about the French camp, grateful to the soldiers for the sake of his tobacco and brandy, and watching his opportunities, took several memorandums very considerable. But [Tomazo] loitering one day carelessly about the quarters of the Prince of Conde, one of the captains of the guard called to Don Tomazo who, believing him not worse than Cerberus and in hopes that a sop would have stopped his mouth, proffered him a taste of his cordial liquor. But the captain, suspecting him to be what he was, ordered him to be searched and kept him upon the guard four whole hours. This was an accident that set all the pulses of Don Tomazo's brain at work, and all little enough to hammer out new spirits to supply the want of those which he had lost in the fright. But those little Vulcans soon recruited his arteries, and the Devil, too, the father of lies, unwilling to lose a servant, gave him a list with a cast of his favour. For after something of a serious study upon such a ticklish point of life or death, Don Tomazo called for the captain and desired he might be carried to the Prince of Conde, at which the captain laughed and saluted Don Tomazo's posteriors with a contemptible kick or two, asking in great derision what business such a beast as he could have with the

Prince. So strangely may a captain be mistaken. But Don Tomazo urged his importunity so home that Mareschal D' Humieres, passing by and hearing the brandyman so boldly demand to speak with the Prince of Conde about business of importance, came up to him and asked him what it was. To whom Don Tomazo made a submissive answer that it was of that high consequence, that for his life he durst not impart it to any but the Prince himself. Away went the Mareschal, little thinking that Satan had sent him of an errand, and gave notice to the Prince of Don Tomazo's importunity, who thereupon sent for the brandy-merchant, not to buy any of his ware, but to understand his business. Then it was that Don Tomazo, with a respectful bow, not like that of a strong-water-man, desired privacy with his Highness, as not daring to give any account of his business to any person living but himself. Thereupon the Prince, considering there were such things as disguises in the world, and frequently made use of, and that it was in his power with one puff of a mortbleu as well to hang a varlet as to reward an instrument, ordered all people to withdraw: which being done, Don Tomazo opening his mouth without fear or trembling thus began.

"Sir, it is intended by the Prince of Orange that his whole army shall march to Oudenarde about four days hence, in order to which all things are in preparation: thirty battering cannon are to be sent from Ghent to meet them. The Prince being resolved to besiege the town with all the vigour imaginable and to render the enterprise more easy, four engineers are to be sent into the garrison tomorrow to dismount the cannon, which is to be done with the consent of some of the gunners already tampered with and made for their purpose. Farther, when the Dutch are ready to open their trenches, the great water dam in the middle of the town is to be sprung by another engineer by the consent of the persons there concerned, of whom they are already assured. Which being done and the water fallen, the enemy intends to attack the town on that side. Now if your Highness think fit, I will return to the Dutch army and make farther inquiry into the particulars of this design, which when I have done, I shall be ready to go to Oudenarde and discover to the persons your Highness shall appoint, the very engineers and their accomplices themselves."

The Prince, hearing such a formal story from such an aniseed-water-robin, as he took Tomazo to be, was not a little surprised, which caused him, as any general of reason would have done, to ask Tomazo what he was, how he had lived, what had induced him to make this discovery, and how he came to be privy to such a considerable secret, adding withal that he could not believe the Prince of Orange would ever communicate a design of such importance to a person of his low degree.

To this Don Tomazo, not thinking it necessary to run through the whole course of his life, replied in short that he was a captain in the Prince of Orange's army, that he was intimately acquainted with all the chief officers, that he had been divers times at their councils of war and often had had the honour privately to discourse [with] the Prince of Orange, the Princes of Curland, Nassau, and Friesland; by which he made it out that there was probability enough that he might be acquainted with part, though not with all, their designs. And lastly, that as to his inducement to make the discovery, it proceeded merely from the great honour and esteem he had for his Majesty of France, whom he was most ambitious to serve.

The Prince, having thus duly weighed the circumstances of the story and finding nothing but what was very likely to be true, surrendered his belief to Don Tomazo's smooth tale and, the more to oblige him, ordered his *valet de chambre* to present him with forty quadruples to the value of £160 sterling, which pleased Don Tomazo much better than the kicks o' the breech which the surly captain gave him. Which being done, the Prince gave him farther hopes of his favour, even to high advancement, if he made out the discovery as he had begun; and so, having enjoined him to return with all possible speed, in order to his going to Oudenarde for the apprehension of Don Tomazo's traitors in the moon, he dismissed the well-satisfied Mundungus-merchant from a most dreadful agony, with the sweet consolation of fiddler's fare.

Don Tomazo, having thus by dint of wit delivered himself out of the lion's den, and finding that he was able to deal with two princes at one time, resolved to play his game out. To this intent, away he goes directly to the Prince of Orange, and to him without any concealment relates all that had past between the Prince of Conde and himself. A story which very much pleased the Prince and caused him to laugh heartily. At the conclusion of his narrative, Don Tomazo was commanded by the Prince to return at the time appointed, which he did accordingly and found immediate admittance to the Prince of Conde, to whom he told the same story as before, only with some alterations and additions. Which so convinced the great general of the truth of the fable, not believing that though a man had counterfeited once, he would ever be such a fool to venture again with the same lie in his mouth, that he ordered Don Tomazo to go directly by such a token to the Marquis de Chamilly, then governor of Oudenarde, and give him an account of the whole matter as from the Prince. All which Don Tomazo exactly performed, but then pretending to the Marquis that the persons were not yet come and that it behooved him therefore to stay till they came, that liberty was soon allowed him. During which time, he made it his business to walk and view all the fortifications, as well private as public, as also to take several memoirs of what he thought proper for his purpose. And though it was not to be expected that the Marquis should be so liberal as the Prince of Conde, yet did Don Tomazo so well order his governorship that he Chamilly'd him out of forty pistols; and so having modeled all his draughts & observations, he watched his opportunity and stole out of the town, though with no small hazard, the French being the most careful in the world how they let any persons pass in or out at their garrisons without a strict examination.

By this time the Prince of Conde had received an account

from some correspondent of his in the Dutch army that the Prince of Orange had sent an engineer to Oudenarde and that he did intend to beleaguer it. Which piece of imperfect intelligence from a known friend, agreeing with Don Tomazo's story, so startled the Prince that he now believed every word Don Tomazo had said. And, thereupon, [he] raises his camp from Charleroy and marches quite cross the country to cover Oudenarde, into which he put 3,000 fresh men with provisions, continuing his camp upon the downs, in expectation of the Prince of Orange's coming. Of whom, in four days after, he heard another story, for the Dutch taking the opportunity of the discamping and long march of the French, presently surrounded Charleroy, the place they had all along had their design upon, which forced the Prince after a tedious march to Oudenarde for the apprehension of Don Tomazo's invisible engineers to hurry back again to the relief of Charleroy, where he had no small trouble to raise the besiegers, not daring to give them battle though he had much the advantage. And it may be truly said that this invented chimera of Don Tomazo's, the product of a mere accident, had so disordered the measures of the French councils, by sending their general from post to pillar, that they could not recover their senses all that summer. From such small beginnings ofttimes arise the most fatal revolutions in the world.

For, to say truth, the siege of Oudenarde was never dreamt of, till Don Tomazo's return from thence with the Marquis's pistols and his presenting the Prince of Orange with the draughts and observations he had made. But then the Prince consulted all his engineers, and divers councils of war were held upon the occasion of Don Tomazo's discoveries, which were found to be of that consequence that the Dutch fell in good earnest to the siege of Oudenarde, which put the Prince of Conde to another dance of attendance upon their masterships to rouse 'em from that haunt. Which happened very much to the loss of the besiegers, and more for the Prince of Conde's honour, though Don Tomazo had put him to trot hard for it. However, there

were some commanders of great experience among the
Dutch who were of opinion that had the directions which
Don Tomazo gave them been rightly managed and kept
private, the success of the enterprise could not have failed.
But that which occasioned the ill successes of the Dutch,
I mean not only in this particular but at other times, was
first their ill conduct in not concealing the good services nor
indeed the names of the persons of those they put upon
such employments as these; and, then, so often communi-
cating their designs to such as gave immediate notice to the
French, by whose advices the Dutch spies were so often
discovered and hanged that others being discouraged, their
intelligence was very insignificant, till Don Tomazo undertook the business, who so ordered it that he had several
emissaries up and down in the French army and some that
waited even upon some of the principal officers themselves,
which he had in daily pay, beside others that continually
trotted between them in the army and himself who, with
Don Pedro, still kept his quarters in some Spanish garrison
nearest his business, modeling collateral designs of another
nature.

The next summer, the face of affairs was somewhat altered, the Prince of Conde being removed into Alsatia, and
the Duke of Luxemburg made General of the Army in
Flanders; which clearly disordered Tomazo's former settlement, so that he was forced to go himself to new model his
affairs, which he effectually performed. For he got Don
Pedro to be a *valet de chambre* to the Duke himself, by
which means Don Pedro became very serviceable to him.
His correspondence being thus settled and carried on for
near four months, Don Tomazo found that some of the
Spanish governors were not so kind to him as he expected,
and therefore he made his complaint to the Prince of
Orange, who soon after procured letters of recommendation from the Duke de Villa Hermosa, not only to those but
to all others which Don Tomazo had occasion to visit. A
certain sort of utensils which he knew how to make use of.

Some time after, there happened certain disorders among

the confederate spies, which could not be well settled unless
Don Tomazo appeared among them in person, and as it
fell out, no other place would serve but the Duke of Luxemburg's quarters themselves. In order to this difficult journey,
Don Tomazo puts on the habit of a merchant, gets as many
passports as were requisite for a man under such circumstances to travel with, and so sets forward on foot towards
the French camp. By the way, he narrowly escaped the
pursuit of several boors in the province of Artois, who would
certainly have stript if not murthered him, had he not
showed them a good pair of heels, the use of which he
well understood, for it was common with him to travel
fifty miles a day in that country. He had no sooner got clear
of this cursed crew, but he met with another party about
half a mile off, as bad as themselves. Through these he had
no other means to escape, but by making his way by main
force. Which so provoked those bloody varlets that some
of them let fly several shot at him from their fuzees, while
others set a-running after him, thinking to have overtaken
him; and perhaps they might have won the race, to the
loss of his life, had he not met with some of the horseguards
of Lisle then scouting abroad, who, observing what had
past between the boors and him, presently seized him
and sent him away to the garrison, where he was detained
by the captain of the guard, notwithstanding that he
showed him his passports, who told Don Tomazo that he
was a spy and only forced in by a party of their men who
were gone out but a little before, and that therefore he
should stay till the party returned. Don Tomazo, vexed at
this stop, acquainted the captain with the real occasion of
his traveling that way, which was to wait upon the Duke of
Luxemburg, but nothing would serve, till at length the soldiers coming back and giving the captain an account how
he had been pursued by the boors and how they had seized
him to secure him out of their clutches, he was presently
discharged, but ordered to attend the governor who was
desirous to see him, having heard of his deliverance out of
the hands of the Sons of Belial. The governor liked Don

Tomazo so well that he would fain have entertained him in his house, as being unwilling to part with him, always acknowledging the great obligations the English had laid upon him in his extremity, in remembrance whereof he thought himself engaged to be kind to Don Tomazo. But he, knowing the urgency of his own affairs far better than the governor, pretended that his errand was to the Duke of Luxemburg and then told him so much of his business as concerned the French interest. Whereupon the governor, sorry that he had detained Don Tomazo so long, to make him amends by expediting his journey, caused his groom to saddle two very good horses and to attend Don Tomazo till he saw him with the Duke. This kindness of the governor Don Tomazo could very well have borne with, had not the groom been ordered to see him with the Duke. For Don Tomazo, being resolved to make the governor, who had given him nothing but a parcel of good words, pay for his loss of time, had already designed to take the horses in execution for his debt. All the matter was how to get rid of this impertinent groom: which put Don Tomazo upon his invention that seldom failed and at this time proved most faithful to him, for as he was riding before by a piece of enclosed ground, upon a pretense that he had seen a hare he had flung his cane over the hedge and therefore prayed the groom to alight and fetch it him again, while he held his horse. Don Tomazo, finding this the only time to prevent his being brought before the Duke of Luxemburg, left his conductor to return home afoot, and rode clear away with the horses to Mons, a garrison of the Spaniards. Upon his arrival there, he was presently carried by two files of musketeers to the governor, then the Duke of Arescot, who had had letters of recommendation in the behalf of Don Tomazo from the Duke de Villa Hermosa before. To the Duke Don Tomazo told the whole story of his travels and how he had served the governor of Lisle for detaining him from his business. Thereupon the Duke caused the horses to be sold by beat of drum, upon the sale of which Don Tomazo received £46, which he put up in his pocket to drink the governor of Lisle's and his groom's health.

Two days after, the Duke sent a convoy of 800 dragoons to Brussels for provisions. Thither with them went Don Tomazo, and there considering the pressing want of his appearance among his confederates in the French army, he resolved to adventure once more. To which purpose he drest himself up in a poor habit like a woman and so, setting forward the next day, made his private entry into the French camp. Where after he had settled all his affairs, scoured and oiled all his wheels, and set 'em at work again, as he was coming away, it being in the evening, a certain lascivious horse-officer, mad to be riding a fresh country wench, would needs have been forcing up Don Tomazo's coats, so that the young Amazon, not willing to be discovered, was forced to use her utmost strength to keep the boisterous officer honest. Thereupon, as all repulses in love beget revenge, the disappointed cavalier, not believing so much strength in that sex and disdaining to be so slighted by a bumpkinly trull, commanded some of his soldiers to search Tomazo, which when those rugged men-midwives had done and made the true discovery, th' enraged Hotspur caused Don Tomazo to be tied neck and heels, and secured as a spy. Now was Don Tomazo in a bushel of troubles and, one would think, past all redemption, but give a man luck and coyt[22] him into the sea. In this condition, therefore, Don Tomazo, arming himself with his wonted confidence, sends to speak in private with his amorous officer, which being condescended to, Don Tomazo gave him such a parcel of demonstrations so satisfactory to a fellow that had more lechery than wit, that he not only ordered no more noise to be made of the business, but at the request of Don Tomazo went himself to tell the Duke of Luxemburg that there was a person stolen out of the Prince of Orange's army in woman's apparel to make some discovery to his Excellency: whereupon the Duke sent for Don Tomazo. But having heard how the Prince of Conde had been trout-tickled and resolving that nobody should make

a gudgeon of him, so soon as Don Tomazo was brought
before him, [he] sent for several officers who had served
in the army when the Prince of Conde commanded, to come
and view Don Tomazo, but it so happened that now there
was not one that could remember him, upon which assurance the Duke was willing to hear what Don Tomazo
had to say, which was to this effect, as close as all the wit
he had could prompt him to lay it: that an English colonel
in the Dutch army had a great inclination to serve the
King of France and, to that purpose, would so order his
business that all his men and officers should privately convey themselves into the French camp, provided the Duke
would assure them of the same employments in his service
as they had under the Prince of Orange: and farther, that
the said colonel had employed him, who was one of his
corporals, to treat with his Excellency about it. This tale
of a roasted horse[23] seemed very probable to the Duke by
reason of the frequent revolts of the English to the French,
in regard of their better pay and usage. Thereupon the
Duke obliged Don Tomazo to assure the officers that they
should not only have the same employments, but also con-
siderations of greater value; and to give Don Tomazo an
occasion to applaud his bounty, with his own hand [he]
put into Don Tomazo's palm ten pistols for a taste, for
which Don Tomazo, having made a scrape or a curtsy he
cannot well remember, with a most cheerful heart withdrew: and being now from a mouse in a trap advanced to
be a man at full liberty, [he] repairs to the Prince of
Orange, to whom he related the good and bad fortune that
had befallen him since the last time that he had waited
upon his Highness: which so well pleased the Prince that
he, remembering the proverb of the pitcher,[24] kindly persuaded Don Tomazo not to venture any more, as indeed
he did not intend, but seemingly refused to give over, keeping his private correspondence still with his agents in pay,
though that knack of his were unknown to the Prince.

But by this time the winter approached, and the rivulets
of money not flowing so freely from the Prince's springs, as

if there were no need of intelligence in the winter, Don Tomazo, who thought he deserved as much in the winter as in the summer and therefore apprehended himself to be slighted, sent for Don Pedro out of the French army, and resolves to set some engine at work. To this purpose, Don Tomazo, taking Don Pedro along with him, went to the governor of Ghent with whom he was sure there lay perdue a letter of recommendation from the Duke de Villa Hermosa in his behalf, as there did with all the rest of the Spanish governors. To this same great man of trust, Don Tomazo pretended that Don Pedro was going upon particular and immediate service into the French camp, but wanted money to defray the necessary expenses of the design. Upon which assertion of such a known minister among them as Don Tomazo, Don Pedro was presently furnished with £30. With which pretense, they visited all the most considerable governors of the Spanish garrisons, which produced a notable heap; for they never got less than £20 at a place.

At length, having no more but one to visit, who was a great grandee, they resolved to strike him home. To which intent, they took up their quarters in Antwerp; and as they never wanted tools (for Don Tomazo had provided himself of a signet with the Prince of Orange's arms), they counterfeited a letter from the Prince to Count Salazar, then governor of Antwerp Castle, in these very words:

SIR,
    Let this person, the bearer hereof, be furnished with 400 pistols and four horses, at the request of
                            P. Orange.

This letter was carried by Don Tomazo alone; and being showed to the Count, who had not the least suspicion that it was written at Don Tomazo's quarters in Antwerp, ordered the money forthwith to be paid and the horses to be delivered, which you may be sure were none of the worst. For the Count was so civil to the Prince as to give Don Tomazo the liberty to go into his stable and make choice of such as he should think most proper for his purpose. And for prevention of the bad effects of second thoughts, as well as for their own ease, Don Tomazo requested the Count that he would permit one of his grooms to ride along with him. A request soon granted to the spy-master general of Holland. Having thus done all their business with success, Don Tomazo and Don Pedro rode directly like Castor and Pollux to Dunkirk; where being stopt by the out-guards, Don Tomazo, with a kind of impatient countenance of business, desired to be carried forthwith before the governor; to whom, so soon as he had the liberty of a private audience, he related in part what he had done to the advantage of the French, that his coming to that garrison was to serve the King his master, and as such a one desired to be entertained. Upon this, the governor received both Don Tomazo and Don Pedro with great civility, giving them permission to dispose of their booty. But Don Tomazo, being willing to lay some kind of obligation upon the governor (for the proverb tells ye, there is daubing in all trades[25]) as an acknowledgment of his favour, presented him with two of the beast; the other two they put i' their pockets, and having given the groom a small gratuity for his attendance, and money to bear his expenses, they dismissed him with as ponderous a compliment to his master as they thought his memory was able to bear, which by that time was as welcome to the Count as the sound of his passing bell. For before the return of the groom with his *vôtre très humbles*, the Prince of Orange passing through Antwerp in his way to the Hague (the campaign being then broke up), the Spanish Count believing he had laid a great obligation upon the Prince never to be forgotten, gave him to understand how ready he had been to observe his Highness's commands in furnishing Don Tomazo according to his request, expecting some mountainous compliment for his great care. But the Prince, not knowing what the Count meant, instead of applauding his sedulity, fell a-laughing, adding withal that it was a trick and that he must pay for his learning. "No, not so," replied the Count, "for I have your Highness's hand to show for what I have done," and presently drew the note out of his pocket. The Prince read it and showed it to all the chief personages about him, who could not gainsay but that it was the Prince's subscription and his secretary's writing. However, in regard the Prince could not remember either the time or the occasion of such a bountiful piece of writing, it was by all condemned for a cheat, and so the Count lost his cause. Nevertheless, the Prince, more sensible than the rest, of the motives that had induced Don Tomazo to make such an ill use of his ingenuity, protested that if Don Tomazo were with him again, he should not be so slighted as he had been, for that he had done him very great services, and therefore could not well be blamed for carving for himself what ought to have been with more freedom allowed him.

Weary now of the land service, for a while they resolved to commit themselves to the mercy of the ocean, and to venture the hazards of three unruly elements, fire, air, and water, all at once. In order to which resolution, the two bold sparks, flush with the spoils of the Flandrian governors, make a league with a privateer at Dunkirk; and so hoisting sail, they steer away for the North-East Sea, where after they had taken several prizes, Don Tomazo was ordered by the captain to officiate in one of the best as his lieutenant. Now would it not vex a man of sense to be in possession of a Peruvian mine and in a moment to lose it again through the folly or rather madness of a company of unruly beasts? For this same prize wherein Tomazo was, being well stored with wine as well as other rich commodities, had given the seamen such a fatal opportunity to steep themselves in the juice of the grape that while their heads swam, the ship run aground upon the Isle of Ameland; in which condition Don Tomazo and the rest of the seamen, having pillaged her of the best of her lading, left her to the mercy of the next tide and got ashore, which being discovered by two Dutchmen that belonged to the vessel before she was made prize, the country rose upon the miserable sons of misfortune, took them every mother's son prisoners, and carried them to Harlingen in Friesland, where after they had stript them and eased them of their rich plunder which in gold, jewels, necklaces of pearl, and other commodities of the highest value found upon no more than thirteen men, amounted to no less than £15,000 sterling, they were so charitable as to deliver them some of their seamen's old clothes to cover their nakedness, and so with 5 shillings apiece to bear their expenses, turned 'em like a sort of Christian dogs out of the town to inquire their way home to Dunkirk, which is near a hundred leagues. So little compassion do malefactors find among the wicked themselves.

In their way, the chiefest place of note was Amsterdam, where Don Tomazo, having entered into a confederacy with two of the stoutest and acutest of the distressed gang, resolved to make a full stop, leaving the rest to take their own course. Here Don Tomazo, hourly instigated by his late sufferings and losses fresh in memory, thinking no injury he could do so merciless an enemy could equalize the miseries which they had caused him to endure, sought all opportunities to satisfy his importunate revenge. Nor needed he long to wait, for those occasions are always at the elbow of those that dare adventure to attempt. And so it now happened, for at that time several East India ships, being newly returned home, lay below a certain place called the Pampus, not being able to get over the sands till they had lightened themselves by unloading some part of their freight. To which purpose, several small vessels of thirty and forty ton apiece were employed to carry the goods so unladen up the river to Amsterdam; all which Don Tomazo and his comrades, with teeth watering and fingers itching, well observed. And therefore knowing their condition to be desperate, and that if their courage did not put an end to their misery, their necessity would soon send them for another world, for which they were not yet ready, they resolved to play at hazard and venture neck or nothing. With which resolution, they made bold to borrow a small boat from Amsterdam and to set sail toward the Pampus upon the trial of their fortune. By the way they met with a vessel of forty tons laden with Indian goods, which in the height of their indigent fury they presently took, though guarded by nine men, whom they made prisoners. With this prize, the three daring adventurers sailed close by the ship from whence the goods were taken, whose company well knowing that was not the way to Amsterdam, let fly several shot at Don Tomazo's prize, however all to no purpose. They had as good ha' thrown their caps at it, for the vessel running right before the wind got presently out of their reach. But coming up with the Texel at the mouth of the river, the gunner of that fort having observed the shot which the East India giant had made at Tomazo's pigmy, sent his iron round robins after him, too, which made several loopholes in the sails and some few in the hull of the vessel, but all to little or no effect, so that now being quite out of their reach and, as they thought, out of danger, they put boldly to sea and steered their course directly for Dunkirk. But when Fortune has a mind to play her Christmas gambols, the Devil's in her, she's as wanton as a kitten. Nobody knows where to have her; sometimes she's as kind as an innkeeper's daughter, sometimes as froppish as a Quaker's wife, sometimes as testy as a losing gamester, as, for example, you shall see how she dealt with poor Don Tomazo before she harboured him in his desired port. For no sooner were he and his two comrades with their prize upon the wide ocean making for Dunkirk, but they were kenned by a Rotterdam man-of-war whose business it was to cruise about and clear the coast, who judging by their course that they were no friends of his, gave them chase, and about an hour after, coming up with them, took the vessel. Upon his first examination, he [the captain of the man-of-war] found the Indian commodities and, upon a farther search, the skipper whom Don Tomazo had stowed in a little hole in the hold, who gave the captain a full accompt of the whole transaction. Whereupon the captain sent away the vessel for Rotterdam, but kept Don Tomazo and his associates in affliction on board his own ship, which was to continue at sea a month longer by order from the States General. Thus much for Don Tomazo, whom Fortune had deprived of the profit of all his fair hazard and confined to an abstemious poor-John diet. Now you shall see how she bobbed the captain of the man-of-war. For about a week after, certain privateers happening to pass the channel being three in number, the captain made all his sail and, coming up with one of their prizes, retook her and after that another, which the three picaroons observing and well knowing their strength, for they had eight or ten guns and a hundred men apiece, two of them resolved to attack the man-of-war, while the other was sent to retake their prizes, which being resolved, the Dutch man-of-war was boarded and, after a smart fight, compelled to yield. The Dutch captain thus bejaded and his ship secured, Don Tomazo appeared in his likeness and gave the French an account of his exploits, which so well pleased the privateers that they highly applauded him. But Don Tomazo, full of revenge for the good booty he had lost, requested the captains to spare him a little money and six men besides his two comrades; for that he was resolved once more to try his fortune upon the same coast, which request of his was not only granted, but one of the French captains, mainly pleased both with Don Tomazo and his proposals, resolved to make one of the company and for his security took his commission with him, which was for both land and sea. By this time, the other privateer had retaken the two lost prizes, and so they all steered directly for Dunkirk, taking the valiant defender of his country along with them to feed upon the same bread of affliction which he had intended for Don Tomazo. So various are the chances of whimsical war. At the same time, Don Tomazo, the captain, and his crew took a small boat and made for the land and, being got ashore, parted company and went by couples directly to Rotterdam, where after they had continued four days, they found probability enough of good store of purchase, though not so rich as what Tomazo had already lost. But the main booty they had fixed their eyes upon was a great flyboat which lay in the road before Rotterdam, but that day returned from Cadiz, very richly laden, having in her a month's provision, twenty-four guns mounted, all her sails furled to the yard, and above half her men gone ashore. This vessel Don Tomazo and his crew resolved to attack in the night. And for the better carrying on of their enterprise, Don Tomazo with the company went to a village called Lyren Damm and set it afire, to the end that while the people were busied for their own security, they might with more freedom do their own work, which fell out very luckily, for the fire had consumed six houses and four ships. During which time, Don Tomazo and his company had taken the flyboat from seventeen men that guarded it, secured without any noise. They cut the cables and let the vessel drive with the tide, before they loosed so much as one sail, till being almost out of sight they spread their canvas wings and made all the way they could. So kindly does one mischief assist another.

Being now got below the Brill, they spied a very gay pleasure-boat under sail and bound for Rotterdam. At the sight of which they brought their ship to an anchor, manned out their longboat, and boarded the little yacht with the usual fury that the hope of purchase inspires, so that they soon made themselves masters of her, four great mynheers and their wives, together with nine men more and four seamen. These fine folks had been taking their pleasure all the day before at sea, but Don Tomazo and his company got the profit of their voyage at night, which consisted of several good watches, jewels, necklaces of pearl, and chains of gold, to a considerable value. The pleasure-boat they sunk, and then carried all their prisoners aboard their great vessel, who being disposed of, they weighed anchor and set sail till they were clear out at sea. At that time, they put the mynheers and their company into the two shallops, which they had made use of for the conquest of their prize, and sent them home to bewail their losses, having above a league to the shore. While the mynheers and their wives were lamenting the sour sauce to their sweet jollity, Don Tomazo and his crew divided the spoil and, being assisted with a thumping gale at Nore Nore-East, in a short time arrived in Ostend road, where being spied by a privateer belonging to the town, who guessed her to be a prize taken by the French, he gave her chase and in two hours reached her. Don Tomazo and the captain, his comrade, would not fire so much as one gun till the Ostender was come within half shot, but then bringing four guns double-laden to bear upon him all at a time, they so raked his sides that not liking his entertainment he sprung his luff and lay by to repair his damages, while Don Tomazo kept on his course and, in twelve or fourteen hours after, arrived safe in the Splinter.

The arrival of Don Tomazo with this prize was more welcome to his owners than summer to the swallow, who, after they had highly caressed and entertained him, exposed the ship and goods to sale, and upon receipt of their money, gave Don Tomazo and his fellow captain £4,600 for their shares, the ship and cargo being worth eight times as much, considering that there was found at the bottom of the vessel a great chest crowded with pieces of eight, not less worth than two thirds of the purchase. Don Tomazo and the captain, thus contented and satisfied, generously rewarded the seamen with £300 a man and gave the prisoners which they had brought along with them twenty crowns apiece to bear their expenses home, wherein they showed nineteen times more full ounces of charity than the Dutch had shown them before at Harlingen.

Don Tomazo, being now at some leisure, began to inquire after his beloved friend, Don Pedro, concerning whom he had this account, that Don Pedro had been also put into another prize, and that they feared he had undergone the same misfortune which Don Tomazo had suffered upon the coast of Ameland. Soon after, Don Tomazo received a letter from Don Pedro that the ship with which he had been entrusted was cast away: which letter was writ, not for any truth that it contained, but only for the cold comfort and satisfaction of the owners. For indeed the company had agreed with Don Pedro to run the ship to Leith and there expose her to sale. But the Scots, being too cunning for them, laid up the vessel and only gave Don Pedro and his mates enough to bear their charges to Dunkirk, so that upon their return they were forced to make good the truth of Don Pedro's letter by affirming the loss of the prize, which was too true to their cost.

The two Dons, being thus reunited and having drowned in the pleasures of the land the memory of their salt-water afflictions, and purged themselves from the scorbutic humours of hung beef and Groynland fish, resolved to try their talents once more upon the terra firma. In pursuit of which resolution, away they went to the Duke of Luxemburg's army then encamped not far from Mons. So soon as they came thither, upon their addresses to the Duke, they were both admitted volunteers in his own regiment of foot and soon after advanced, Don Pedro to be youngest lieutenant and Don Tomazo to be youngest ensign in the same regiment, the Duke not suspecting in the least that one of these two was the person that had put so many fourberies upon himself and the Prince of Conde, his predecessor. About half a year had these two Dons enjoyed their commissions, at what time the French and Dutch armies met at Seneffe, which occasioned a most terrible fight wherein, to the unspeakable grief of Don Tomazo, Don Pedro was slain, and Don Tomazo himself taken prisoner, and which was worst of all by a party of horse that belonged to Salazar, governor of Antwerp Castle, of whom Don Tomazo had borrowed the money and horses in the Prince of Orange's name. These needy Spaniards, having uncased Don Tomazo, found in his pockets several rough draughts of Antwerp, Mechelen, Ieper, Louvain, Ghent, and several other Spanish garrisons; upon which they conjectured him to be a spy and so publicly declared him to be. The noise of a spy's being taken in time of fight, and by his own men, made the old count eagerly

desirous to see this same thief of intelligence. No sooner
did Don Tomazo appear in his sight, but the cunning governor at first view, without spectacles, knew him to be the
person that he had furnished with the money and horses,
as already has been related, so that without any farther examination Don Tomazo was committed close prisoner to
Antwerp Castle and by the count's order guarded day and
night by four sentinels to prevent any discourse or conveyance of letters. This severe confinement lasted about four
months, in which time the misfortunes of an English gentleman had entered the College of Jesuits at Antwerp and
were more particularly taken notice of by one Father
Worsley, who was the only man among them that made it
his business to gain proselytes. He, therefore, at the instigation of his zeal prevailed with the count to discourse
[with] Don Tomazo, a request easily obtained by one of
his order and function. When Father Worsley came to discourse [with] Don Tomazo in English, heavens, what a refreshing it was to him! For he had not spoken to any person
whatever in ten weeks before. Presently Don Tomazo besought the old father to take his confession (for Don
Tomazo, shrewdly guessing at the occasion of his charitable
visit, was resolved to prevent him of the trouble of a con-
version), which he did accordingly, and therein, as Don
Tomazo had ordered it, had some sort of information of
Don Tomazo's case. From thence forward, the old father
looked upon him as his pupil, procured him a better provision of diet and lodging, and came often to visit him, as well
to confirm him in his faith as to fathom the bottom of his
crime. And at length, the father's good opinion of his penitent moved him to so much compassion that having thoroughly sifted his case, and understanding that the draughts
which the Spaniards found in his pockets were the effects
of his employment under the Prince of Orange and that
the Prince had been presented with all the copies of them,
he resolved to take a journey to the Prince to know the
truth of the matter, which he soon found to be real and
that the Prince was sorry for Tomazo's misfortune.

During these negotiations of the old father, Don Tomazo was brought before a court-martial, convicted for a spy, and sentenced to be shot to death by two files of musketeers; but upon Don Tomazo's application, he was allowed five days' time for him to prepare himself for another world, neither he knowing of the father's journey, nor the father of his condition. But it luckily fell out that the old father returned before two of the five days were expired, and brought along with him a letter from the Prince of Orange to the Duke de Villa Hermosa, purporting the great desire he had that Don Tomazo should be discharged. But the old father, having all the count's revenge and interest at court to deal with, found it hard to get the Prince's letter allowed, so that all he could obtain for the present was a reprieve for fourteen days longer. In that time the father made another journey to the Prince and then returned with two letters, one to the duke and another to the count, which gave them both such satisfaction that Don Tomazo was ordered to be discharged. But the old father, desirous to try whether Don Tomazo were a true son of the Church or no, kept him still in ignorance of his proceedings, and still admonished him to prepare for death, as Don Tomazo did according to all the ceremonies of the Romish Church, as being indifferent to him since he must die of what religion he died, so that now the time prefixed being quite expired, Tomazo was brought to the tree, bound fast, the soldiers in his sight ready presented, the old man on his right hand, the few ejaculations he had were spent, and he ready to give the sign, when the old father, seeing the constancy of his devout son, unbound him, and with tears embraced him (an odd kind of ambition in those people to heighten the merits of their obligations), crying out, "My Son, thou shalt not die, for God has intended thee for some good and pious work."

Don Tomazo, thus discharged, was taken by the old father to the Jesuits' College where the members of the order raised him a collection of £37, which put him into an equipage to return to the French army, where he was no

sooner arrived, but he was informed by an English soldier
that Don Pedro was slain, that all their equipage and
money were seized, for that the Duke of Luxemburg had
understood, as indeed their papers demonstrated no less,
that his lieutenant and ensign had been both spies for the
Prince of Orange. It was a hard case for a man to lose all
the treasure and sweet booty for which he had so often
ventured his life, but Don Tomazo rather chose to abandon
all than stand to the mercy of the Duke of Luxemburg,
and so with a heavy and disconsolate heart he took his way
for Calais. From thence he crossed over to Dover, and so
came directly to London.

Being come to London, his first endeavour was to find
out an associate fit for his turn, of which he could not well
miss among so much variety, so that having leagued himself
with one (as he thought) according to his heart's desire
and raised a small sum of money, they two fell to the old
trade of counterfeiting gold, so that in a short time they
had made and uttered a considerable quantity, presuming
to visit several parts wherein Don Tomazo had been before,
which bold attempt proved very unsuccessful. For having
dispersed several of their illegitimate guineas in Wiltshire,
Dorset and Hampshire, they were pursued and taken in
Dorsetshire, and both upon information committed to Dor-
chester Prison.

Some time after, Don Tomazo was removed to Sarum,
there to be tried according to the law for his offenses committed in those parts, a thing that could not be avoided,
so that he was convicted and suffered the penalty of his
sentence: and what added to his affliction, he had no fair
prospect of his release, as not having wherewithal to satisfy
the irresistible demands of the jailor. But Fortune, sometimes his friend as well as sometimes his foe, soon found
out a way to bring him out of this labyrinth. For in a short
time after, one of the tender sex, among whom he had always a friend in a corner, came and made him a visit so full
handed that Don Tomazo soon purchased the liberty of
his heels. Which being obtained, away he comes for Lon-

don, where he first sought out and soon found a companion. For iniquity seldom prospers without confederacy. This companion of his lent him his helping hand to the old profession, for they knew that the readiest way to have money was to make it themselves. And therefore, after they had stored themselves with a sufficient parcel of their own manufacture and were able to set up for themselves, away they gallop to Newmarket, where it was their course to bet high, but never both of the same side, so that if the one lost, the other was sure to win; and the gains of the one easily made good the other's losses. For the loss of near a hundred guineas of Don Tomazo's quaint sort of metal did not amount to above £7. This trade continued for some time with good success, there being hardly a horse race or a cock-match that escaped the two guinea-merchants. But that trade failing at length, Don Tomazo and his companion turned graziers and, frequenting the fairs and markets up and down the country, bought several droves of cattle with their unlawful coin; for which, when they had driven them off to another place, they soon found chapmen, as being persons that could easily afford good pennyworths. But the cries of the country farmers began to be so loud when they found what a bad exchange they had made that Don Tomazo and his companion, not able to endure the noise, were forced, after a trade of four months' continuance, to quit a calling so prejudicial to all the landlords and tenants in the country. So true is the proverb that "nothing violent is of long continuance."

Thus, nowhere safe and continually lying under the curse of wasting perpetually what was ill-got, the two knights of the Order of Industry resolved to take their pleasure at sea. To which purpose they bought them a vessel of about forty tons, and having manned her with persons fit for their purpose, they lay perdue, sometimes in the River's mouth, sometimes in the Channel, to meet with merchants' vessels that were homeward bound. Out of which, Don Tomazo and his friend bought several good pennyworths of the seamen with their counterfeit gold, till they had al-

most loaded their vessel. Which done, away they made for
some convenient port and exposed their goods to sale for
good money. This was a way less hazardous, but very expensive, and therefore, not answering expectation, was
soon laid aside.

The sea-trade failing for this reason and the two merchants near broke, Don Tomazo and his comrade parted,
after which Don Tomazo, taking a journey into Berkshire
to sow his yellow grain in that soil, was apprehended and
committed to prison for endeavouring to enrich that county
with his precious wealth. There he was kept half a year in
durance and sorely threatened to be sent to heaven in a
string; but not liking that way of traveling to bliss, he so
ordered his affairs that he was discharged without any trial,
though cruelly gripped with the pangs of poverty. For when
the prison doors were opened to him, all his revenue was
but 3 shillings. But industry soon increased it. For out of
that small sum, one being a milled shilling, he presently
made a counterfeit guinea and past it off with a "certio-
rari" for good, which fruitful return soon produced a new
recruit, so that in a short time he saw himself the father
of two goodly twins or bags of a £100 apiece, begot by his
own labour. This round sum warmed his invention and put
him in an equipage to go on with a new project. In order
to which, away he returns for London, hires several servants
fit for his purpose, according to the method of trimtram,
and takes at least fourteen or fifteen lodgings of good note
in the City, which lodgings were generally near the shopkeeper or the merchant that was to suffer under his contrivance. These boroughs of his he would visit several times
in a day, lying sometimes at one and sometimes at another,
till he had lain a night apiece in each, which being, as he
thought, long enough, he began his frolic as follows.

Don Tomazo stayed in his lodging and sent a servant, as
it might be, 'cross the way to a goldsmith to bring him such
and such parcels of rings and jewels of such a sort to show
them his master. Presently either the goldsmith or his man
came along with the servant in hopes of some great cus-

tomer. But when Don Tomazo had fixed upon such jewels and rings which he seemed to like best and agreed upon the price, the goldsmith, having left the main purchase with Don Tomazo, was desired to walk up another pair of stairs with his servant, if the house admitted of such a conveniency, there to receive his money. But no sooner was the goldsmith in the trap, but the servant, who you may be sure was a special trout, locked the door upon the poor mouse, and presently both master and man slipt away together. At another place, having bought another parcel of the same commodities at the same rate, he would send his servant with the owner of the goods to some cashier or banker of note, to be there paid for his costly ware, and while his trusty servant and the goldsmith were trotting to the receipt of custom, away tript Don Tomazo to another lodging, leaving his servant to make his escape and shift for himself as well as he could. And of such an exploit as this, a certain goldsmith in Lombard Street had the misfortune to have the woeful experience to the loss of £275/17s/6d. Now you are to understand that when Don Tomazo had once begun his diabolical progress, he used all the expedition imaginable in his dispatches and removals from place to place, in regard it behooved him never to leave off till he had made an effectual visit at all his particular abodes, which was done to all intents and purposes in the space of nine hours, by which he got more than the best day laborer that works at Paul's: the reward of those few hours' pains amounting to no less than £1,625. For he looked upon it as a calling too mean for one of his quality to make children's shoes.

But this trick made too great a noise to be played over again, so that Don Tomazo was resolved to knock off and live for some time upon the spoil. In order whereunto like an honest master, he first discharged all his servants, to whom he gave £35 apiece, which amounted to £525, there being fifteen in all, and then retired into the country. But neither could he there rest long; for though he went under the most absolute disguise imaginable, yet it would so hap-

pen that some or other still knew him, so that in short by
removing from place to place and living at the rate of a
lord, his massy sum in two years was reduced to £150, with
which Don Tomazo set forward again for London, the only
stage proper for a Guzman to act his parts upon, in order to
the projecting some new enterprise. But no sooner was he
come to town, but a gentleman of Worcestershire, with
whom Don Tomazo had been trafficking by way of exchange
to the value of £170, met him in the street and began to
make a noise, which Don Tomazo finding no way convenient for his interest, whispered the gentleman in the ear.
Which gentle motion of Don Tomazo's lips, having conveyed to his irritated senses a short promise of satisfaction,
stopt the violent motion of the gentleman's tongue. Thereupon away they went to the tavern, where Don Tomazo
would fain have been rid of his troublesome companion,
but he stuck so close to him and kept him so charily within
the reach of his eye that Don Tomazo, to his unspeakable
grief, was forced to come to composition and to pay the
gentleman £120. This forced putt of moral satisfaction
brought Don Tomazo very low. Hating therefore that want
should be his master, he resolved to have one stroke more
with his hammer, and so fell to the old trade of coining.
Which work by the help of two more assistants being com-
pleted, and a good stock of pieces being made, they had
laid their design to take a ramble into Essex to dispose of
their gold that made others poor and themselves rich. Being upon their journey, they took Hackney in their way,
where one of the sparks, having his pockets full of gold,
would needs have the world to take notice of it and to that
end, at a place where he and his companions had called to
drink a bottle of wine, pulled out his gold by handfuls and
exchanged one of his counterfeit guineas to pay the reckoning. The King's picture dazzled the vintner's eyes at first,
but they were no sooner gone but, happily for Essex, the
cheat was discovered, which put the whole town upon a
swift pursuit, and such a one as proved indeed so very
swift that the whole knot of money-changers was quite un-

tied, all of them taken and carried over the fields to a justice of the peace. By which means Don Tomazo took the advantage to dispose of his guineas in the long grass. Nevertheless, that poor shift would not do; Don Tomazo was sent to Newgate for company, tried at the Old Bailey for company, and fined £50 for company, and so was remanded to Newgate for company, where he lay a whole year not able to pay his fine, and at length obtained His Majesty's most gracious pardon, by which he was discharged.

Having this ill luck in company, he fell to the old trade alone, with the assistance only of one servant. But whether Fortune had taken a pique against coiners, or whether Mercury were turned honest and had disposed of his influences another way, so it happened that Don Tomazo, having sent his boy to the silver market one evening in the shape of a vintner's servant to exchange some few counterfeit guineas, the raw messenger was taken, carried before a magistrate, examined, and upon his examination discovered his master. Whereupon Don Tomazo was as soon apprehended and sent to wait upon his man to Newgate. 'Twas an ill job for one misfortune so soon to fall upon the neck of one another, but there was no avoiding these home-thrusts of Fate. And therefore Don Tomazo, to make the best of a bad market, made all his applications to his servant and so far prevailed upon his good nature to recant his charge against his master and take the whole business upon himself; which he did, with that exactness and fidelity that Don Tomazo, being tried first, was acquitted. But being forced to lie a good while before he could purchase his liberty, as being charged with actions to a great value, then it was that Mrs. Cellier, having heard of Don Tomazo's fame and believing him brisk for her turn, gave him her first visits which produced those transactions between them that have lately made so great a noise in the world. For an account whereof, the reader is referred to the *Narratives* themselves.[26]

FINIS.

THE COMPLETE MEMOIRS OF THE LIFE OF THAT NOTORIOUS IMPOSTOR WILL. MORRELL

(1694)

Elkanah Settle

FOREWORD

William Morrell's exploits, once suspected of being fictitious, may now be seen in a new light. Typical of the old attitude was the point of view held by the greatest authority on rogue literature, Frank Wadleigh Chandler, who classified this notorious impostor among the "English rogues of reality," but then voiced the suspicion that "the story . . . reads like fiction." However, on the basis of recently found evidence, it is possible to define more exactly the "real" in Morrell's story. That the criminal was a real person can now be proved by an entry in the registers of St. Clement Danes for January 12, 1692: "William Morrell alias Bowier a man bur[ied] poor." Indirectly, the burial record also confirms the whole last episode of the culprit's life as it appears in *The Complete Memoirs*, especially the statement that "in a coffin of 4 shillings price, he was laid in the earth in a nook of St. Clement's Churchyard." Not only in *The Complete Memoirs* but also in the much earlier criminal biography by Elkanah Settle, *The Life and Death of Major Clancie, the Grandest Cheat of this Age* (1680), the central character had been a flesh-and-blood personality.

Although well known as a dramatist and as one of Dryden's and Pope's dunces, Elkanah Settle is hardly ever mentioned as a writer of criminal fiction. At the time he wrote *The Life and Death of Major Clancie,* he was, according to his biographer, "the chief literary supporter of the powerful Shaftesbury" in the strongly middle-class Whig party. In *Major Clancie,* which purports to narrate "real matter of fact," Settle succeeds, now and then, in making ordinary people come dramatically alive. Here he tries out a theme that reappears in the William Morrell narratives, namely, the ability of natural wit to triumph over birthright. A mischievous hero-villain, Major Clancie thrives on family deceptions and jewel thefts not very different from Morrell's. Starting out as a humble page in a gentleman's retinue and using a fertile ingenuity, Clancie soon moves about freely in a social circle of lords and ladies. He impersonates important people like the Duke of Ormonde and forges letters from the Earl of Carbery. In one of his pranks he makes the Bishop of London an unwitting accomplice in the cheating of a creditor. Even Charles II pays his respects to the Major's roguish brilliance. Episodes like these, indeed, sound more like fiction than fact. And the contemporary Anthony Wood notes that Major Clancie was "an Irishman, hanged at Tyburn in the latter end of the year (as I remember) 1678," but "several stories in this book which belong to other persons are fathered on the said major, who, as I remember, was in Oxon in the plague year 1665 when the King and the Queen kept their respective courts there." Wood then contributes a few of his own pungent stories about the Major, which have no counterpart in Settle's narrative. Where the two writers provide parallel accounts, the "fiction" of *Major Clancie* appears to be based on a substratum of truth surviving in current anecdotes. Settle's verisimilitude had an effect on Theophilus Lucas's *Memoirs of the Lives, Intrigues, and Comical Adventures of the Most Famous Gamesters and Celebrated Sharpers* (1714), which begins with a condensed version of the criminal biography as if it were entirely true.

Settle's next criminal narrative grew out of the mysterious circumstances attending the death of the notorious William Morrell. On January 3, 1692, a man who called himself Humphrey Wickham, Esq., of Swalcliffe in the county of Oxon, had died at Mr. Cullen's, baker in the Strand. He had left behind a will in which he divided up his worldly estate with especially generous portions for the tradespeople who befriended him in his last days. The whole affair soon became very complicated by Mr. Cullen's discovery that his deceased tenant was really William Morrell, a specialist for the past twenty years in impersonation. While the event was still the talk of London, the bookseller Abel Roper rushed his biographies into print. The first to appear was the short, newsy *Diego Redivivus,* which was entered in the Stationers' Register for January 12, exactly the day of Morrell's humble burial. Although its title page promised a "full relation" of the impostor's cheats, the anonymous *Diego Redivivus* presented only the "will" episode—but with all the colors of a sensational news item.

Early in the 1690s Elkanah Settle, finding himself in desperate circumstances, needed something like the William Morrell story that would sell. Thoroughly disgusted with politics and in low finances, he had returned to the stage. As he states in his dedication to *Distressed Innocence* (1691), he wanted "to quit all pretensions to state-craft, and honestly skulk into a corner of the stage, and there die contented." In 1691, appointed City Poet, he started producing the annual pageants for the Lord Mayor's Day. The work did not pay well, and already he had squandered the inheritance left him by an uncle. The City Poet, wrote one of his enemies, "underneath his glorious pageants starved." In these conditions, Settle brought out *The Notorious Impostor,* Part One, over the imprint of Abel Roper. The book was being advertised in the February issue of *The Term Catalogues,* and Anthony Wood noted that he bought his copy "in the beginning of March." Part One met with such a "general reception" that Settle hurried out *The Second Part of the Notorious Impostor,* a fortnight after Part One.

Interest in the grand impostor remained strong throughout
February. "The death of William Morrell," complained *The
Gentleman's Journal* of this month, "hath made too much
noise not to have reached you before this. . . . Had not his
Will and Life been printed, I would have given you a large
acount of both." The unknown writer refers here, perhaps,
to *Diego Redivivus* ("Will") and *The Notorious Impostor*
("Life") in the order of their publication. Next, turning to
verse, he launches a fourth brief biographical account,
"William Morrell's Epitaph," in which he ironically lauds
the great skill of the impostor ("Columbus-like I a new
world descried, / Of roguery before untried").

Elkanah Settle's two parts of *The Notorious Impostor*
were finally published together in 1694 as *The Complete
Memoirs of the Life of that Notorious Impostor Will. Morrell,* a reprint of which was also advertised in *The Post Boy*
from February 17 to April 23, 1698. So extensive are the
rearrangements of the episodes taken from Parts One and
Two that *The Complete Memoirs* may be regarded as a
fifth, very different narrative. The two earlier parts retain
the scaffolding which the author used to construct his story.
Near the conclusion of Part One, for instance, Settle admits
to a lack of further information, "which yet we have not
received," but refuses "to load our rambles with romance
or fiction." Later—it seems he now has enough material for
one pamphlet—he boldly interrupts: "We have reason to
conclude he [Morrell] fell into smaller games, in which his
walks have lain something more obscure, and thereupon by
reason of our unacquaintance with the truth of that part of
his life, we shall overleap some years and bring him to his
conclusion." But this obscurity in Morrell's career is soon
dispelled. For Settle begins *The Second Part* by protesting
"we are so over furnished with matter of fact that we have
not the least need to load him with the least untruth; and
therefore we make this real profession that, excepting a
little garniture (that common pardonable liberty), the
whole feast we treat you with, has not one borrowed dish."
All his information he claims to draw from most reliable

sources, nay, even "from the persons' own mouths that were
the suffering parties in our narrative." The gaps in Part One
are then deftly filled in by *The Second Part*. In *The Complete Memoirs*, finally, these obiter dicta (of considerable
value for the theory of fiction, since they assert the primacy
of realism over romance) are dropped, and the various episodes are dovetailed into a fairly smooth, chronologically
consistent "history." As the title page announces, *The Complete Memoirs* also appends "considerable additions never
before published." In these new adventures appear the
servant Tom, arrested for stealing a wealthy heiress, and
"our grand Guzman," involved in "the very first of all his
wedlock feats." Like *The Counterfeit Lady Unveiled* published two decades earlier, *The Complete Memoirs* is truly
a composite narrative. By examining its connections with
the other William Morrell narratives, we are really watching
the compilation of a criminal biography in slow motion.

In its theme, *The Complete Memoirs* is more English
than Spanish picaresque. It is true, on the one hand, that
there are surface resemblances to Francisco de Quevedo's
Historia de la vida del Buscón, llamado Don Pablos (1626),
an English translation of which was published in 1657.
Both Morrell and Don Pablos, as F. W. Chandler points
out, practice the same trick of enhancing their prestige by
leaving forged letters where they can be "accidentally" read.
And in general, according to E. A. Baker, Morrell "merrily
emulated the exploits of a Don Pablos de Segovia." On the
other hand, it is also true that the English and Spanish
"histories" are separated by a chasm of moral difference.
Don Pablos, in his "education" from Segovia to Seville, experiences inner crises. One of the severest is, in Chapter 10,
the disgust that overwhelms him when he observes his
uncle, the public hangman, enthusiastically whipping the
criminals. Later he becomes so deeply enmeshed in crime
for its own sake that he says in comic seriousness: "I began
to realize that hell, which usually comes cheap, had begun
to cost me a pretty penny. I saw that I was becoming the

architect of my own perdition . . ." (*Masterpieces of the Spanish Golden Age*, ed. Angel Flores, Rinehart, 1957, p. 228). This kind of introspection is precisely what William Morrell lacks.

Settle's forte is not character development, but trenchant satire of the social-climbing middle class "taken in" by the clever impostor. Morrell hardly feels the impact of his varied experience. He ends, as he starts: facetious, witty, vulnerable to a pretty face, always ready to insinuate himself "into the society of the best quality roundabout." The satire hits mainly at the mercenary motives that underlie marriages. The ladies, deceived by Morrell the "wife-merchant" disguised as a gentleman, are alike in being dazzled by the title of ladyship. But they differ, strikingly, as types: "the pretty country girl" of Brailes, the romantic elder sister of Ludlow, the "hard-faithed" innkeeper's daughter of Bath, the "sweet country innocence" of Slough, the boarding-school heiress of Wells, Nan the cookmaid of the Castle Tavern, "dear sweet Betty" of Portsmouth, and (of course!) the single legitimate wife of Banbury. In a unified series of episodes, Settle rings the changes on a favorite theme of Restoration comedy: love versus money. As he woos each beauty, Morrell disclaims any interest in portion or estate. Yet, as it turns out, "without a spill of yellow boys [guineas], naked white and red has but indifferent charms with him." In each affair he drops "the luggage of a wife" and holds on to the groats that came with her.

Settle's tone here, as in *Major Clancie*, is one of great admiration for the rogue's ingenuity. Major Clancie impersonates Lord Ormonde, and Morrell assumes the identity of country gentlemen like Sir William Walters and Sir Charles Bowyer. Implicit in the impersonations is a secondary theme, namely, that natural wit can prosper without help from high birth. This theme becomes explicit, near the conclusion of the memoirs, in Morrell's rejoinder to his deserted "wife" Betty. Exposed in his pretensions to an estate in Worcester, he scornfully displays whole handfuls of gold "to show her that though his birth, 'tis true, had bestowed no patrimonies upon him, his wit and sense could make his own fortune, and accordingly [he] valued not that inconsiderable want of birthright." Twenty years later, during his last grim cheating of the world, he was still impersonating a country gentleman. In the Epistle Dedicatory of *The Notorious Impostor*, Part One, Settle points out the *real* triumph of William Morrell's ingenuity: "And whereas there are famous examples of old, that have perpetuated their names at no less price than the burning of temples, his better husbandry, to his glory be it recorded, has purchased immortality much cheaper."

ABOUT THE BOOK: Alfred Beesley, *The History of Banbury*, 1841; Frank Wadleigh Chandler, *The Literature of Roguery*, The Riverside Press, 1907, Vol. I; Frank C. Brown, *Elkanah Settle: His Life and Works*, The University of Chicago Press, 1910; *The Complete Newgate Calendar*, ed. G. T. Crook, The Navarre Society, 1926, Vol. II; Ernest A. Baker, *The History of the English Novel*, Barnes & Noble, 1950, Vol. III; Spiro Peterson (introd.), *Elkanah Settle: The Notorious Impostor* (1692), *Diego Redivivus* (1692), The Augustan Reprint Society, No. 68, 1958.

THE COMPLETE MEMOIRS OF THE LIFE OF THAT NOTORIOUS IMPOSTOR WILL. MORRELL, *Alias Bowyer, Alias Wickham, &c. Who Died at Mr. Cullen's the Baker's in the Strand, Jan. 3, 1692. With Considerable Additions Never Before Published*

THE EPISTLE DEDICATORY
TO GABRIEL BALAM, ESQ.

SIR,

A fair name in the frontispiece of a book is by long custom reckoned as essential a part of it as a portico is of a temple. And yet as panegyrics are their common furniture, dedication is the nicest part of writing.

For though the honest poet, like the faithful painter, draws not beyond the life, 'tis still but a sort of labour lost. For as modesty is the finishing stroke to the complete gentleman, that patron that is the most worthy of praise is the least fond of it.

And if we stretch into that nauseous extreme of flattery, the panegyric is turned into a libel, by exposing what we pretend to praise.

'Tis true, the pretense of dedications is the borrowed protection a piece of scribble receives from the noble patron, under whose umbrage 'tis ushered into the world—when, alas, a great patron is no more a protection to a dull book than a Caesar's face to a leaden shilling. Wit and sense stand only upon their own legs, and go no farther than their own intrinsic merit carries them. The world, at least the judicious part of it, is not to be so cheated. There's no passing off that false coin for which every man of sense has both a scales and a touchstone. Wit runs the fate of Belshazzar: the "Mene Tekel"[1] is certainly written over our heads, if we are once weighed and found too light.

But supposing some favoured author, cherished by the smiles of a noble or generous patron, takes this occasion (for that's the fairest dedicatory pretext) of avowing his gratitude to the whole world for such signal obligations; yet this public acknowledgment of past favours looks very suspiciously like a design of drawing on of new ones, too, so that to sum up the cause, the brotherhood of the quill, if they would fairly unmask, should plainly tell the world that there's a private gratification goes along with the public acknowledgment. For men make dedications as votaries make thanksgivings: the bent knee is not wholly for blessings received, but for some little continuation, too, of the kind descending smiles.

And, 'faith, now I am playing the tell-troth, and making thus bold with the poetic fraternity; this common fault amongst them may well be excused, for to apologize for the Muses in their own native dialect, I need but quote a stanza in *Gondibert*:

O hireless science, and of all alone
*   The liberal! Meanly the rest each state*
With pension treats: but this depends of none,
*   Whose worth they reverently forbear to rate.*[2]

If poor poetry is put to such hard shifts (for maugre our
Gondibert's fair flourish, that's the plain English) to be so
wholly unprovided for, that the Muses have neither lands
nor livings annexed to their foundation, but are wholly supported by goodness and favour; whilst all other studies,
whether in the long or black robe, have their preferments,
as warm gowns, soft furs, fat glebes, and fruitful crops, and
what not. And poetry, as much as 'tis charged with fiction,
yet like truth goes almost naked: under these melancholy
circumstances it may well be permitted some grains of allowance, as an unhappy dependent upon courtesy.

But whilst I am thus plain in correcting faults abroad, I
ought to look at home, as having a much weaker plea for
my own Dedication, when being so altogether a stranger to
you, I dare be guilty of this presumption. This indeed I
ought to have considered, but when I find the ingenious
every day making their court to you, and the more eminent
priests of Apollo, the more successful and no less deservingly
so, all assiduous suitors to your favour; so many fair examples are that warrant for my ambition, that I lay hold of
any occasion, though at a farther distance, of making one
of the train.

You have that air of sweetness and obliging temper, a
conversation so grateful, as renders you the favourite even
of both sexes.

But if I proceed to sum up your fair character, I shall
transgress the laws I have laid down, and offend that modesty as has an ear too tender for that subject. Not to enlarge therefore upon your other merits, 'tis sufficient you
are so great a cherisher of the Muses and the state that
that single virtue alone has encouraged me to the confidence
of this address.

All I have truly to blush at, is the slenderness of the

present, this inconsiderable trifle I offer you. However, as the crow presented to Caesar, be pleased to give it the same favourable acceptance, as indeed (like that poor crow) saluting you with the same "hail" only with more zeal, and tendering you the humble obedience of

Sir,

Your Most Devoted Servant,

E. Settle.

THE NOTORIOUS IMPOSTOR: OR THE HISTORY OF THE LIFE OF WILL. MORRELL, ALIAS BOWYER, &C.

This famous rover, from the multitude of his titles, to begin with his right name William Morrell, was by profession a chirurgeon, and more than twenty years ago, for many years together, a practitioner of good credit in Banbury, where his industry honestly got him by his practice a comfortable subsistence, with which he maintained himself, his wife and family very handsomely, till about twenty years ago he began to be very lazy and much addicted to hanker after the conversation of the gentry thereabouts. And being a person very facetious, and his company not disacceptable, he screwed himself into the society of the best quality round about and would be a month or two a guest at several great men's houses. More particularly he some time since insinuated himself into the favour of a worthy gentleman near Banbury, viz., Humphrey Wickham of Swalcliffe, Esq., whose person and character he pretended to represent, and in which imposture he made his last exit. His original, it was very obscure, and his first start into the world was in no higher a post than a journeyman shoemaker, in which character he lived some considerable time at Worcester, understanding so little of what he professed at Banbury, viz., chirurgery, that he knew the virtue of no other plaister than his own cobbler's wax. From that employment, he took a frolic to sea; from whence returned, he came to Swalcliffe with the true privilege of a traveler, his authority unquestionable; he talked miracles both of his voyages and adventures, for example, that he had made a voyage to Constantinople and Barbados (for east and west were all one in his geography), and so amused the country-people with his rodomontades that they looked upon him as a prodigy of a man. His great art he professed was chirurgery (the little he had of it being indeed gotten on ship-board), and what with promised wonders and great words, the common crutch of little abilities, together with some favours and countenance received from Captain Wickham (a common charity from so worthy a gentleman), which very much heightened his reception, he made shift to rub through the world.

But to begin our history in order, from his conversing with gentlemen and herding with quality, business began to fall off; his many rambles from home soon made his practice flag; when the glass and the bottle came into play, the salvatory and plaister-box went out. And his patients could not well stay for the setting of a broken limb or tenting a green wound, till our Aesculapius was to be called, the Lord knows where, and found the Devil knows when. This trade continuing, the other fell to decay, till at last poverty began to peep in at his window, and duns to hover about his door. In these little exigencies and necessities (for the gentlemen's tables abroad would not fill the bellies at home; nor would hunting or hawking pay landlord's rent) his wants put him upon shifts and artifices for his subsistence; and what with a natural wit and a pretty large talent of confidence, the pressing hand of Fortune threw him upon several tricks and frauds to hold his head aboveboard. But not to trouble you with any of his lesser diminutive exploits, the infancy and nonage of his activity, we do not think fit to treat you with these pettier adventures, but e'en set him out in one of his noblest achievements, and paint our new Guzman in some of his boldest and fairest colours.

Accordingly, he equips himself with a sturdy, young

country-fellow, a Ralpho to our Hudibras, and takes a
knight-errantry one day to a fair at Brailes in Warwick-
shire, his habit between a grazier and a plain country gentleman, where sauntering about with his man Tom (for so
his squire was titled), at last spying a knot of good likely
kine (near a score of them). "Ah, master," says Tom, "what
a parcel of brave cattle are these?" "Ay, Tom," replies the
master, "I am sorry I saw them no sooner; these would do
my business to a 'T,' but as the Devil and ill luck would
have it, I have laid out my whole stock already, and so
I'll e'en set my heart at rest." The country-fellow, the owner
of the cattle, seeing a gentleman of his honest appearance
surveying his beasts, and hearing every word that passed
between the man and master (for they took care to talk
loud enough to be heard), thought he had got a good chapman and desired the gentleman to draw nearer and handle
the cattle. "Handle?" answers Tom. "What for? You know,
sir, you have laid out all your money already, and what
should we handle cattle unless we had cole[3] to buy 'em.
I confess they are for your turn above any I have zeen in
the whole vair, but that's nothing, the money, master, the
money." "The money?" replies the countryman. "Troth,
that shall make no difference, nor break squares between
us; if you and I can agree, the cattle are at your service.
I suppose you are some honest gentleman hereabouts, and
the money will do my work next market day. Pray, what
may I call your name?" "My name is Walters," replies our
cattle-merchant. "Walters, master?" answers our countryman. "What, any relation to his worship the noble Sir William Walters?" "Ay, friend, a small relation, a brother of
his." "A brother of Sir William's!" Off goes the countryman's
bonnet at the next word, and a long scrape made, for no
respect was too great for a brother to a person of such
eminent quality. "My cattle, noble squire, ay with all my
heart." In short, after much ado to make the countryman
be covered before him, he fell to treat about the price of the
cattle, in which he bargained so warily that they had almost
parted for a single shilling in dispute between them. But at

last the bargain and sale concluded, Tom is commanded to drive home the cattle, the money to be paid next market day, and the countryman has the honour to drink a pot at parting with his worshipful chapman, our Sir William's brother. This feat performed, he takes a walk round the fair and picks up a pretty country girl, a mason's daughter, at a small town about four miles off, and gives her the common country civility of a fair, viz., a glass of white wine and sugar. During this entertainment of our young damsel, he is most desperately smitten with her beauty, insomuch that our inamorato must wait upon her home to her father's house, nothing but death and despair attending if he cannot have that extraordinary happiness. The girl, who by this time had learnt his name and quality, was not a little confounded at the pressing importunities of a person of his worth to a poor girl of her little capacity, and notwithstanding her modest refusals, felt a secret pride from so kind an offer, and at last accepted of his service home. No sooner was she got safe handed home, and her mother and daddy were privately whispered what honour they received from such a visitant, but the best the house could afford was not good enough for him. After the coarser compliments of "Lord, sir, such a person of quality under our poor roof!" and the like, the best welcome that could be made him was not wanting. Nay, for what was deficient at home, the whole neighbourhood was ransacked to lend help toward the accommodation. Our new lover, not to balk a good cause, openly professes no less than honourable matrimonial affection to his dear conqueror. Estate he wants none, and portion or quality are below his consideration: the satisfaction of love is the only thing in the world he resolves to gratify.

The father and mother are much astonished at such an addresser to their daughter. Nor is the daughter herself a little surprised at it, though of the two her wonder is the least, for her sex's natural frailty was so apt to make her think it the pure effect of her own sweet face that the power of her charms and the quality of her captive were not altogether (she fancied) so extraordinary an adventure. In fine, our passionate admirer pushes on his suit with all the vigour and application imaginable, and truly you may well conceive so weak a resistance could not well hold out long against so puissant an assailer: the siege is pressed home, and in three short days the white flag is hung out, a parley beat, articles concluded, and the fort surrendered. Our damsel, in short, commits matrimony, and the whole family is not a little transported at such a noble alliance. Thus wedded and bedded, our new couple are all honey and sweetness, and though Sir William Walter's house was not above a dozen miles from thence, his adopted brother all safe and secure sleeps in the soft arms of his young bride with all the rapture of pleasure and delight. After three reveling days were spent in feasting and joy, the father-in-law and himself enter in a close cabinet consult about providing for family and settlement. He tells the old man that truly his brother the knight will undoubtedly take no little dudgeon at this match, not that he cares a farthing for't. He has married the only creature of the world he can love, and he is resolved to cherish her accordingly. But, however, to manage affairs with discretion, he thinks it his best prudence and policy to get his trunks and the writings of his estate safe out of his brother's hands, before he publishes the marriage. And for that purpose he has no better way than for his father-in-law to help him to a small cart and a couple of able horses, and to drive to his brother's and take up his trunks, &c. And considering he had laid out all his ready money in cattle at Brailes Fair, he desired the favour to furnish him with £10 that he might not be unprovided with a little of the ready about him, in case of any rupture between his brother and himself, till he could furnish himself better amongst his tenants.

The old man very readily embraced this reasonable proposition, and though truly the sum of £10 was above his stock, nevertheless, living in repute amongst his neighbours, through great solicitation, some 40 and some 30 shillings, and such-like sums, with much ado he raises the £10 desired; and more and above he procures two very able horses and a cart to bring away the treasure aforesaid, &c.

By this time his man Tom, having sold the cattle, is come to wish his noble master joy of his fair bride, and so the master and Tom, attended by a brother of his bride, an honest country swain, who though so highly honoured with his new affinity is at present planted in no higher a post than to be a mate to his man Tom to drive the cart, set forwards, &c.

The brother-in-law, cheek by jowl with the fore-horse of his small team, drives on very merrily for about nine of the twelve miles to Sir William's, entertaining his worshipful relation with the very best tune he could whistle all the way they traveled.

But now within three miles of home, our politic bridegroom thinks it advisable that one of his carters, the brother, should make a halt at an alehouse where they stopped, and the whole management of the cart and horses be entrusted with Tom, for fear the sight of a stranger to come to take up goods at his brother's might give occasion of curiosity and inquiry, whereas Tom, an old servant in the family, with less suspicion and inspection might do it.

These strong reasons (or indeed weaker would have served turn) were satisfactory enough, and so the gentleman equipping his brother Clodpate with a George to stay and drink till they returned, the master and man fairly drive on for the remaining three miles to bring off the bag and baggage, &c.

The potent sum of a whole half crown to be laid out in ale set in our country youth to a hearty carouse with the kind hostess of the house, where the esquire's health was over and over remembered, not forgetting the great man at the great house about three miles off where, as simple a country-fellow as he was, he expected one day to be better acquainted.

But to draw this adventure towards a conclusion, our waiting carter, long expecting the return of the brother, the palfreys and the cargo, notwithstanding the strength of powerful ale and his sweet landlady's diverting company, began at last to be impatient. Sometimes he fancied the loading was too heavy for the poor beasts, and he thought it his best way to walk out and see if he could meet them. But all inquiry was in vain, night at last drew on, and the best part of his half crown melted down; at length, though very uneasy and restless, he is persuaded by his kind hostess to take a hard nap till morning. The cock was not so soon awake as he, for to tell truth he ne'er slept at all, though indeed he dreamt all night, for he could not think less than that some retainers of the family had undoubtedly followed the cart and murdered the squire to run away with the treasure; and what his poor sister would suffer to be a widow so early, was little less than a mortal apprehension. Thereupon, very betimes in the morning, he pads to Sir William's and very earnestly inquires what was become of the squire, the knight's brother. "Sir William's brother?" replied the servants. "We know none he has; 'tis true, he had one some years beyond sea, but whether dead or alive is more than any man upon English ground (God wot) can tell." How! No brother-in-law squire! No Sir William's family! No sister like to be a lady, nor brother a gentleman! Nor no horses nor cart neither! This staggering account put him into so doleful a dumps that he stood almost thunderstruck. And truly the twelve miles home again was so tedious a journey, and the lamentable narrative he must make 'em at home, so killing a fancy that it was a great mercy he did not make a stay upon some convenient twig in some hedge in the road, rather than live to be the messenger of such a woeful, sad tale—but ill news at last must out. The bird and the beasts were all flown; the poor bride sweetly brought to bed, a cart and two horses to pay for, a son-in-law to find when the Devil was blind, the daughter's sweet plaything lost, the father and mother dipt ten whole pounds in chalk, and the whole family under the suffering of a whole chamber pot full of wailings and tears for their calamities and misfortunes.

But to return to our rover, by the sale of cart and team, £10 in cole the last lump, and the price of his kine the other, his pockets were pretty well lined; and considering this spot might soon grow too hot for him, he thinks it wisest to shift the scene, and thereupon dismissing for some time his man Tom, who had pretty well licked his fingers in so profitable a service, our grazier now transmogrifies into a spark and, very sprucely rigged, takes a ramble westward, where meeting with no adventure worth recital, in some small time he gets to Ludlow. There taking up the first night at an inn, his garb (though unattended by servants) soon made him good reception. His first inquiry was to learn out the eminentest people in the town, of which being readily informed by the drawers, he learnt amongst other relations that there was a substantial, wealthy tradesman, had two pretty, marriageable daughters. Being directed to the house, he addresses the father, telling him he was a Berkshire gentleman; and intending to make some small abode in Ludlow, he did not think fit to continue in a public house, but would gladly gain admission to some private family. The tradesman (whose name we will not mention), being a widower and taken with the manner of his discourse, kindly invited him to his own house, which our traveling gallant as kindly embracing, accommodation was made, and he was lodged that very night at this private landlord's.

His entrance here gave him the opportunity of daily conversing with no mean wit and charms in the two sweet daughters of the family; and our gallant, very apt to take fire at but a small matter of beauty especially with a portion at the tail of it, felt no little wamblings at the extraordinary accomplishments of the elder, somewhat the sweeter creature. But this new adventure was not an enterprise so easy as the last; this sire of some fashion was so far above the education and extract of his former father-in-law, a man of mortar and trowel, and his daughters of a reach and understanding so much beyond the other's humbler capacity that measures must be quite altered here from those that he took before. Accordingly, now his discourse was always upon foreign subjects, himself and his own affairs the least

part of his talk; and if any inquisitive question, either by
father or daughters, were made relating to his family or
concerns, he answered with that modesty and almost silence
to all demands of that kind, that he left their curiosity still
in the dark, and which indeed was so much heightening to
the favourable imaginations they had conceived of him that
they doubted not in the least, but he was of eminent quality;
and what any boasting vanity would have made 'em rather
suspect, his modesty on the contrary confirmed. 'Twas some
few days before they inquired his name, for which he had
ready at his tongue's end the name of a very great family
in Berkshire, but not descending to particulars; the remote-
ness of the place did not gain 'em much intelligence of his
quality from only the bare name. All this while, at some
little distance, he dropt a great many complaisant words to
the elder sister which looked very much like love, and which
he indeed desired should be so interpreted. In this conversation, now of a fortnight's continuance, he had rendered
himself so acceptable to the whole family that a great many
favourable thoughts on all sides inclined towards him. The
address to the daughter at last looked a little more plain
and barefaced; and at that time a fair, happening at Ludlow, where he had been diverting himself with seeing of
fashions, he came home in much concern and some kind
of passion, much greater than hitherto they had at any
time seen from him.

"Certainly there is no place in the world," says he passionately, "so retired, but some devil or other will still find
out and haunt me." The oddness of this expression invited
the elder sister to ask him what he meant. "Why truly,
Madam," he replied, "I have been hunted from three or
four towns already, for in spite of all my resolutions of living incognito, some unlucky person or other comes full in
my mouth, and will betray me in spite of my soul." This
answer did but heighten her curiosity; and having, as she
thought, some little interest in him as a professed servant
of hers, she was a little the bolder in pressing the question,
and therefore plainly asked him why he lived incognito, and

what accident had now discovered him. To this at last, with a little more frankness than he had hitherto used, he replied, the reason of his ramble from his family, with his living three or four months past unknown to the whole world, was only to prevent the ruin of a sister, who like a foolish girl was in much danger to be undone by a beggarly match she was too fond of; and her portion being in his hands, he had absented himself from his home lest the softness of her tears, the importunities of several advocates in behalf of this indigent lover, together with the weakness of his own tender heart, might at last be prevailed upon to grant his consent to what he knew would be his shame and her undoing. And as ill luck would have it, he had unfortunately tumbled upon a countryman of his, now at the fair, who would infallibly run openmouthed to his sister and his family, and tell 'em all where he was. This discovery gave a good occasion to the fair examiner to be not only a pleader for her own sex in the person and cause of his unknown sister, but likewise to be a champion for love. For now she plainly told him that a great many grains of allowance were to be made where hearts were inseparable. If this lover of his sister's was a man of sense and quality (as neither of those he could deny him), it was a little barbarous in him to oppose the whole repose and contentment of so near a relation as a sister for so sordid a consideration as a little worldly interest. Besides, there was a Providence always attended faith and truth in love, and undoubtedly sooner or later would provide for their well-being, or else enable 'em to bear a meaner portion of riches, which others perhaps might less contentedly possess. This argument was almost the daily discourse, in which she seemed to gain some little ground, but not enough to persuade him to the unreasonable grant of his sister's desires.

About five days after comes a letter directed to him at Ludlow, with the postmark upon it very authentically, which in a very legible woman's hand contained these words:

Dear Brother,

What unhappy star am I born under to suffer all this miserable persecution? Certainly, when my father left me to your disposal and tied my portion to your liking of the man that must marry me, surely he could never have died reconciled to Heaven, could he have foreseen the slavery he tied his poor child to, in putting me into the power of so cruel a brother. To run so many months from your house, your family, nay, your honour, too (for what must the censuring world talk of you?), and all to break a poor sister's heart. Oh, shameful! To hide yourself from the world and run from mankind, only to shut your ears against justice and to be deaf to all goodness and humanity! Alas, what capital crime have I committed, who only loved a gentleman in birth and blood no ways my inferior; and what if an unfortunate younger brother's slender patrimony of a hundred a year is not answerable to a portion of £2,000? A wonderful cause to make me the most unhappy creature living, in refusing me the only blessing the world has to give. How many fair steps to preferment and honour lie in the way of so accomplished and so well-related a gentleman, notwithstanding his elder brother run away with the estate; and what good Fortune have I not to hope for, if your barbarous aversion did not interpose between my felicity and me? In short, resolve to return home, and be kind to your languishing and almost despairing sister, or else expect very speedily to be visited by her at your bedside in her winding sheet. For if ghosts can walk, and your barbarity has sworn my death, expect to be eternally haunted, as you shall deserve from—

Your Distracted—

The next post four or five letters more came after him: one from his bailiff to desire him for God's sake to come home again, for the Devil a farthing would his tenants pay till they saw their landlord. A second from one of his tenants, complaining of his bad crop and the low price of corn, and that unless he would bate him £20 a year rent, he could never hold his farm, earnestly desiring his worship to come home and take care of his poor tenants, &c. A third condoling his misfortune in the loss of his eldest son and desiring to see his sweet worship's face, that he might get him to put his second boy's life into his copyhold; and others of the like import.

These letters our spark left in his closet window; and one whole day going abroad, by a pretended negligence he shot the bolt of his closet lock out of the staple, and so left his door ajar, and his letters exposed to anybody that would please to read 'em. This stratagem succeeded to his wish, for the daughter, whom I may now call his mistress, knowing him safe abroad, had dropt into his chamber when the maid was making the bed, and finding the closet door open, made bold to peep, and spying his letters there, tips the wink upon the maid, whom she made of the council, and read 'em all out. The contents put her mightily upon the gog; for certainly she concluded he must be a man of a mighty estate, so many tenants, and the Lord knows what; and if a sister had £2,000, what must an elder brother possess? After she had conjured the maid to silence, she could not forbear running to her father and telling him all she had discovered. The father at first reprimanded her curiosity, but considering he had found out a love intrigue between his daughter and him, he thought it no unwelcome discovery. At last looking very steadfastly upon his daughter's face, with a sort of a kind fatherly leer, he cried, "Ah, child, would he were abed with thee." "How, father," replied the girl blushing. "Nay, no harm," quoth the father. "Chicken, that's all. Thou sayst he makes love to thee, and troth I must own it no small part of my ambition to have a person of his quality and fortunes for a son-in-law." In short, the father gave her very seasonable admonition; for having sounded her inclinations and found 'em to his own wish, with a fatherly authority he commanded her, if his

addresses hinted at marriage, to make him all reasonable
advances that way.

Our gallant found his plot had taken; for he had criti-
cally observed in what most particular manner and station,
to a quarter of an inch, he had laid his letters, and finding
all of 'em displaced more or less from the exact point he
had left 'em, he plainly perceived they had all of 'em been
read. Besides, in compliance to her father's orders, and indeed a little to her own inclinations, he discovered her usual
coldness to him a little diminished and her aspect more
favourable, which plainly told him the bait had taken.
Whereupon one evening, finding her alone in her garden,
with a confidence more than usual he plainly spoke home,
telling her what an inestimable blessing he should acquire
in possessing so much sweetness for a wife.

A long courtship ensued, the particulars too tedious.
Only, the girl was a little more pliant than ordinary, but
much doubting the integrity of his protestations, alleging
it was very unlikely he would debase himself to marry a
creature of her mean fortune, for all she could at present
challenge, except what her father might do for her after
his decease, was only £100 left her in her father's hands
by an uncle deceased. Our gallant presently, with much
disdain, seemed to slight all thoughts of her fortune, for
that he thanked Heaven he wanted not, and truly her dear
person was the only consideration that had fixed his heart
entirely her captive. To bring him to the happy point,
forty-eight hours are not past, before he comes to reap the
fair fruit. The marriage knot is tied, and the nuptials consummated, and joy and felicity runs high between them.

In this happy state and uninterrupted delights, they continued some days, when of a sudden his old servant Tom,
booted and spurred, comes to Ludlow, and now in a little
higher station than before, in the garb and figure of one
of his bailiffs, he comes post thus far; first, to tell him the
distraction of his family, occasioned by his absence; secondly, the lady his sister's sudden departure, God knows
whither, for she went away by night two days before he set

out from home, and has not been heard of since. And that
a letter was come from Bristol, intimating that his venture
in sherry was safely landed there, and that the King's customs came to £97, but his correspondent at Bristol being
lately dead, the custom was yet unsatisfied; and truly for
his part none of the tenants would pay him one groat till
they saw their landlord again, and therefore he could not
raise the money to satisfy it. Our new bridegroom, hearing
all this, presently communicates the whole matter to his
sweet bedfellow, desiring her to get her father to accommodate him with that sum; not that he asked it as any part
of her uncle's legacy, he scorned to be so poor-spirited; no,
he requested it as a boon, and the moneys should speedily
be repaid with thanks: which if he pleased to do for him,
his servant should fall down the Severn and take care of
his wines, of which his dear father-in-law should have one
hogshead to drink to her "Hans-en-Kelder."[4] The daughter
was a speedy and successful ambassadress, for the money
was presently laid him down in gold, for the more ease of
his servant's carriage of it. Tom had not been two hours
gone, but a footboy in a very fine livery brings him a letter
from his sister, signifying her extreme concern for his de-
serting his affairs and family, and that her griefs and dis-
quiets had made her take a long ramble to see him once
more, and that she was now at Hereford, not daring to approach any nearer till she had his gracious warrant and permission, which she humbly upon her bended knees entreated of him, with a great deal more passionate courtship
to him upon that subject. Upon perusal of this letter he
seemed to melt into a great deal of good nature and compassion for his dear sister, insomuch that a tear stood in his
eyes, which his sweet bride very kindly drank in a kiss, at
length launching out into a great many tender expressions
towards his sister, which goodness his kind bride much applauded and encouraged, throwing in many a kind word in
her sister's behalf. At last the brother concluded he would
be so civil to her that since her extravagant affection had
brought her thus far to visit him, he would return her the

favour of riding himself to Hereford to fetch her, if his kind father would procure him a horse. Ay, with all his heart. Nay, both father and daughter proffered to take the same journey with him to pay their respects to the young lady and attend upon her as part of her train to Ludlow. "No, by no means," replied our spark. That was more than the rules of honour would allow. For his dear bride, as his wife, was a person in quality above her, and whatever kindnesses she pleased to show her, when at Ludlow, were in her free power, but this complaisance was too great a condescension, and consequently he begged her leave, that the tenderness he had of her honour might absolutely forbid her any such thought. And, indeed, his father's was much the same condescension, which he must likewise no way suffer.

The father and daughter, both silenced with this answer, acquiesced with his reasons, as being much a more experienced master of ceremonies than they could pretend to, consenting to let him go alone, only attended by the sister's page; in the meanwhile resolving to apply their officious respects to this fair, tho yet unknown relation, another way, viz., in making a suitable preparation for her honourable reception. But first a very stately horse was borrowed, one that a colonel of the guards had lately bid a lumping sum for, with all accoutrements answerable. And at mounting, our cavalier whispering in his father's ear, and telling him he had been long from home, and not knowing whether his remaining stock might hold out to his present occasions, he desired . . . The father would not hear out the speech, but running upstairs presently, fetched down, and stole into his hand a silk purse richly lined with twenty broad pieces.

Our squire, thus every way obliged, after his due congees all made, bids them all farewell till tomorrow and so prances off. Here let us leave the father and daughter as busy for the credit of the cause as may be imagined, making all suitable provision for tomorrow's entertainment; the kitchen and pantry, the bedchamber, and the court-cup-board must all appear in splendor extraordinary.

And now to return to our traveler, Heaven knows he had the misfortune to miss his way, for he never found Here-ford nor sister. His barb, too, found another chapman than the colonel of the guards; for both horse and accoutrements all embargoed, and the dismounted cavalier slipt into a frieze-coat of his man Tom's providing, who waited his coming, the master, page, and Tom, in a small prepared vessel, trolled down the Severn as fast as tide and good speed could carry them.

As we thundered down the Severn, one of our strollers being at present useless, our page (well rewarded for play-ing his part in the farce) is dropt at Worcester, from whence we continue our voyage to Bristol. Arrived there pretty late in a summer's evening, 'tis not thought con-venient to appear in any dress whatever had been seen be-fore at Ludlow, nor indeed to expose his face, lest any in-quiry might be made there about him as a sherry-merchant; and so trunking up all his best raiment, he gets himself new rigged at a salesman's in a genteel garb, but something modester than his Ludlow bravery, and Tom and he next morning move off to Bath.

It fortunes, here, that he quarters at one of the great inns, it being the beginning of the summer, just before Bath time, where was a brisk daughter of the house, about halfway stage between twenty and thirty, and consequently much inclinable manwards. A girl that had had the honour of many a slap 'cross the mouth and chuck under the chin by lords and earls in her time, her father's honourable guests at Bath season. Our most constant lover of every new face feels the old itch again; business he finds will thicken upon him, and therefore flushed with his late successes, he resolves to throw out his winning hand as far as it will run.

But now to know what portion this damsel had, for with-out a spill of yellow boys,[5] naked white and red has but indifferent charms with him. This intelligence was quickly

made, without asking the question, for there was a jest in
the family of one of the drawers being suitor there, who
belike wanted a tight sum of £80 to set up withal (a small
portion of hers formerly left her by a grandfather, and now
at use). This drawer, forsooth, was a rival, but not an over-
formidable one. For truly our innkeeper's daughter had so
often been tickled with the addresses of quality that (foh!)
her father's drawer was scarce worthy to hold up her train:
a gentleman or nothing for her. Nay, if she has not the happiness to strike in for a lease for life at bed and board with
some honourable person, rather than die in ignorance, keep
a stale maidenhead, and so lead apes,[6] she has long since
resolved not to stand out at a lower game, and e'en admit
a tenant at will to an inmate of fashion and quality, and
was grossly suspected she had tried the constitution of her
body under a load of honour long before her present year
of twenty-five. But true or false, that's a small blot in her
scutcheon.

Our Don John is absolutely captivated, and plies her
home with all the rhetoric that love can afford. Our man
Tom, in the meanwhile, but very modestly, is whispering
amongst his mates, the lower tier of the family, the servants, what a worthy gentleman his master is, being a rich
Norfolk gentleman (a pretty large stride from Bath) of 500
a year. This narrative passes pretty well amongst the shal-
lower pates, the chamberlain, the tapster, the hostler, and
the rest of the inferior domestics; but our hard-faithed
young mistress of the house, whether bit before or naturally
not overcredulous, does as good as declare that her principles are to look before she leaps. Our Norfolk suitor finds
his addresses very acceptable, but still with a reserve, provided he be the man he appears. He plainly sees that the
girl, upon good grounds, is very pliable, but she's a little
past the years of being dandled and kist out of her reason:
he or any man else (any tooth, good barber) with honour
and estate may go far with her, but demonstration is the
only argument that must carry her cause. As many years as
she has lived (or at least past for) a maid, she is not so

hard set, but she can tarry till substantial testimony (as far off as Norfolk lies) can make out the lands and tenements, before she consents to an enclosure. Our spark therefore, put to his last trumps, finds this last a craggier and more difficult enterprise than any he had ever yet encountered; however, thinking it a very great scandal to his wit to lie down before her and shamefully, for want of ammunition, be forced to raise the siege, he sets all his brains at work for one last mine to blow her up; or if that take not, he is resolved to quit the field. In a day or two after, he begins to be melancholy and indisposed; during this fit, he is very cold in his love and applies him to religious books, talks much of very odd dreams he has had, till at last he takes his bed. Physicians are sent for, whether they found any real indications of sickness or no, or acquiesced to his own declaration of the pains he felt, no medicinal application was wanting. His distemper increasing, he desires a man of law to be sent for. Accordingly, a scriv'ner of the town is called, who draws up his will, in which he gives away about £3,000 in several legacies, leaving his nephew his full and sole executor. The will is sealed up and delivered to his man Tom; and all the cognizance taken of his mistress is only £10 to buy her mourning. Next, a man of God is sent for, and all the necessary preparations for a man of another world are made: his conscience settled, and his viaticum for his long journey most devoutly furnished. But it pleases Fate, or the sick man rather, in some few days after, to give some small symptoms of amendment; and to shorten the matter, in eight or ten days' time, he is pretty well recovered, and the next talk is of fancying his own native Norfolk air for perfecting his health. All this while, the young damsel who, though not called to the will-making, knew all the contents of it, and finding from all hands the great uprightness and devotion of her humble servant, could not fancy that so much religion and piety could be an impostor, and therefore she doubted not in the least, but the estate in Norfolk was unquestionable; and though indeed her prudence would still incline her to a full inquiry and satisfactory account, yet 'tis now too late; her cooling admirer talks of speeding to London, and though he professes he will leave his heart behind with her, she is afraid that new faces and better fortunes will soon shake her hold there, and therefore taking her pillow upon the business, she resolves not to slip so favourable an opportunity, but to lay hold of the forelock and take a good offer whilst she may have it. For with all her natural pride, she considers herself but the lees of a tap, and 'tis not every rich gudgeon will bite at a bait so blown and so stale.

Her departing lover still pressing for his journey, the good-natured girl watches the next amorous sally of her gallant and takes him at his word, and without asking advice thinks her own wit sufficient, and in two days' time enters into "for better, for worse." The town bells soon rung all joy, and the best hogshead in daddy's cellar run claret. His honourable guest and son-in-law was the little idol of all the virgins of the town, and the envied preferment of sweet Mrs. Betty had filled all tongues, and scarce a prayer offered up for a husband, but Mrs. Betty's felicity was made the pattern of their devotion.

But now, as the Devil would have it, our dignified bride is for having her dear spouse by all means doing her and her father the honour of staying out the whole Bath season (now coming on) amongst 'em, and nothing can divert her from that resolution. This is a very unwelcome proposal; for the multitude of faces from all quarters of the kingdom may not only be very dangerous to his circumstances, but likewise his Norfolk abilities long before that time may be examined too narrowly; and therefore not being able to make any harsh refusal of his fair bride's request, lest it should look like design, and to marry a young girl and be ashamed of her parentage would appear so unkind, he has no artifice to wean her from Bath and drill her out of town but by pretending a small relapse of his indisposition, which he acted so well that he denied himself the very pleasures of love and fell off from family duties. This curtain-failure began to moderate her passion for staying at Bath, for her tame bedfellow still preaching up the virtues of his own native Norfolk air, his poor defeated bride could not but have a womanly longing for so necessary a restorative, and thereupon for so important a medicine to her feeble yokemate, she consented to go along with him.

All her fine clothes were boxed up, together with several bed and table linen, &c. (for she had pretty good moveables, all the legacies of deceased aunts and grannies, and other good kin), and all sent by her man Tom to the carriers, and two days after, places took in the flying coach for their speeding to London.

But one main thing was almost forgotten. She had called in her portion, which for a guinea's gratification the scriv'ner had ready at an hour's warning, having at that time some other people's money by him undisposed; and hers being out upon mortgage, the owners were very well pleased to make an exchange upon the same security. This money was not to be trusted by the wagon, but to be carried up with her in the coach box, for which her man Tom begged her acceptance of a little gilt-leathered trunk that happened to be just small enough to go into the coach box. The day of setting out being on the morrow, her thoughtful spouse had nicely considered that the coach would be in London half a day before the carrier, which for some reasons you'll find in the sequel was not altogether for his convenience, and therefore he made a shift to put off the journey till next coach day.

Against that time, the gilt-leathered trunk, and the key to it was delivered her (though by the bye he had got two keys), and the £80, some broad pieces, a caudle-cup, half a dozen of silver spoons, and some other toys were all stowed in it; and the kind couple are trundling away for London, with the man well-mounted riding by.

Now, as a man of his estate, he had freely given her all her own portion, a small privy purse to buy her pins with, having married her only for beauty and much disdaining the addition of so small a sum to his plentiful fortune. The first stage being done (for they had but one night to lie by the way), the small cabinet of treasure was carefully taken out of the coach, and lodged in a closet in the chamber, and next morning delivered to Tom to see safely laid in the coach box as before.

The next night arriving both at London (whither Tom about Brentford was commanded by his master to speed a little before to prepare for their reception), a very fair lodging near St. James was ready to entertain her, but no Tom had been there; and coming to open the trunk, instead of the gold and silver entrails, there was nothing but a bag of stones and a piece of a brickbat to supply their places, enclosed in a few rags that stuffed up the trunk. This amazing sight threw the poor lady into a most violent distraction, and 'twas very hard to hold her from falling into a fit, her husband seeming as much amazed as herself and joining in the complaint as loud as she. But to abate her rage, he told her the wicked rogue should not so escape, he had very sufficient security from able friends for his honest and faithful service, and their purses should make her reparation, till when the loss should be made up out of his own pocket. Nor would he sleep till he had made her some farther satisfaction, and therefore begged her excuse but for one half hour till he took coach and made that search and quest that perhaps would bring her some considerable light into the villainy. Her zeal for her loss never looked any farther, and accordingly well pleased with the kind motion, she took leave of him for the half hour aforesaid.

But, alas, a long half hour, for half the evening, nay, the whole night was gone, and neither man nor master to be heard of. So husband and portion all departed, she thought fit to secure her goods and clothes at the carriers, but the same calamity attended there likewise, for Tom had been there, too, and swept all.

To describe the distress and anguish of our present female sufferer, or either of her two foregoing sisters in affliction, being a work beyond our power, we shall e'en do as the painter did of old, that is, draw a veil before the face of sorrow, the lineaments of true grief being above the pen or pencil's skill.

His continued good luck at the female quarry succeeding so prosperously, he has hardly snapped and gorged one before he's for flying at a second.

Leaving therefore this last wife to shift home, not only penniless, but almost naked, too, it being then in the gay time of summer, he buys him a very stately gelding and prances down to Slough near Windsor. There taking a genteel lodging and throwing off his old, now hackneyfied disguise of the country gentleman, he assumes the character of a London merchant; and tho the little distance of twenty miles laid the scene very nigh and consequently (one would think) exposed him to something more hazard than any of his former remoter pretensions, however, he is so flushed with success and thereupon so hardy an enterpriser that he reckons upon Fortune now entirely his own, as no less than bound to his cause, and her smiles as secure as himself, her now darling favourite, is fearless and undaunted.

His tent therefore pitched at Slough for the best part of this summer's campaign, with sufficient of gold and whatnot in his pockets he contracts (amongst other country-acquaintance) a great intimacy with the minister there. And at length, praising the good air of that country and the sweetness he tastes in the conversation thereabouts, he desires the parson (his now intimate) to inform him of some purchase of 50, 60, or (rather than fail) 70 pound *per annum* somewhere near there; if a good house upon it, so much the better; otherwise it will put him to some few hundreds extraordinary expense. If any such purchase can be found, he shall be gratefully thankful to him. For resolving to get him some countryseat for a little summer's retirement from his fatigue at London, he has not met that place in the world that pleases him better. The parson kindly replied that truly he did not yet know of any such purchase, but he would make it his business to inquire and inform him accordingly.

It falls out, here, that he insinuates into the conversation of a country gentleman that had a very pretty daughter, to whom he could give £500 portion. Through his acquaintance with the father, he finds opportunity and access to the daughter, and in a little time professes downright love. Now besides a great deal of wit and sense in the daughter, here was a very judicious and sensible man to her father, and likewise a very ingenious young gentleman, her brother, all three to be coped with, insomuch that the highest of prudence ought to be used to manage the amusement and fence off all curiosity and inquiry which (considering how near London lay) might dash the whole plot. For that purpose he no sooner declares his passion, but at the same time he utterly abjures all pretensions to a farthing of portion (if he may be so happy as to succeed in his love), that truly his affairs and circumstances are far above so poor a thought. Whatever her father's goodness did or might have intended for her, he is free to keep for the bettering the fortune of so hopeful an heir of the family as the young gentleman, her brother: it is enough that the possession of her dear person is all his ambition, and if after all his prosperous ventures both at sea and land, to crown his felicity he can but carry this last dear prize, he has all he wants in this world. Nor is beauty the only charm he finds in his dear mistress; her virtue is her most captivating perfection. Alas, if he had sought either face or fortune, those were to have been found nearer home, and possibly where he was better known, viz., in his walks upon the Exchange and thereabouts, whatever personal wants he had, however his other qualifications would have made him no hard access to very considerable fortunes. But as his natural jealousy of town beauties had all along made him somewhat colder in the choice of a London wife, he declares that the vanquishing of his heart was reserved only for some sweet country innocence, which truly he had never met with till now.

This declaration carries a very pleasing face every way. Here the daughter for her part has the heart of a rich merchant of such vast estate that her inconsiderable portion is not worth his acceptance, and consequently if she can like the man, she has all the reason in the world to embrace the addresses of so qualified a suitor. Here are father and son likewise under no occasion of complaint, for one is like to save £500 by the bargain, and the other to get as much. And therefore 'tis a match they ought not to oppose. And to put all suspicions out of their head, what reasons have they to misdoubt his being the man he pretends, for he had then a pretty many years upon his back and therefore unlikely to commit so boyish a folly, to take the luggage of a wife with never a groat with her, unless he had wherewithal of his own to supply that defect. Besides, here was all the appearances possible both of honour and honesty in his daughter's inamorato, for more and above the daily management of his discourse, and his prompt answers and insight [in]to all affairs in the world, which discovered a person certainly of public business, his port and figure he made amongst them, together with the grandeur of his way of living, confirmed their entire belief and confidence. And to conclude all, who could suspect a counterfeit that would cheat for nothing?

During his courtship he presented his mistress with a very rich gold watch, and as he gained ground not only upon her, but went a great stroke with the father and son, who were mighty inclinable to the match, at last he pushed home and gained the consent of all parties concerned. The father and son were of opinion that they should all go to London, and the wedding and bedding work should be all done there at his own house in the City. With all his heart, replied the spark. Only one inconvenience attended that proposition: for it would be impossible for him to marry in London without dragging a great deal of noise and trouble at his heels, for unless he would disoblige more than a hundred eminent citizens, his particular friends (which in honour he could not well do), he must be forced to make a public wedding of it and so draw on a great deal of ceremony and hurry, which truly (might he be chooser) did not agree with his inclination. Nevertheless, if they so

pleased, he was ready to acquiesce to their absolute commands. But otherwise, for prevention of all that, if he might
direct, he would desire to divide his blessings between the
country and city, viz., have the happiness of marrying her
in the morning at Slough and then have the honour of
their good companies with him to London, and there bed
her at his own house.

This appeared so highly reasonable that three places are
ordered to be taken in the Windsor coach tomorrow for
London, and the marriage to be solemnized early before
the coach sets out. And accordingly our lovers, who wake
with the lark, are the next morning devoutly joined together. When the nuptial rites were performed, and a small
collation prepared before setting out, he publicly again
declared his protestations against all pretenses to a portion.
However, as he had now taken the dearest creature in the
world into his arms without any such claim or pretension,
and the longest day of his life he should maintain her to
the highest dignity and grandeur of a city merchant's lady,
as much as if she had brought him thousands of her own
to do it with, yet as perhaps there might be some wedding-
garments and other small matters wanting suitable to his
bride, he durst not presume to make her any present of
that kind, lest possible it might be some little indignity
and reflection upon her own honour in accepting of any
such offer; and therefore that part he left to her and her
relations' pleasure and discretion. His putting them in
mind of that necessary point appeared more like a piece
of gallantry than anything else from him. And thereupon
both the father and bride take a whisper privately together,
and immediately the closets and cabinets were rummaged,
and near a hundred guineas mustered up and stowed in a
small casket to carry with her to London, to rig her in all
ample manner accordingly. As they merrily travel along,
the father, bride and brother in the coach, and the bridegroom *en cavalier* riding by, taking a little start before 'em
upon Hounslow Heath, he comes back furiously galloping
to the coach-side and with much concern bids 'em have a

care, for he was certain there were highwaymen before in the road, and he much feared the coach would be robbed. This put the travelers into some small fright, and all of 'em (for the coach was full) into a very great care how to preserve the small treasure they had about them. "Nay, gentlemen," replies the spark, "for that small matter I have about me, I fear not all the thieves in Christendom to take from me, for though I profess myself no swordman to fight for it, yet, I thank God, I have a horse has such a pair of heels as I defy any man in England (especially upon this open plain) to outride me." This hint made the poor bride immediately request his securing some small things of hers, and thereupon she gave him her little casket and her gold watch to carry for her, withal desiring him to speed off the safest way he could and tarry for the coach at the Red Lion in Brentford. Her prudent example encouraged some other passengers in the coach to desire him to do them the like favour; one lady in the coach desired him to secure a diamond and a gold ring of hers, which she took from her finger; another gentleman clapt a purse of near twenty pieces of gold into his silver tobacco box, and besought him to give it sanctuary in his pocket to Brentford. In short, some other small matters were presently entrusted to his protection and preservation; and so being desired to troop off with all speed and to meet them at the general rendezvous aforesaid, our merchant puts spurs to his steed, and the coach trundles leisurely after him.

At Brentford they arrive safely in some little time after, and making a halt at the Red Lion, inquiry is made if a gentleman so mounted and so dressed was there. No, answer was made, no such man was there; but upon examining, the horse and the rider they had described, that very gentleman, about half an hour ago, was seen to ride almost full speed through the town towards London.

The bridegroom's so strangely outriding his stage put the whole company into some little consternation, but the bride more especially, it being a matter of no mean surprise to her to have a bridegroom so unkind, or so frolic-

some at least, to ramble away from her on her very wedding
day in so odd a manner. A great many several descants
were made upon it by the whole company, but as all of
them happened to be some small neighbours to Slough and
had either conversed with this honourable merchant during
his abode there or at least had heard of his fame, it was
concluded of all hands 'twas only intended as a jest, and
so they all moved on towards London, not doubting in the
least but to find it so.

When they arrived at London, the young Lady, as guar-
antee for her bridegroom, though she could not well invite
them with convenience that night, besought all their good
companies tomorrow at dinner with her at her house in
Lime Street, there to call their trustee to an account and to
laugh out an afternoon with her upon their traveling adventures.

Having thus dismissed their fellow travelers, a hackney
coach is taken to drive to Lime Street. When they came
there and such a merchant's house was asked for, a name
very like it was found in that precinct, but both the gentleman and house they inquired for were utterly strangers
to all the inhabitants round, and neither that night nor
next whole day could give them any tale or tidings of her
new husband. However, in all this utter darkness, as she is
left in ignorance, she has the comfort to be left in innocence, too, for thanks to her kind stars there was no consummation in the case; as much a wife as she is, she is a
virgin bride at least; and as much cheated as they have all
been, our young spouse has the satisfaction of that single
happy escape to counterbalance all the rest of her losses.
What reparation our fair promiser made to her fellow sufferers in the coach, our story mentions not, but the father,
son, and bride, returning by Weeping Cross, they found
this farewell epistle at their arrival at Slough:

My Sweet Bride,
     Ay too sweet, God wot, to be so lost. Had we but
consummated, my chicken, had I but got the virgin

toy signed and sealed, my sweeting, it had been a prize worth all the other treasure. But my hard Fate had otherwise decreed, and I must e'en sit down by my losing bargain. But, my dear, notwithstanding my abrupt parting, prithee do not conceive hard thoughts nor fancy me a masquerader, for though my house is removed from Lime Street, upon my honest word, I am a true merchant and have hooked in my venture. Pray, comfort your condoling fellow travelers, and assure them their moveables I took into my protection are all very safe, and that I shall take all possible care in performing my trust in keeping them so. And now, child, if thy defeat of a bedfellow should set thee agog for a new husband, for thy consolation let me tell thee that I am fairly drawn off to make room for a happier successor; and at thy next prayers for a man in thy tables to fill up the blot I leave open, thank Heaven thou hast scaped so well, for thou hast received the first mercy I ever showed thy sex before; and so, dear widowed turtle, farewell.

This adventure so luckily concluded, our wife-merchant takes a little recreation in London, and then tired with ease and idleness, he thinks it high time to look out for new game. His rambles have hitherto mostly lain westward, and his success he has gotten there invites him to try his farther fortune afield the same road. Down therefore his galloper and he set out, and meeting nothing in the way worthy his achievement, he fixes at last at the town of Wells. Here he is a country gentleman again, his name Bowyer, brother to Sir Charles Bowyer. This town happily afforded a boarding school for young girls, where the fair recluses generally are not altogether nun's flesh and where notwithstanding the watchful oversight of those guardian dragons, the governesses and superintendents, love too often leaps the pale, and many a bold Jason very luckily moves off with a Golden Fleece.

At this castle 'tis resolved our next batteries shall be levelled; only all the hardest work here is the making his approaches. For that purpose he inquires, first, who and what the fair inhabitants are, and the like, where he is soon informed of several considerable fortunes amongst 'em, but most of 'em either under guardianship or parents, and though allied to pretty considerable effects, the lash is in hucksters' hands. The carrying the damsel will not finger the gold,[7] and our business being only to snap and away, a lighter cargo than those unwieldy portions does our job. And accordingly he discovers one just sizable for his turn: a tradesman's daughter, her small portion about £150, and all in her own hands or at least in her own power, her parents and friends all dead, and therefore at her own disposal, and likewise something of the elderliest for a schoolmiss, being indeed about twenty years of age.

'Tis resolved then to fix here; and for a handsome initiation, his first attack is only from his eyes; he sees her first at church, where his whole devotion is so intent upon no other object that he gives her occasion to observe him. His genteel equipage, and in a stranger, too, might very well draw some eyes in a country congregation; and this young devotee's were not so wholly tied to her prayer book, but hers might rove a little. She no sooner saw him, but she met a very passionate and long-wishing look returned her. If her curiosity peeped a second time, she found him in the same posture, his eye never off of her. And this he continued forenoon and afternoon, in such a manner that it was impossible even for indifference itself not to remark him.

Next morning he makes some means to get the company and ear of one of the sub-governantes of the school, a matronly kind of a tutoress. He cannot tell what malleable metal she's made of, and how far she may be tempted to betray a little trust. However, he resolves to try. And if she be to be shaken, at least he'll use the most persuasive arguments to assail her.

Accordingly, having first begged the favour of a full hearing, he begins to lay open his case in manner following.

First, he discovers his birth and quality, a brother to the honourable Sir Charles Bowyer; secondly, though a younger brother, yet provided with a plentiful patrimony to keep up the port of a gentleman; then, that yesterday at church, he had seen the only sweetness upon earth that he could truly love; that it was some extraordinary destiny that had brought him thither to lose his heart to so lovely a creature: and then telling her name (which his love had made him inquire into), the present suit he had was to obtain the conversation of that sweet gentlewoman, that he might have the favourable opportunity of declaring his passion to her; which access, understanding the strictness of the family in which she now lived and under what confinement she lay, he had no hopes of accomplishing, but through her means; and that if she would vouchsafe to be the kind instrument in gaining him his request, he should not only be bound to her the longest day of his life, but likewise make her a gratification suitable to so signal an obligation. The gravity of our tutoress seemed a little surprised at this motion, but before she could make any reply, he continued his supplication to her by telling her that for Heaven's sake she would believe his intentions to the young lady were nothing but honourable, that had his designs been so wicked as to aim at or overreach any young fortune in the house, as such he understood there were several there, he should be the greatest of villains. But that love, and only love, was his design was manifest in his addresses to this young gentlewoman who (as he was informed) was but a tradesman's daughter, of little or no fortune, or at least very inconsiderable to a person of his circumstances and birth; and therefore she had all the reason in the world to believe him a person of honour and integrity, and 'twas as such he desired her to serve him in the request he had made her. She, hearing him protest so heartily and profess so honourably, could not but be a little attentive to so reasonable a suit.

But being herself a woman of principle and naturally faithful to her trust, she could not forbear making him this

answer: "Sir," says she, "you have the least reason in the
world to seek my assistance in this matter, for if you are
that lover and that gentleman you profess yourself, your
quality and pretensions to this young woman are sufficient
to make your own way to her, without wanting my help.
What need has a gentleman of your fortune and honour to
seek to a poor servant, as I am, to introduce you so meanly
as a private suitor to this young maid, when you have it in
your own power to make a more public declaration of your
love, and undoubtedly, so qualified as you are, have all encouragement to hope for success? If you please, therefore,
I'll tell the governess, and when she shall have examined
all things requisite to the discharge of that honest duty,
as the tuition and care she has undertaken shall require of
her, she will be so far from opposing your access that certainly you may expect all the fair reception your heart can
wish." This answer being not the present point we must
gain, our squire (before prepared for a reply) seemed extremely pleased with her for her fidelity, that truly she was
highly to be commended for so conscientious a scruple as
to the admitting of a stranger (as he was) to anything under her guardianship, and that truly the advice she had
given him was but very reasonable, and that if he should
make open love to this young gentlewoman, he might possibly have hopes of succeeding. And really it was the only
course he would take, but for one only obstacle, which was
that though indeed, as a younger brother, he had above
£300 *per annum* already in good land of inheritance, a com-
petence sufficient to maintain a family indifferently well,
yet as he was next brother and indeed as the presumptive
heir to Sir Charles, an unmarried man of thousands a year,
and was at present transacting with him about a considerable addition to his estate and other very eminent friend-
ships expected from him, he was under an invincible necessity of making an amour of this kind one of the greatest
secrets in the world, lest his marrying so inconsiderably
might lose him his brother's favour and thereby defeat so
advantageous an expectation. Not but he loved the young

creature enough to run a thousand times greater hazards
for obtaining so sweet a blessing: but what folly and prodigality would it be to expose so main a part of his well-
being to so dangerous a venture, when there was so little
occasion for it? For he, could he reach so great a blessing
as to obtain her for his bride, yet it would be worth his
while to make both his wooing and marriage, for some
time, an absolute secret, for so valuable a consideration.
And he that resolved to enter into matrimony was, in all
duty, bound to take the best measures to make a married
life comfortable, by making the best provision to support it
with credit and reputation. And therefore 'twas that he was
forced to supplicate her private assistance in the affair
which she could not well blame under so important a circumstance; and therefore stealing a brace of guineas into
her hand, he once more entreated her to gain him some
admittance to the young lady's conversation, as silently as
possibly her goodness could contrive. I cannot tell whether
the arguments, or the gold, or both together, prevailed, but
to shorten the discourse, 'twas agreed that evening, an hour
after sunset, that he should come to the garden back gate,
which was accordingly done.

And not to tire the reader with the narration of the
wooing, let it suffice that he obtained three or four private
meetings, and a little courtship well managed prevailed
and conquered. By the assistance of this matronly confident, the business is concluded, and the girl steals out one
morning and marries him. He had not been long married,
but continuing the old plea of silence and secrecy so necessary on his brother's account, he gets her to call in her
small portion for her own use, making it his free wedding
gift, all to be disposed in buying her clothes and the like,
and so makes all speed to London with her. At London
he provides her a very genteel lodging, still leaving all her
portion in her own custody. He had not kept her company
two days in Town, but he comes home in great haste and
surprise, telling her that his brother, by some accident or
other, had heard of his marriage. But as 'twas impossible

he should know what woman he had married, he had one favour to beg of her which she must not deny him, which was to pretend herself to be a young Devonshire lady of such a great family and such a fortune. By this means he should win his brother's heart and hasten that additional settlement and the other favours he expected from him; and though indeed it was a little piece of fraud, which truly he was never guilty of before in all his whole life, yet considering the advantage so innocent a deceit might gain them, he conjured her by all their loves to join with him in it and carry on the mask till he had gained his point. The poor creature, soon persuaded, consents to his request, promising her acting the best part she could in the disguise, since it was his pleasure and command to have it so.

Having obtained her concurrence in it, he tells her these lodgings were too mean for a woman of her birth, and therefore he would presently take her a fine house at Greenwich, four miles out of Town, and have it furnished suitable to his and her quality.

At Greenwich a house is instantly provided; and what by the pretensions of this great match, he strikes in with a confiding upholster for a rich bed, tapestry hangings, and very sumptuous furniture in most ample manner. Nay, he carries it on so far as to gain credit for several hogsheads of wine, which were likewise wafted down to Greenwich. The young wife all this while, seeing him make such splendid provision for her, never in the least suspected him for less than high quality and indeed was utterly ignorant that all this gallantry was taken up upon trust and mostly raised upon the noise of her vast Devonshire portion that was very speedily to pay for all.

After this country house was thus richly set out, pretending business one morning early to London, he returns again between ten and eleven in great haste, that truly he had occasion for about an £100, and having laid out more cash than his returns from his estate in the country could at present supply him, he desired her to accommodate him with that sum out of her money, which in a fortnight at farthest should be made her up again. The poor girl very readily gave him the keys of her closet and her cabinet, desiring him to take what he wanted. Immediately he goes to the treasury, and having not leisure to stay to tell out the sum, he took the whole bag, which in silver and gold was about £140, which he would tell over at London and bring back the remainder, whither he desired her company along with him in the boat that stayed to carry him back. Yes, with all her heart, if he would please to stay till she dressed herself, being then only in her morning gown. No, by no means, he replied, no matter for dressing herself; she was well enough dressed for that little company she should see today. And so without farther ceremony she trips into the boat with him, and so away to London.

When he came there and had fixed her at her old lodgings, he desired her to have a little patience till his return from Lombard Street, where he was going to pay this money. But before he went, giving her a kind kiss or two, "Lord, my dear," says he, "this plain wedding ring upon thy finger is too poor for my wife! I am going to pay this money to a goldsmith, and prithee give me thy ring along with me, and I'll put a diamond into it."

The ring, upon so good an account, was presently delivered him, and a very low curtsy dropt him for the promised diamond. Away goes husband, money, and ring; and the wife, staying with her old landlady, waits for the return of her kind spouse, after a great deal of patience pretty well tired and many a sigh to pass away time. Evening at last draws on, and no husband appears. To Greenwich she dares not return; 'tis now too late at night and too dangerous traveling so unseasonably. And so taking a soft bed, but a hard night's rest in Town, she gets up early the next morning for Greenwich, where instead of husband or house, she finds the furniture, bedding, nay, the very wine in the cellar all carried off, and so neither husband, money, nor clothes, but the loose undress she had upon her back; she is left to a whole deluge of lamentation, and the King's

highway fair open for her to steer back to Wells or what
other hospitable coast she could find in the wide world before her.

This marriage-trade thriving so well with him, he left it
not off till he arrived at the number of eighteen wives, in
which several various cheats and disguises were practiced
according to time, place, and circumstance. At Kidder-
minster he passed for Sir Charles Bowyer's brother again,
and there married an innkeeper's daughter, from whom he
hooked out several pounds besides sponging upon her father, where he continued a very considerable time and
wrought himself into that entire credit with his father-in-
law that when some of his neighbours made bold to ask
him, how he could repose so much confidence in a mere
stranger and, after his daughter had been so long married
to him, to make no inquiry into him all this while. "Inquiry!" he replied very briskly. "Trouble not your heads
about that business. I am very well satisfied in him, and
know well enough what he is. His wit and breeding, and a
hundred other genteel qualities, sufficiently assure me.
Nay, a gentleman he must be most certainly, for I have
observed him, he will never dine without a bottle of wine."
In Holborn he courted a rich vintner's widow (but there
he was a little higher advanced into the honourable family
of the Bowyers, for then he was Sir Charles himself) and
so far tickled her out of her small reason, by the high sound
of a ladyship, that the wedding-clothes were making. Nay,
he took her along with him to a goldsmith's in Cheapside
to bespeak a very large quantity of plate, amounting to
about £200. No sooner did he enter the goldsmith's shop,
but he kindly shook him by the hand and gave him so
many familiar how-do-ye's, as if he had been his long and
intimate acquaintance, where bespeaking so much plate
and such a coat of arms to be engraved upon it, the day
was set when it was to be called for. Before that day, he
was to receive £600 from his steward in the country, which
he had sent for up to pay for this plate and other necessary

nuptial habiliments. But the day drawing on, a letter comes up by the post from his steward, intimating that amongst all his tenants he could at present raise but 150 of the £600 he desired, and truly that small pittance he did not think fit to return up, till he could make it a larger sum, &c. This letter was received in his mistress's presence, and the knight so enraged at his steward's neglect that he fell into a very great passion to be so defeated of his expectation, especially at so critical a juncture. The kind widow, seeing him so concerned, desired him not to be troubled at it, for if his present occasions required, she was very willing to furnish him with it and, in fine, lent him 200 guineas to fetch home the plate. But neither was the plate sent home, nor knight or guineas ever seen afterwards. The widow, somewhat impatient, trips away to the goldsmith to inquire if he had been there, and being answered in the negative, she asked him if he were not acquainted with Sir Charles? "What Sir Charles?" "Sir Charles Bowyer that bespoke the plate." Truly, not he; for to his best knowledge, he never saw him before that day. "How," replies the widow, "never saw him before, when he knew you so well, talked so familiarly with you, discoursed of so many affairs relating to yourself, that I durst have sworn he had known you this seven years and dealt in at least a thousand pounds with you." "Yes," replied the goldsmith, "all this familiarity he expressed, which as much surprised me as it does you. But it was none of my business to inquire of a customer how he came so acquainted with my concerns, or why he treated me so courteously at first sight. He laid me down earnest in part for my plate, and if 'tis your pleasure to pay me the remainder, the plate is forthcoming. But when or where the gentleman can be found forthcoming, that you know better than I. For as I told you, he is a person I never saw before nor after."

To prosecute the full relation of all his wooings and marriages would be dwelling too long upon one kind of subject, and therefore not so divertising to the reader, for which reason we have selected only these as most entertaining of all his amours.

After he had accomplished near a score of marriages, he neatly counterfeited a bill for £700 drawn upon an eminent citizen, and so well managed all conduct and matters relating to it that he received the money. But what with his wives and this last grand cheat, he began to think little England would soon be too hot for him. And therefore buying three very gallant horses, and equipage and accoutrements suitable, he got him 'cross the herring-pond and went a volunteer to the Duke of Monmouth then before Maastricht. His business, here, was more flourish and bravado than any great feats of war, any martial wonders he intended to perform. In Flanders he made a pretty long campaign, for he stirred not from thence till all his money was spent; and at length, when his dwindling stock was so small that his very horses' heads grew a little too big, for a new supply he converted them into ready money; and when that last stake was almost run out, and he had just enough left to land him safe upon English ground again, he returned for London, and there setting in again at his old play of wiving, he wooed a parson's daughter of £500 portion, and by virtue of the great name of Sir Charles Bowyer and other winning arts he used, he married her and gained so far upon her father that he got £100 in part of the five into his clutches. But not satisfied with that modicum, but resolving to grip the whole remainder, too, he takes a house for her at Hampstead where he lived some time very kindly with her, still plying her father with all the softest and tenderest management to hook in the £400.

But here, as Fortune will not always smile, a turn of her wheel gives him a little stop to the current of his felicities. His Ludlow wife had made no little outcry with her wrongs and, amongst other search and inquiries, comes up to London, being the last place she has to make her quest after this impostor and monster, for those are the gentlest names her sufferings and resentments can give him. She has a great opinion that Newgate or Newgate-roll, or some other such chronicles of his renown, will give her some light into his life and fortune; and perhaps the justice of Heaven afford her a sight of him at least, if not a power to execute Heaven's and her just vengeance on so egregious a reprobate.

Her inn being at Holborn Bridge, she lights into the company of a good motherly woman just come from Oxfordshire; the sorrow in so young a face, and the swollen eyes which were not yet dried, the fountain being indeed inexhaustible, the curiosity of the elder traveler made bold to ask her the cause of so doleful a look, &c. The young one (who now had no reserves) plainly told her whole sufferings, to which the matron replied, "Alas, young woman, what are your griefs to mine? I have been many years the wife of the most infamous miscreant that the earth ever bore, deserted and abandoned by the wickedest of men after long years of honest and loyal fidelity to his bed, and exposed to perish (which you, thanks to able friends, need not fear)," &c. with a great deal more, bitter invectives against him, till at last upon further conferring of notes and describing of characters and persons, they came to jump together and found themselves both abused by the very same monster, the eldest being indeed his old Banbury wife. What amazement this accident produced may easily be conjectured. It will be enough to tell you that the anguish of both their souls and the bitterness of gall on each side made them swear an inviolable friendship, determining to search (if possible) the whole world to hunt down this devil. Accordingly, they take a lodging a little higher in Holborn, where making no secret of both their hard cases, they open their whole souls to their new landlady to engage her assistance in the quarrel. The landlady, transported at both their narrations, fell upon her knees and blessed God He had sent them to her house, for this Lucifer they had described was certainly the very man that next week was to marry her daughter. This surprise put them all into new confusion, and the daughter being called to the council, it was evident that this very fellow had made love to the daughter of the house, the day of marriage concluded, the ring and wedding-clothes preparing, &c. This last deliverance made the poor old woman, and the daughter no less, melt into tears at this happy discovery.

Well, 'tis agreed between them all that they shall not stir till he comes thither, which will be in twenty-four hours at most; and all their united vengeance, constables, warrants, and what not, shall be prepared for his reception.

This resolution was heartily fixed amongst them, only the Banbury wife would that evening take a walk to a cousin's, a citizen, where she had some important affairs, but nothing should stay her abroad above an hour. She had not walked half a furlong, but destiny, or some other ruling power, threw her full in the mouth of her husband. Her passion at sight of him rose so high that at first it could not find vent for words, which he, perceiving, desired her to walk into a tavern which was just before them and there recover her confusion. You may conceive she was very ready to accept the invitation, her stomach being so full that 'twas the only thing she wanted, to have her full swing at him. The discourse [on] her part you may well guess at, but his answer was so tender and his confession so open that at last she grew patient enough to hear him out. He plainly told her all he had done or at least the greatest part: that it was only the effects of his wants and necessities; that now he had raised enough to re-establish him in the world; that the honeymoon of love had been almost over between them; and that if he had made any lapse in disloyalty to her marriage-right, it was not infidelity but interest that had enforced him to all. And so showing her handfuls of gold and silver, he humbly entreated a reconciliation betwixt them, which good words and address at last so perfectly obtained that he persuaded her to send for all her household goods and to live with him somewhere in the liberties of Westminster, where disguising his name and amending his faults, he doubted not, through his practice, to recover a plentiful being and maintain her like a woman.

The poor creature, absolutely mollified, promises fidelity

to him and, never returning to her new lodging, takes him along with her, defeating the whole vengeance that was hatching against him, and not stirring from him till all her goods were come up from Banbury, and a new house furnished with them. She had not lived there three days, till finding a gossiping errand for her to keep her from home a whole day, at her return at night to bed, she finds neither husband nor goods, bed to lie or stool to sit upon, the whole house being utterly dismantled, and nothing but nakedness and empty walls to receive her.

This last cruelty of her barbarian made her almost run stark mad, and returning to her Holborn lodging to own her frailty in believing an infidel and the just judgment that had befallen her upon it, she found the poor Ludlow mourner departed, and all her relief left was to return to Banbury to live upon the alms of the parish.

This libertine life of our renegade did not long continue, till found at last by the Ludlow wife he was thrown into Worcester jail, from thence by Habeas Corpus (at the charge of a parson in Southwark whose daughter he had likewise married) removed to Newgate; and upon an indictment of six wives appearing against him, being then tried by the name of Morrell, alias Bowyer (a name of a worthy person of quality, for personating of whom he had stood in the pillory), he pleaded guilty to those six, and twelve more, and thereby received only the punishment of a squeeze in the fist. Nevertheless, the judges were pleased so far to commiserate the unhappy poor women he had undone, but especially the parson's daughter, that they gave her leave to lay an action upon him of £5,000, by virtue of which, being still detained a prisoner, he removed himself to the King's Bench. Here, being kept within the gaol, he behaved himself so winningly that he gained some favour with the then marshal and had now and then the liberty to peep abroad. Improving and advancing in the farther good graces of the marshal, he obtained at last that extraordinary credit from him that himself and three or four more prisoners were one day permitted to take a little

ramble to a merrymaking some little way out of Town,
which lucky slip of their necks from the collar they took
that wise care to make so good use of, that neither our
Sir Charles nor his fellow travelers, the master or mates,
ever returned again. This escape made such a clamour that
£100 reward was set upon his head, if to be caught in England. But this pursuit soon cooled, for upon the change of
marshal which soon followed, the cause dropt, and he had
full freedom to creep from his covert and turn practitioner
at his old craft again, his deliverance being in a manner
complete and his £5,000 and the rest of his load discharged.

After his heels were at liberty, his pocket run but low,
and he was forced to truckle to little shifts to put him in
stock again. His pranks are scarce to be numbered; nor dare
we pretend to trace them successively, and therefore we
shall not tie ourselves up to time and order.

For one of his common feats, he got him a large seal ring
and several other gold rings, all variety, as plain, mourning,
and enameled, value together about £4—with these, by
confederacy, he would sham an arrest upon himself by a
couple of marshal's men; and being hurried into some alehouse, he would call for the landlord, pretend himself a
tradesman and housekeeper as far as Wapping, Stepney, or
some such remote place. Then opening his grievance, that
he was arrested for 40 or 50 shillings and being too far
from home to send for money, he desired the landlord to
carry his rings to the next goldsmith and see what he valued
them at. The landlord returns with the rings and tells him
the goldsmith would give him something above £3 for
them. Upon this, he desires the landlord to pleasure him
with 50 shillings upon that pledge, and he would come
himself or send (by such a token) the money the next day,
and redeem them. The landlord, ready to aid a man in his
distress in so reasonable a request, lends the money, whilst
instead of the gold rings, he puts the legerdemain and
leaves him a set of brass ones well-gilt, shaped, enameled,
&c. to a tittle, in every point resembling the true rings,
and worth about half a crown.

One day about high noon he came to the Poultry Compter gate, wanting a sergeant to execute an attachment for
him. So giving him his instructions and fee, he desires him
and his yeoman to follow him to such an alehouse in Leadenhall Street where he would wait for them. To the alehouse he goes and takes a lower room which looked into
the street, where calling for a tankard of ale and soon after
spying the bum[8] and his follower approaching, he whips
out of his codpiece a pewter tankard, slaps the drink into
it, and returns the silver one into his breeches. As soon as
they entered and asked him for the gentleman, he told
them he would cross the way and see if he had dined yet,
and come over, and call them immediately to do their office. Out he trips and, there being a thoroughfare over the
way, neatly conveys himself off, till at last the sergeant,
waiting beyond his patience, calls for the landlord and desires him to fill the tankard again. "Fill the tankard!" quoth
the host. "What tankard! This is none of mine. My tankard
is a silver one." "How, a silver tankard?" replies our man-
catcher. This was all the tankard in the room since he came
there. That won't serve turn: their comrogue and confederate that had left them had a tankard of him, price £6/10s
—and tankard or so much money must be found before
they parted. A great many hard words rose on both sides,
but in fine the attacher himself was now under attachment,
and moved not off till a reckoning of £6, an angel, and
some odd pence, was discharged.

At Woolwich he pretended to be a doctor of physic and
professed an infallible remedy he had for the gout. A gentleman, an inhabitant there, long afflicted with that distemper, retained him as his physician; but his grand receipt requiring a fortnight's preparation, he squeezes some
money out of him for materials to the operation and puts
several earthen pots, with the pretended ingredients, for
fourteen days under ground, against which time the expected effects were to be produced. But it so unhappily
fell out that before the elixir came to perfection, he was
arrested by the name of Bowyer and thrown into the Mar-

shalsea. The fourteen days expired and the doctor in durance, the patient made bold to dig for the treasure and examine the pots where, to his great satisfaction, in each pot
he found about half a dozen straggling maggots, which indeed was their whole contents. But what cures they wrought
our history mentions not.

Between five and six years since, he tries one touch more
at marrying; but truly not so high a flier as formerly, he
contents himself to lay siege to Nan, the cookmaid at the
Castle Tavern at Fetter Lane end, and to attack her in no
less formidable a figure than the old Sir Charles still. So
worshipful a matrimonial suitor (you may imagine) tickled her not a little, for the title of a ladyship could not
but make a strange rumbling in a kitchen-stuff pot. The
poor girl was soon inclinable to listen to such potent love.
Our Sir Charles makes quick work on't; and though her
kind master and mistress daily laughed at her for fancying
him in earnest with her, our lover was so well furnished
with rhetoric to set her to rights again, and so absolutely
persuaded her that he meant nothing more than to marry
her, that at last she contrived to feign herself sick, whilst
her knight, under pretense of a condoling visit, was to steal
her downstairs and march off with her. This plot taking
effect, he kept her out ten or twelve days, in which time he
wheedled her out of all the money she could raise in the
world, being about the sum of £12. But when he had
drained all he could get from her, at last he began to grow
so cold to her that he denied her one morning a pennyworth of milk, which being no longer able to bear, she returned to her master with a very sad heart, much wailing
the barbarity she had received and the ruin she suffered.
At the return of poor Nancy, the knight was flown; and
though unsuspected before, now her master and mistress
with good reason believed him a cheat; and being concerned for vindicating the injuries of their servant, they
dogged him at last into Whitefriars; and fetching him out
thence by a constable and warrant, he was committed to

gaol, tried for an impostor, and stood in the pillory before their door.

One very notorious cheat was much in use with him within a twelvemonth before his death. For instance, he comes one morning to an eminent tavern in Holborn near Hatton Garden end, his habit a plain countryman, with an oilskin hat, a shabby periwig, a large buff belt round his waist, a pair of boots without tops, a whip in his hand, and a hundred-pound bag under his arm. Here he bargains for a hogshead of sack to be sent into the country. Whilst the carman is loading his wine, he pretends very urgent business he had to do before the carrier goes out of town, insomuch that he cannot well stay and pay for his wine, for which reason he desires the master to lay up his bag of money for him till he can call in the afternoon and reckon with him; but first taking out (for a blind) a handful of money, between 30 or 40 shillings for present occasion, he seals up the bag again and leaves the rest in the vintner's hands.

And now resolved to play the good husband and do two jobs with one trouble, whilst the car is loading, he goes to a linendraper's in Newgate Street where he buys a parcel of linen near £30, and as the carman comes by, he packs up the linen and mounts it into the car. Here pretending his old haste, with another hundred-pound load under his arm, he plays the former prank and gives the draper the bag, too. Now no countryman coming to reckon (as promised), they both make bold the next day to unseal their treasure and see what security they had in their custody, when to their great surprise they found a parcel of new halfpence stowed round the bag, with a lesser bag in the belly on't, filled with fragments of old iron. This prank was hitherto pretty well carried; but Fortune, of late years a mere jade to him, had a very unhappy after-game to play him. For the vintner and draper happening to meet together to condole losses and confer notes, they chanced to remember that one of the carman's steeds was a remarkable piebald horse. Hereupon, making inquiry amongst the fra-

ternity of carmen, by the marks and tokens of that horse
they found out the very man that drove off the chattels,
who what by threats and other persuading arguments they
prevailed to lead them at last to a house in the mint where
the wine and the drapery were both lodged. Here they
made a shift to recover the whole prize, excepting about
five pounds' worth already embezzled, being pretty well
content to sit down by no greater loss.

In much the like manner, and much such a habit, he
came to a cutler's in Fleet Street, and leaving such another
bag there under pretense of showing some swords to his
master at a coffeehouse hard by, he carried off three silver
swords.

For the same feat of activity, he came to a coffeehouse
adjacent to Paternoster Row, where the master of the house
was a tailor, whose company and advice he entreated, desiring him to go along with him to some of the mercers in
the Row to look upon some rich silks which he wanted for
a country gentleman's (his master's) and a young lady's
wedding-clothes. The tailor, in kindness, handed him once
or twice to several shops. But one morning, leaving his bag
behind him at the coffeehouse, he went alone to a mercer's,
a corner shop in the Row; where he cheapening some rich
stuffs flowered with silver and gold, a haberdasher of small
wares, passing by and happening to set eye upon our chapman, made bold to lay hands upon him and carry him off
to the Cock in Amen Corner. His charge against him was
for leaving him the bag, too, for about £30 in small wares.
But noise and crowd coming about him, fearing that other
complaints might appear against him and so load him
heavier than possibly he might be able to stand under, our
haberdasher, wisely resolving to take care of nobody but
himself, danced him from house to house, till his country-
chapman could raise effects to make him satisfaction; and
so having with much ado hooked in his own bet, he turned
him loose again for the other open mouths against him to
take as fair a hunt for him as he had done. After this
mortifying adventure, whether out of a principle of modesty,

a virtue not often in fashion with him, or some other forget-fulness, the bag left in the coffeehouse was never called for from that day to this; and keeping of it about three months sealed, at last they ventured to break it open, in which they found about 6 shillings in new halfpence and a lesser bag filled with pieces of old iron, a great deal of which, as memorials of his renown, they have kept by them for relics.

About the year 1672, he pretended to a great estate in Northamptonshire and carried it on so far as to borrow £400 upon the mortgage of it, of a Hampshire gentleman. At Hannington, likewise in Hampshire, he married a min-ister's daughter and entered into bond and judgment of £1,000 to jointure her in £50 a year, by which he got £250 out of her father as part of her portion.

In Piccadilly, about five years since, he went to a horse courser's to buy a horse, and after he had bargained for and bought him, he desired to back him to try his goings, and rode off with him before the horse courser's face, and sold him in the country for £4.

But now to hand our great master actor off the stage, we must bring him to his exit. Some few days before Christmas he came to one Mr. Cullen's, a baker in the Strand, to seek him a lodging, his habit but indifferent and his stock not above 2 shillings, pretending himself to be a person of worth and honour, viz., Humphrey Wickham of Swalcliffe in the county of Oxon, Esq.,[9] a person whose name and reputation was well known to Mrs. Cullen, being born not far from him, which contributed much to the swallowing of the imposture. His pretense for leaving his family in the country, and living here incognito, was occasioned (he said) to avoid the payment of £500 which he stood engaged for, and for which the principal had left him in the lurch, and which he had made a rash vow he would not pay.

Mr. Cullen's family, thus imposed upon, supplied all his wants and paid him the due respects to the quality he per-sonated, till falling sick, on the 28th of December he made a will as follows:

His Will

In the name of God, amen. I, Humphrey Wickham of Swalcliffe in the county of Oxon, Esq., being sick and weak in body, but of sound mind and memory, do make this my last will and testament, revoking all wills by me formerly made. And as touching such worldly estate as God hath been pleased to bless me withal, I do hereby give and bequeath the same in manner following.

Imprimis, I do give, devise, and bequeath to my kinsman, William Wickham, of Garsington in the county of Oxon, all that my mansion-house of Swalcliffe aforesaid, and all the lands, tenements, and hereditaments thereunto belonging, to hold unto him the said William Wickham and his heirs forever.

Item, I give and bequeath unto John Cullen, son of Thomas Cullen, of the parish of St. Clement Danes, in the county of Middlesex, baker, all that my impropriated parsonage of Sulgrave in the county of Northampton, with the rents, issues, and profits thereof.

Item, I give unto Anne Cullen, sister of the said John Cullen, the sum of £250.

Item, I give unto Thomas Cullen, son of the said Thomas Cullen, the sum of £300.

Item, I give unto Dorothy Halford of Halford, in the county of Warwick, the sum of £200.

Item, I give unto Richard Davis, son of William Davis, of the said parish of St. Clement Danes, the sum of £400.

Item, I give unto William Davis, son of the said William Davis, the sum of £200.

Item, I give unto Anne Fowkes, for her care and diligence in looking after me in my sickness, the sum of £100.

Item, I give unto Robert Croker, son of William Croker of Sandford in the said county of Oxon (being my godson) the sum of £500.

Item, I give unto the said William Croker the sum of £500.

Item, I give unto Robert Penniston, son of Sir Thomas Penniston, and younger brother to Sir Farmalis Penniston of Cornhill, in the said county of Oxon, the sum of £300.

Item, I give unto Mrs. Jane Penniston, sister of the said Mr. Robert Penniston, the sum of £200.

Item, I do hereby give, devise, and bequeath all my lands, tenements, and hereditaments whatsoever, called by the name of Appletree Ducy in Cropredy, in the county of Northampton, unto John Brooking of Rashleigh, in the county of Devon, Esq., and the said William Davis, Sen., and Thomas Cullen, Sen., and the survivor of them, and their heirs, and the survivor of them upon trust and confidence. Nevertheless, that they the said John Brooking, William Davis, and Thomas Cullen shall sell and dispose of the same; and out of the money thereby raised, pay, or cause to be paid, the respective legacies herein before bequeathed unto the said Anne Cullen, Thomas Cullen, Jr., Dorothy Halford, Richard Davis, William Davis, Jr., and Anne Fowkes. And whereas I have herein before bequeathed unto my kinsman William Wickham and his heirs all my mansion-house at Swalcliffe aforesaid, with the lands, tenements, and hereditaments thereunto belonging, my true will and meaning is that the same devise is upon this special trust and confidence that the said William Wickham shall pay, or cause to be paid, the several legacies herein before bequeathed unto the said Robert Croker and William Croker, Robert Penniston and Jane Penniston; and also pay and discharge one bond for the principal sum of £500, with interest, which I became bound for, with Thomas Walker, to one Thomas Irons, anything herein before contained, to the contrary thereof in any wise notwithstanding; and also that he the said William Wickham shall out of his legacy, and lands, and premises aforesaid, to him devised, pay, or cause to be paid, unto my executors, hereafter named, the sum of £500, to be by them bestowed, distributed, or employed for the use and benefit of the poor of the parish of Swalcliffe aforesaid, in such manner as they, or the major part of them, shall think fit and convenient.

Item, I give and bequeath unto the said John Brooking out of the moneys that shall be raised of the sale of the lands and tenements, called Appletree Ducy aforesaid, the sum of £500. And all the rest and residue of the moneys that shall be thereby raised, I do hereby give and bequeath unto the said William Davis, Sen., and Thomas Cullen, Sen., to be equally divided between them and the survivor of them.

Item, I give and bequeath unto Alice Cullen, wife of the said Thomas Cullen, Sen., the sum of £600 to her own proper use and disposal.

Item, I give and bequeath in like manner the sum of £600 unto Jane Davis, the wife of the said William Davis.

Item, I give unto the said Robert Croker and William Croker the sum of £10 apiece to buy them mourning, and also to each of them a ring of 12 shillings.

Item, I give unto Jane Croker and Mary Croker, and also to the said Robert Penniston and Jane Penniston, and all other my legatees herein before mentioned, and to every of them, the sum of £10 apiece to buy them mourning, and a ring of 12 shillings.

Item, whereas I have the sum of £700 lying at interest in the hands of Mr. Ambrose Holbech, in the name of Oliver Charles, my servant, I do hereby give and bequeath the same to and amongst my four servants, Oliver Charles, John Harbert, Sarah Winn, and Margery Smith, and the survivor of them, to be equally divided amongst them, share and share alike.

Item, I give and bequeath my three geldings, and all my accoutrements belonging to them, unto the said John Brooking, William Davis, Sen., and Thomas Cullen, Sen., viz., my bright-bay gelding to the said Thomas Cullen, and my black gelding to the said William Davis, and my dapple-grey gelding to the said John Brooking. All the arrears of rent in my tenants' hands at the time of my decease, I do hereby freely acquit and discharge. And all the rest and residue of my personal estate, not herein before devised, after my debts, legacies, and funeral expenses paid and discharged, I do hereby give and bequeath unto my said kinsman, William Wickham.

And, lastly, I do hereby nominate, constitute, and appoint the said William Wickham, John Brooking, William Davis, Sen., and Thomas Cullen, Sen., executors of this my will, hereby revoking and making void all other and former will or wills by me made.

In witness whereof, I, the said Humphrey Wickham, have to this my last will, containing one side of a sheet of paper and almost half the back thereof, set my hand and seal this twentieth day of December, Anno Dom. 1691.

Humphrey Wickham

Signed, sealed, published and declared in the presence of us, with the words (William Wickham) being first interlined, Rob. Smith, Jo. Chapman, Rich. Chapman, Mart. Pinckard.

I, the above-named Humphrey Wickham, having omitted out of my will, above-mentioned, the disposition of my estate in Huntingtonshire, do hereby make this addition to, and part of, my said will, in manner following: I give and bequeath all my lands, tenements and hereditaments, called Pryor's Farm, and all other my estate in Holywell and Needingworth, unto the above-named John Brooking, William Davis, Sen., and Thomas Cullen, Sen., and the survivor of them, and their heirs, and the heirs of the survivor of them, under this special trust and confidence that the said John Brooking, William Davis, and Thomas Cullen shall sell and dispose of the same; and out of the moneys thereby raised, pay, or cause to be paid, the respective legacies hereafter named, viz., I give and bequeath to Humphrey Longford the sum of £600, and to his sister Mary Longford the like sum of £600.

Item, I give and bequeath unto the said Thomas Cullen, Sen., the further sum of £800; and all the remainder of the moneys thereby raised, I give and bequeath unto the said William Davis, Sen., and Jane his wife, and the survivor of them.

Item, whereas I have by will, above-said, given unto John Cullen, son of the said Thomas Cullen, the impropri-

ated parsonage of Sulgrave, my true meaning is that I do
give and devise the same to the said John Cullen and his
heirs forever. In witness whereof, I, the said Humphrey
Wickham, have to this codicil addition, or further part of
my said will, set my hand and seal, this twenty-eighth day
of December, Anno Dom. 1691.

Humphrey Wickham

Signed, sealed, published and declared in the presence
of us, Robert Smith, John Chapman, Richard Chapman,
Martin Pinckard. *Probatum fuit*, &c.

This stupendous confidence of a dying man is very amazing. Nay, he drove on the masquerade at that strange rate,
that he may be truly said to have ended as he began,
having received the blessed Sacrament, pretended the settlement of his conscience, and making peace with Heaven
with that seeming sincerity, as if he had resolved to pre-
varicate with God with the same assurance he had all along
done with mankind. The credulity of these deluded persons, his landlord and the rest, is not much to be wondered
at, when the last gasps of death could carry so fair an
hypocrisy; and their transports for his extravagant legacies
bequeathed them are rather to be pitied than ridiculed.
And if they have been faulty in any little overfondness of
their imaginary good fortune, the jests and gibes they have
received have been their sufficient punishment, besides Mr.
Cullen's being run out of above £30.

After his death, care was taken to provide him a coffin
of about £10 value, and the embalmers were paid for some
of their office of preserving him sweet, till preparations for
a solemn and sumptuous funeral could be made, suitable
to the remains of the honourable deceased. And this letter
was sent as follows:

SIR,

These serve to inform you that Humphrey Wickham, Esq., of Swalcliffe in the county of Oxon, died
this morning at my house, where he has been about

ten days. He has made his will, and you are one of his executors with me and others. A very great share of his estate is given to you; therefore, pray, sir, speed to London, that we may take care of his funeral and other matters necessary to be done upon this occasion.

I think it may not be amiss that you keep this private, lest any thing may be purloined or embezzled by any of the deceased's servants or any else at his seat at Swalcliffe, which is all given to you, some legacies thereout to be paid. I am, sir, your servant,

Thomas Cullen.

London, January 3, 1692. From my house at the Wheatsheaf near St. Clement's Church over against Arundel Street, Strand.

To Mr. William Wickham of Garsington, inquire at the Blue Boar's Head in Oxon.

These following lines were enclosed from the aforesaid executors in the said letter, being left by the deceased.

Whereas, I, Humphrey Wickham, Esq., in company with my own man, John Harbert, and John Austin, son of Nicholas Austin, did carry a black hogskin trunk marked with the letters "H. W. 1688," wherein are the deeds of my estate at Sulgrave and Appletree Ducy, these are to desire you to deliver them to the executors, signed with his own name thus

Humphrey Wickham.

Memorandum, that there are two mortgages, in the hands of Austin the one for £1,400, and the other for £400 in the name of Oliver Charles, in the hands of Mr. Ambrose Holbech.

In answer to this letter came a gentleman from Oxford to tell Mr. Cullen that the Christian name of this Mr. Wickham of Garsington was mistaken, which gave the first alarm of an imposture. Otherwise, hearse and mourning had been provided to have carried him down to Swalcliffe for his interment there.

Mr. Cullen, being not overapt to believe himself cheated, but more to satisfy the rest of the world, sent down a messenger to Swalcliffe with 15 shillings in his pocket, mounted upon a poor hackney, but ordered to return upon the bright-bay gelding bequeathed him in his will, being not convinced of the delusion till his messenger's return, notwithstanding several persons of reputation had declared him a counterfeit, and Major Richardson and Mr. Compton had both inspected the corpse and averred him to be the very man formerly judged for six wives, as before mentioned, and more than once their prisoner in Newgate.

The messenger returning Tuesday, the 12th of Jan., 1692, he brought a compliment to the executors from Captain Wickham (who had treated the messenger very civilly) to this effect, that he gave them his hearty thanks for their intended kindness to him, and if they would please to come to Swalcliffe for a month or more, they should be very welcome and have the use of all the geldings, viz., the black, the bright-bay, the dapple-grey, though he could not well part with them for good and all.

Upon this full satisfaction received, about three the next morning, with no more than a watchman and a lanthorn, in a coffin of 4 shillings price, he was laid in the earth in a nook of St. Clement's Churchyard.

The nurse and assistants that attended him in his sickness now call to mind that they once or twice observed him to laugh to himself very pleasantly, which they suppose proceeded from the pleasure he took in cheating the world he was then just upon leaving.

To conclude with his frauds and impostures, (besides the grandest and boldest of them all that he left the world in) he was charged with one cheat after his very death. Amongst the numerous visitants that came to see him that week that he lay above ground, it happened that a man and his wife living at Whitechapel, pressing in amongst the crowd of gazers, immediately remembered his face; and seeing the clothes there which he wore before he died, he presently owned himself the tailor that made them, and that they were not only unpaid for still, but likewise he was cozened out of them by one of the lewdest shams that ever was put upon man. Upon which he repeated the whole story at length, viz., that about Bartholomewtide before, the now deceased came overnight and took a pretty handsome lodging at Whitechapel, pretending himself newly come up by the stagecoach out of the country, his name Bowyer; and desiring his landlord to help him to a tailor, 'twas his ill luck to be the man that was sent for. When he came to him, he found him in a threadbare black coat and very much in want of repair. He had not talked with him long, before he was desired to take measure of him; and whilst that was doing, up came a footman in a genteel livery and, paying him much respect and reverence, told him that Sir John, his master, desired his company at dinner. "At dinner!" answers our threadbare spark. "No, 'faith, he must excuse me. I am not in a pickle (pox of my dog-rogue[10]) to stir out of doors. No, sirrah, these rags upon my arse are no dress for dining at Whitehall. And so, pray, go tell your master that I am forced to keep my chamber at present, for I have been robbed since I saw him last night."

The footboy presently asked him, "By whom?" "By a young son of a whore, a footman of mine, the Devil go with him." And so desiring the boy to carry the whole relation to his master, he tells him very formally that sending his boy last night to the carrier's for his trunk, in which were two suits of clothes, all his linen and point, and fifty pieces of gold, the rogue was run away with it. And though this old suit upon his back served him well enough to come to Town in, Sir John must pardon him if he durst not stir out till he was a little better rigged. The footman, making a long scrape and departing with his message, our country squire gave a hundred hard names to this runaway man of his, threatening a great deal of vengeance if ever he caught him; for hanging was too good for him. Whilst this alarm held, there came another visitant to our esquire and told him, he hoped he had drawn it up to his liking. So the man producing a paper, the esquire took it and read it, which was a long advertisement to be put into the *Gazette*, describing the marks of his man, and £5 reward to him that should apprehend him. So having read it out and approved of the wording of it, he put his hand in his pocket and gave the fellow 10 shillings to pay for entering of it, giving him a strict charge to be sure of getting it into the next *Gazette*. After this, he began to treat about his clothes, which he desired might be neither rich nor gaudy, for he was past those vanities. The tailor, accordingly, by next day at noon, brings him his clothes, his bill between 5 and 6 pounds, which truly he must be forced to stay for till next week; for the villain and thief, his man, had put him out of money, but he had sent down last night by the post for new supplies and by the middle of next week should be furnished, and pay him very thankfully. The poor tailor, not in the least doubting his money, was very well satisfied, for he was sufficiently convinced that he was a gentleman of fashion, and hoped to find a good customer of him. But no sooner were the accoutrements upon his back and he had now liberty (no disgrace to his gentility) to walk by daylight, his first progress is down to Sir John's at Whitehall, who was belike so fond of his company that he would never let him find the way home again; for from that hour, neither his Whitechapel landlord nor tailor could ever set eye of him.

But to give him a little farther visit at the baker's (the hospitable roof under which he finished his last masterpiece) and lend the reader some few farther observations upon what passed there, more and above his own personal performance in that grand masquerade of the pretended Captain Wickham, several accidents both before and after his death contributed much to corroborate and support the impostor. To instance one remarkable one, his kind landlord sending for the worthy Dr. F—— to take care of him in his sickness, he asked the doctor if he did not know him, or had never seen him before; which the doctor (as with good reason) not well recollecting, our patient was pleased to remember him that he had the honour to dine with him such a day, in such a year, when the doctor was mayor of Gloucester. Now it happening that that very day the true Captain Wickham had really dined with him at Gloucester. The doctor who was not much acquainted with the true Captain, and thereby not ready to distinguish faces, yet very well remembering such a worthy gentleman one of his honourable guests that day in his mayoralty, was very ready (upon so convincing a circumstance) to swallow the juggle and to acknowledge him the person he presented, which very much influenced the credulity of the family.

The Monday, the next day after his death, a noble peer, attended by several persons of honour, came to see the body and was so satisfied in his being his country neighbour, the true Captain Wickham, that he questioned the family why the coroner did not sit upon him, upon which being answered that such a physician took care of him and that, besides, the honesty of the house in which he died gave no occasion for any such reflecting inquiry into his death. His lordship was pleased to reply that if he was not "murthered," he must certainly die mad, it being impossible that in his right senses he should give such extravagant legacies to mere strangers. Nor would his lordship be satisfied till he consulted both his bodily and ghostly physician, his minister and the doctor, about his outward and inward man, &c.

Another very confirming credential happened, viz., a grave citizen of London, a near neighbour to our capital cathedral, who likewise inspected the corpse, was pleased to say, he had fifty guineas in his fob and would make them an hundred with any man, that it was Captain Wickham. Nay, Mr. T——, the proctor, was so confident of his integrity that he deposited five guineas with the baker's wife, to a wager of five more, to buy him a pair of gold-fringe gloves, that he was the true Captain Wickham; and not only so, but made two wagers more with her, of two guineas each, upon the same fund. Which wagers she was so unwilling to lay

with him, as being herself so confident of his truth that
she gave them for lost, nor had been drawn into them, but
by this argument of the nurses, who told her that if he
was the true Wickham, nine guineas' loss would be nothing
out of their great legacies; and if he was otherwise, the
winning of so many guineas would make some help towards
the charges they had been out upon him.

Besides all this, a great many Oxfordshire gentlemen that
frequented Kn——t's Coffeehouse in Essex Buildings were
so concerned at his executor's happiness that, rather than
the baker should run away with so much of his estate,
declared they were resolved to make a Parliament business
of it. So many affirmatives so strengthened the believing
baker that he offered to give his maid £50 for her 100, to
which she pertly answered, no, she was not in so much
haste to compound at that rate; she was as well able to
tarry for her money, as he was for his. And talking of the
poor maid, one thing must not be forgotten: the day before
he died, he told her he had left her £100 to buy her a
husband, but have a care she did not marry a rogue that
should beat her, for if she did, he had that kindness for
her, he was sure it would disturb him in his grave and
make him walk when he was dead.

But to return to his death. When the searchers came to
do their necessary office, upon inspection they found some
little extraordinary mortification upon some nameless part
about him, that put them upon the smile. Their respect to
the worshipful deceased made them somewhat modest in
the discovery, which occasioned the nurse to inquire into
the cause of their fleering and asked them plainly if the
Captain were under the covenant of circumcision. Yes,
truly, they replied, some such kind of corporal defect they
had found about him. This put the churchwarden into
some surprise, who, inclinable to fancy better things of this
pious benefactor defunct, would by no means believe either
searchers or nurse, till he played the searcher, too, and
made a peep for his satisfaction. But, alas, he no sooner
cast his eye that way, but he found our bachelor Captain

was in no danger of leading apes.[11] He discovered him an old soldier under Cupid's banner, for by a sad token he had been a loser in the wars. But eighteen wives might do much, and so the wonder is not so extraordinary.

By a letter dated January the 21st, 1692, from a credible hand, we received a short relation of the man Tom, the famous Sancho Pancho to our deceased Don Quixote, so often mentioned and formerly so great a sharer in his master's adventures.

This squire to our late knight-errant, through his long service now grown master of his art and consequently setting up for himself, was then taken at Putnam, near Godalming in Surrey, for running away with an heiress of £150 *per annum*. This wealthy heiress he had married in very good season, our bridegroom truly being not overrich (the common fate of great wits), for he had hardly money enough to pay for his marriage. However, accepted "for richer, or poorer," he had bedded her seven or eight nights, and was so long pursued and hunted from place to place, before her relations could catch him, being taken at last in bed with her. The farther particulars we are not yet informed.

Since the first publication of our foregoing history of our grand Guzman, we have received some comical adventures worth inserting in his *Memoirs*, which though they now bring up the rear of his chronicle, however they were the very first of all his wedlock feats, and which take as follows.

As our young Machiavel was bred up a brother of the Crispin fraternity, in which he lived some years a journeyman to a cordwainer at Worcester, some little worldly calamities, chiefly the product of a natural laziness, unfortunately run him into Worcester gaol, where he lay some months, till partly by charity and partly by the mercy of his creditors, who were softened into a composition of his debts, at length he shook off his stone doublet. From hence, his reputation being a little sunk in that part of the world, he made shift to pick up a small load of St. Hugh's bones,[12] and so strolled down the Severn to Bristol; and after he had tired out his new acquaintance there and made that town, too, almost a little too warm for him, he packed up his awls and moved farther abroad. Our wandering itinerant, not to mention his more inconsiderable rambles, comes at last to the town of Petersfield within seventeen miles of Portsmouth. Here (as in all places) being a boon pot-companion, he fell in at all-fours with a surgeon's pren-tice, who on his master's account had some business in that part of the country; and with the good fortune of a lucky hand and some little help of a dexterous cut and shuffle, the kind Devil's books[13] were so favourable to him that our young bone-setter lost all his money to him, to the doleful tune of upwards of £3. Nay, when his losing hand was in, his plaister-box and salvatory, pretty well furnished with all silver-tipped instruments, were staked and lost, too. The poor young fellow was not a little mortified at this loss, but being a man of some little fashion, he knew himself able, when he sent home not above a dozen miles off to his friends, to have money enough returned him to redeem his implements and supply the cash of his master he had thus unfortunately embezzled. Accordingly, he desires the fa-vour of silence, and that he would let him have the kind equity of redemption for his plaister-box, upon honest re-payment of the money lost upon it. All this was readily agreed to, and a good hearty oath by way of honourable engagement was thrown into the bargain, that his instru-ments should be forthcoming upon the reasonable terms aforesaid and that he might hear of him at Goodman-such-a-one's, a shoemaker in the town, where he worked journeywork.

No sooner came our fortunate gamester home, but he surveyed his prize and found it, as he thought, worth twice the sum lost upon it; and therefore, having a long time been weary of his own mechanic occupation, a mercurial thought comes into his head of roving to sea. Accordingly, early the next morning, he sells his Hugh's bones for a small matter of silver to a brother Crispiano; and pretending to foot it up to London, he wheels round the town and marches directly the clean contrary way, viz., to Portsmouth, resolving to prevent all manner of hunt after him from the young Aesculapius for his plaister-box in tribulation.

Here he lights into a public house that generally entertained seamen, the mistress of which was a young buxom dame, not long, or rather too long, a widow. Here he soon found himself a tar-mate that he made his bedfellow, with whom he quickly contracted a great intimacy, and also gained some considerable light into sea affairs. His landlady, to give her her due, was a pretty, handsome, little, tight woman; but what was her yet greater charm, she was worth above a hundred good pounds. Here, our traveler, upon the authority of the fair credentials in his pocket, pretends himself a surgeon to such a ship that lay out at sea, and that his chest of medicines [was] coming down from London in order to his Straits voyage. Though the instruments in the pocket seemed some small testimonial of his doctorship's capacity, yet the breeches that held them, and the rest of his outward furniture (being indeed something shabby and threadbare), did not altogether look like the habiliments of a graduate medicinal professor. And truly his good hostess, from that slender outward appearance, was not apt to have overmuch faith in the case. Besides, he had that cloudy hand for a learned manual operator, that she would sometimes merrily joke upon his not overneat palm for a chirurgeon. But that objection was soon answered, and she was readily given to understand that he professed chymistry as well as surgery, and the making up of his own medicines had a little tinctured his hands; and so the remains of the cobbler's wax were slurred off under a more honourable pretension.

Our brisk youth now makes bold suit to his landlady in no less capacity than an humble servant of hers. The cunning gypsy, not easily overreached and besides not much taken with his person, gave him but slender reception. 'Tis true he spent his money briskly, and so far she could hear of that ear, but was somewhat deaf on the other; for truly, as I said before, she wanted faith. However, her passionate admirer was not wanting, not only in pushing on heartily, but likewise in great rodomontades of an estate he had at Worcester of £30 *per annum* free land, with twenty other high romances. But all this wrought but little upon his too cold and too coy mistress, till at last by the help of his tarpaulin chamber-mate, whom he had made of his party, a very comical project was formed to try what titillation could best work upon her.

Our sea friend, therefore, an old weather-beaten tar, who had several times lodged at this house and by that means was very intimate with the good dame, takes an occasion one evening to drink a pot and a quartern with her privately, to tell her something that very nearly concerned her. This private interview was no sooner obtained, but our tar, with a very serious face, began by the way of a counselor and friend to bid her have a care of his bedfellow, not but he loved him well enough as a chamber-fellow, but not half so well as he loved his good landlady, whom he had known so many years together and received so many civilities from. In short, he had discovered that this doctor made love to her, and he supposed to marry her. But take heed what she does; for to his certain knowledge, instead of a man, he was rather a monster. "A monster?" replied the hostess somewhat amazed. Ay, a monster, for he was his bedfellow, and he could swear what he had seen and known. Truly, under the rose, he was such a devil of a fellow that he was more a horse than a man. Nay, she might do what she pleased; yet he was sure that if he once came to lay her aboard, a poor little creature as she was, he would certainly tear her to pieces from the very stern to the poop. For, as he said before, never was such a monster of a man. The good dame mighty kindly thanked him for his friendly advice, and she should take her measures accordingly. In fine, a great deal of kind caution he gave her, and came so far to particulars as almost to tell her the very dimensions, how many half crowns he could sweep off, &c.

The next morning our young doctor desired the favour of a morning's draught with his fair landlady, which was readily granted; and when he came to drink to her, he found the bowl so extraordinary spiced and sugared, so much sweeter than usual, that he could not but make her a kind salute.

In fine, both the bowl and the fair Ganymede, the hospitality and the hostess, all sweetened at a strange rate; and our happy inamorato had that access to her soft warm lips, that he never billed half so close before. This kind morning's entertainment was not concluded till the generous widow proposes a frolic tomorrow morning to Chichester to visit some relations there, in which she desires the honour of the doctor's good company. Our spark received the invitation very thankfully. Only, he must deny himself that happiness, by reason he was at present (his wardrobe being not yet arrived from London) in that dishabille, that he should disgrace both her and her friends by his too poor outward appearance. The widow immediately excused that want by telling him that fault should be mended, the town of Portsmouth should furnish him, &c. The spark replied very frankly that truly till his return from London, he was not at present strong enough in pocket for such a purchase. The generous widow bid him not trouble himself in that point, for she would accommodate him and wait his time for his repayment. And, accordingly, that very afternoon he was, at the kind widow's own proper charge, equipped cap-a-pie with a new suit, hat, and all other accoutrements, to the tune of upwards of £7, besides some very fine linen, relics of her old husband. And the next morning, a brace of very fine gallopers were provided, and our mounted doctor, *à la mode de cavalier*, pranced with the gay widow to Chichester.

When he came thither he was very courteously received by the widow's relations, being people of pretty good fashion, where the widow, a little profuse in her new gallant's commendations, gave an extraordinary character both of his quality, his parts, his profession, and what not. What a fair estate he had at Worcester, and what a fairer name he had amongst the College of Physicians and the whole world that knew his merit, which in respect to their relation much heightened the reception he found amongst them.

Matters going on thus swimmingly and a great deal of mirth passing of all hands, the doctor publicly avowed his pretensions to the widow, and the widow as frankly acknowledged the honour he did her in his favourable thoughts towards her. To conclude, the affair went on so briskly that the match, before the whole kindred, was struck up that very night, and execution resolved the very next morning, which was accordingly performed. But now, by the bye, the reader is to consider how her tarpaulin's advice had warned her of the dangers of marrying this monster of a man, and that the least she must expect was to be downright killed. Nevertheless, by a certain kind of courage natural to the whole sex, of running the risk of that sweet sort of martyrdom, she resolves to venture her whole mortality and, in spite of predictions, marry this formidable desperado.

Here let us slip over the nuptial ceremony and bring her to the grand work consummation. When the brisk bridegroom came to attack the fort and enter the breach of love, the fair bride, who had conceived most prodigious imaginations of the assault, had her expectations so far defeated that instead of the monster, the Hercules, the *gigant*, &c. she found him but a mere man. Nay, as the malicious devil of love would have it, the dimensions of her felicity were so far short that, what with remembrance and comparison (those unlucky critics), she found the furniture of the whole new magazine not answerable even to the poor defunct in the grave. The very worms were now feasting of that more substantial *quondam* dish that 'tis not a small untowardly reflection upon her present slenderer bill of fare.

Not but to do our bridegroom all right and justice, he behaved himself in all points as briskly as manhood of between a score and a half could perform, and really there was no reasonable objection to be made against him. However, expectation had raped her into those extravagant notions and phenomenas that 'tis no little damp to her high flights to be so frustrated and disappointed.

Our young couple had not slept the first whole night together, I mean as much as a first night's sleep generally is, but the bride before morning was heard to sigh very often, which much surprised the bridegroom and made him a little inquisitive into the occasion of so untuneable a music for a wedding night. To which she made answer, she much feared that she should be a very miserable woman, for truly she had made a vow to her old husband upon his deathbed to mourn a double widowhood for him; and now so notoriously contrary to her promise and all the decencies of her sex, to marry in less than half a year after his death, not one quarter of the time engaged, was both that shame and trouble to her, that she had just reason to dread some exemplary vengeance from Heaven, at least to be haunted by his ghost, a due punishment for so wicked a perjury. The bridegroom gave her a great many mollifying arguments in answer to so ridiculous a scruple of conscience, but God wot to little purpose; all her *quondam* sweetness was perfectly soured to all intents and purposes. The goodman, the new spouse, found her still more and more in her melancholy dumps, especially after her return to Portsmouth, for to tell truth 'twas one of the shortest honeymoons of love that ever new-wedded couple had. Amongst her daily invectives against her unhappy marriage, the old lodger, the tarpaulin, took occasion to remind her of the fair warning he had given her against marrying this man. "Ay," replied the dame, "you did advise me in the Devil's name, a pox of such plaguy counselors." For his part, like a lying, cozening, cheating loon, as he was, she turned him out of her doors and would suffer him to lie no longer in her house.

The husband who, upon conferring notes with his tar-friend and other remarks, guessed where the shoe pinched, began to think upon raising a little of the rhino[14] out of her; and therefore before he had been a week married, a letter comes down from London to tell him his lodging in Town, by an accidental fire, was burnt down, in which his trunk, clothes, sea chest, and everything he had there, were unhappily lost in the flames. Upon this he made strange moan for £10 to recruit his chest, otherwise his voyage would be lost; and to send home to Worcester for money of his own would be longer work than the time he had on shore would grant him. For which cause he must request his dear wife to do that great favour for him. She raise £10! God knows where should she have it. She swears 'tis twice as much as she is worth in the whole world. Nay, then, replied our young doctor, 'tis but losing his voyage and giving over all sea affairs. He'll e'en set up a doctor in Portsmouth; his ability will find him practice enough to live like a gentleman, and so live and die in the arms of his dear sweet Betty. And therefore he would immediately write to his friends at Worcester that his tenant might know his resolution.

This last proposal was worse than the £10 demand, for to live all days of his life with her was so mortal an apprehension to her that she had rather pay twice that sum to be rid of him; to sea, to the Devil, any whither, so she can but see his backside, and £10 well laid out. And accordingly, upon second thoughts, she told him that truly that town was overstocked with his profession already; and therefore, rather than lose him his employ, she would try all her friends to raise it, which was done the next day after, whilst our operator, under pretense of a journey to London to new furnish his laboratory, lays in a stock of brandy and other comfortable importance into a merchant's ship, and in no higher a post than before the mast, sets out a voyage for Venice.

Our young traveler being thus set out with a fair gale and his dear turtle's, his fair spouse's best wishes, by the way of a witch's prayer for his good voyage and safe return, we have little of moment through his voyage, only that he was very bounteous to the seamen and doled his brandy and the rest of his good stowage amongst them, which excused him from the greatest part of his duty, they being all ready to serve him. More particularly, he ingratiated himself with the surgeon of the vessel and gained some small experience in chirurgery and some little insight into physic. At his arrival at Venice, by virtue of his pretty decent appearance in habit and some little matter of money in his pocket, but chiefly by his natural talent of confidence, he set up for a spark and gained an intimate acquaintance with a young Venetian merchant, who traded with the English and had a little smattering in the tongue, enough to be understood. With this young merchant he went now and then to a *bona roba*, some of the fair wantons of Venice. During which extraordinary familiarity between them, the merchant was so frank as to unbosom some few of his secrets to him: one above the rest, that he had debauched a young girl of some considerable quality there, which had run away from her relations; that, 'tis true, her friends knew not who 'twas had dishonoured their family; and that if by any accident it should be discovered, the least he must expect was to have his throat cut, as the common revenge of that nation upon much lesser injuries. Our young doctor, seeming very much concerned for his friend's danger, offered his service of a projection that should make all safe and happy, which was, if he thought fit, by a plot that he would lay, to marry this unhappy damsel to a very rich Venetian of his acquaintance. The merchant was highly pleased at such a proposal, if feasible, an honourable marriage being the only thing that would salve and reconcile all. Accordingly, upon a close cabal between them, this following intrigue was managed, to our young doctor's immortal reputation in politics.

He was mighty well acquainted with a public notary in Venice, a very rich man, to whom he had often boasted of his great medicinal learning; and one day he took an

occasion to tell him that he had the honour to take care
of a young merchant's widow, at present desperately ill,
who had thought fit to select him for her physician before
all the best and ablest of her own country doctors who had
experienced all their best skill in vain and had given her
over for lost. Notwithstanding this universal despair of her
recovery, he had some more than ordinary hopes of performing wonders that should amaze the world. Not but
her life was in the hand of Heaven, and he durst absolutely
warrant nothing that was mortal. Amongst the loud enco-
miums of his own skill, he sprinkled some tender expressions of pity towards the poor young lady whose extraordinary beauty, as much as sickness had defaced it, was no
little object of admiration. In two or three days after, this
young lady takes occasion to make her will, and who should
be sent for to do that office but this notary, as being partly
recommended to her by her doctor. Our man of law, who
from the descriptions of this languishing lady had received
a strange impression of her extraordinary, though yet un-
seen charms, was mightily pleased that this opportunity
should give him a sight of that prodigy of beauty his
Aesculapian friend had described. Accordingly, being conducted to a most magnificent stately house, he was ushered
through several most sumptuous apartments to the bedchamber of the sick lady, so prodigiously richly furnished
as had almost amazed him, had not the fairer object before
him, by a much greater surprise, diverted that poorer
thought and fixed his wonder upon a nobler contemplation.

But to bring him to do his office, viz., drawing up her
last will and testament: after she had bequeathed her soul
to him that gave it, and her body to the earth from whence
it came, a too rich legacy, God knows, for poor worms.
For, indeed, what with her own natural sweetness, the dress
and light she appeared in, and withal the prepossession of
the notary that much heightened her charms, she seemed
no little miracle. But as I was saying, to come to her worldly
capacities, she bequeathed very large sums of wealth to several relations, insomuch that the astonished notary, now

her absolute captive, could not but think that Heaven had done the highest justice to so delicate a piece of its own fairest handiwork, in matching the blessings of so many charms with an equal addition of fortune. And that there wanted nothing from her kind stars, but the restoration of her sweet health, to complete the smiles of Providence, all but too justly due to so lovely a sweetness that so highly deserved even the extraordinary care of Heaven.

The transported young scribe was extremely raped with the wonders he had seen in this bewitching face, and truly by the favour of his good friend, our kind Mr. Doctor, had the happiness several times after to accompany him thither, when called to visit his fair patient, who in some little time after began to be in a fair way of recovery.

Our long-robed inamorato, thus happily introduced, is not wanting to improve so favourable an opportunity, and continues his daily visits to the fair widow still after her perfect recovery (for our famous operator has set her upon her legs again). And though accesses to the soft sex in that country are generally not so easy as in our English clime (treaties of love being there carried on, like love itself, a little blindfold), yet under the notion of a widow those concessions were granted, which from a maiden mistress, through strictness of custom, might have been denied him.

Our law-courtier (to bless his kind stars) gains ground, makes a formidable attack, and is not very vigorously repulsed. For though there is no virgin wax in the case, here's something as soft, and the impression not over-difficult. The fair adored makes him all the suitable advances fit for a woman of her quality and figure. And her humble servant, though perhaps as zealous an idolater of a fair portion as of a fair face, nevertheless makes no further inquiry into that particular, but takes her fortunes upon trust, being as amply satisfied of her capacity that way by virtue of the late large will he had made her, as his own eyes had made him of her other more visible accomplishments.

Matters, in fine, are so handled, and the siege so pushed on, that at last the white flag is hung out, and the fort upon articles of discretion comes to surrender. For truly the widow, not to be behind in generosity, makes as little scrutiny into his worldly effects as he had done into hers, and consequently without any interrogatories upon that subject, gives up the cause; and accordingly hymen is celebrated between them, the transported bridegroom not a little charmed with his fair prize.

It is not worthwhile to prosecute this part of our history any further. Only, we must tell the reader that whatever lumping prize the bridegroom found, his Anglican doctorship, the kind mediator, made a good bargain of it. For the generous merchant, for his assistant part in putting off the above-named fair but somewhat damaged commodity, generously presented him with 200 crowns, besides a cask of rich wine to cheer his voyage for England.

Our spark, thus nobly equipped, returned homewards, now no longer in the capacity of a private seaman, but in a manner a mate to the master of the vessel, but especially with his old friend the doctor of the ship; for now medicine is his professed study.

At his arrival at England (though the vessel was bound for London), it happened they touched in their way at Portsmouth, till a fair wind offered for the Thames mouth. Here our flourishing traveler resolves to make a visit on shore to his good Portsmouth dame, poor Betty, he left behind him. But when she came to set eye upon his lovely phiz, never was such a roaring welcome made. The not overfond spouse, during his more than six months' absence, had unluckily inquired news of him about Worcester, where she had discovered he had no more of an estate than he had in Transylvania, and was no more a doctor than he was a major general. In short, his whole pedigree, extract, and occupation were fully discovered; and consequently not a few civil compliments of "rogue," "cheat," "counterfeit" and "impostor" were very heartily bestowed upon him. Nay, she could hardly forbear telling him that his pretended estate was as wholly imaginary as the boasted di-

mensions of his manhood. He was all forgery and lies, inside and outside.

Our young doctor, who expected no less than all this
fury, was beforehand prepared for it and received her with
a scorn as great on his side as the rage was on hers, pulled
out whole handfuls of gold to show her that though his
birth, 'tis true, had bestowed no patrimonies upon him,
his wit and sense could make his own fortune, and accordingly [he] valued not that inconsiderable want of birthright. But to sum up the whole conference between them:
the dame was for never seeing his face more; and no love
lost on his side, he was as ready to make a drawn battle
of it himself. However, if she would purchase a general
release from all pretensions to him, he demanded an acknowledgment of ten guineas for the signing and sealing
such a full discharge; which though 'twas a little hard, she
consented to pay down the sum, and our young doctor drew
up a paper under the penalty of a £1,000 never to claim
her as a wife or give her any trouble whatever, but to allow her free liberty to dispose of herself to any man she
should like better. No sooner was this formal divorce signed
and sealed, and the ten guineas paid upon the aforesaid
agreement, but they fairly bid each other an eternal adieu
—the young dame being so very frank with him as to tell
him she had already had a better man in her tables since
he went away, and had some very fair effects of it, being
four months gone with child by him, that being a particular
piece of justice she owed him before for the impudent
cheat he had put upon her. So a good riddance on both
sides. Our doctor returned for London with his pockets
well lined, sets up for a town spark, and lets his gold fly;
till at last, the mine pretty well sunk, he sets his brains at
work for a recruit, and here he got acquaintance with an
innkeeper of Kingston on Thames, a person principled for
his purpose, and to him he communicated a design to get
money, which he readily embraced. The innkeeper, upon
pretended business, gets well mounted with a £150 in
money, and a watch, rings, and other rich moveables worth

£50 more; and accordingly, his road lying upon Clapham
Common, he is there accosted in a very hostile manner,
though by a not over-formidable enemy, being our young
doctor transformed to a cavalier, who with the rough compliment of "stand and deliver" disburthened him of his
brace of hundreds, for which a loud hue and cry is immediately made, though with no great design of taking
the thief. This project succeeded so well that with a hardy
front and a little natural assurance, our innkeeper makes
so bold with the Evangelists as to swear heartily to the
robbery and accordingly sues the county and recovers the
money, which was very fairly and honestly snacked between them.[15] With this last prize he thinks it high time
to fly no longer at rovers, but to take up and settle, and
accordingly carries himself, his impudence, and plaister-
box, to Banbury and there sets up a professed chirurgeon,
as the beginning of our history has already set forth.

FINIS.

NOTES

Kirkman: *The Counterfeit Lady Unveiled*

NOTE

1. The German Princess's story had been the subject of at least twenty-three books and pamphlets. A complete check-list may be found in C. F. Main, "The German Princess; or, Mary Carleton in Fact and Fiction," *Harvard Library Bulletin*, X (1956), 181–85.

2. *The Case of Madam Mary Carleton* was registered on June 26, 1663, twenty days after her acquittal from the bigamy charge. Kirkman must have used a copy of the *Case* (1663): he places so much emphasis on its frontispiece, the lady's portrait.

3. "M. C., at the age of twenty-one, 1663, around January 22, New Style."

4. *tower*: a very high headdress.

5. The fabricated story of her birth in Cologne, of well-to-do parents, is given in the *Case*, pp. 6, 9–10.

6. Sweden supported the Protestant cause against the Imperialists in one phase (1630–35) of the Thirty Years' War.

7. Of the five romances favored here, Kirkman translated the

NOTE

sixth part of *Amadis de Gaul* (1652) and *Don Bellianis* (1671).

8. On the title page of Thomas Deloney's *The Gentle Craft* (reprinted in 1648 and 1652), there is the "assertion" mentioned by Kirkman: "Shoemaker's son is prince born."

9. Spoken by South Germans.

10. In the Preface to *The Wits* (1673), Kirkman reminisces about how "that well known natural, Jack Adams of Clerkenwell," interrupted a performance of the droll *Simpleton the Smith* to the great amusement of the audience. The name "Jack Adams" became almost synonymous with "idiot."

11. In the *Case*, pp. 26–27.

12. In the Thirty Years' War, Breda was captured (1625) by Ambrogio di Spinola. Kirkman's *"soldado"* had also served under the Count of Tilly, commander of the Army of the Catholic League. The King of Sweden, Gustavus Adolphus, was killed at Lützen in 1632.

13. *conveniency:* a passenger vehicle.

14. Here Kirkman inserts, practically verbatim, a large section from the *Case*, pp. 40–76.

15. *celebrious:* attended or observed by throngs.

16. *The Replication, or Certain Vindicatory Depositions . . . Written by John Carleton of the Middle Temple, London, Gent.* (1663). He makes the joke about "my old Grandsire Adam" on p. 6.

17. These verses and the others in this section are borrowed from a contemporary lampoon written "by F. B. Gent.," entitled *Vercingetorixa: or, The German Princess Reduced to an English Habit* (1663).

18. *cock-a-hoop:* rampant or transported.

19. *justicore:* a knee-length coat; *night-rail:* a woman's loose wrap "when in undress."

NOTE

20. Reputed to be a prophetess around 1641, but probably an entirely mythical person.

21. The Epilogue was taken from Thomas Porter's *A Witty Comedy: or, the Female Victor* (1663).

22. *farendine:* cloth part silk and part wool or hair.

23. In backgammon, a "hit" is a game won by a player after his opponent has thrown off one man or more from the board, whereas a "blot" is an exposed piece liable to be taken.

24. Kirkman's indebtedness to *The Memoires of Mary Carleton* (1673) for incidents like the swindle of the apothecary is fully discussed in Ernest Bernbaum's *The Mary Carleton Narratives* (1914), ch. v.

The Triumph of Truth

1. *figgaries:* pranks.

2. The delinquents were Royalists who had fallen behind in their taxes to the Commonwealth. According to acts passed by Parliament in 1651 and after, delinquents forfeited estates that had been concealed and uncompounded for. Clerks and solicitors, according to *Memoirs of the Life of Colonel Hutchinson* (Everyman's Library, 1913), p. 259, "made a trade of hunting out such discoveries, and making them known to such as had any arrears due to them."

3. This pamphlet has not been identified.

4. A prison named the Poultry Compter.

5. Francis Tryon, merchant, was sufficiently wealthy to purchase and sell "six pieces of arras, of the story of Vulcan and Venus," which had once belonged to Charles I. He also bought "a picture of the late King's five children" by Sir Anthony Vandyke. These facts were reported in May, 1660, by a committee appointed to find Charles I's goods and restore them to his successor.

NOTE

6. *coles:* tricksters (?).

7. Proverbs xxviii, 13.

8. Isaiah xxxviii, 1.

9. Numbers xxii, 11, 31, 34; xxiii, 11.

10. *copse:* a wagon top.

11. *quarrel:* a square of glass, set diagonally.

12. Semi-hanging and subsequent resuscitation of the criminal were not uncommon practices. See Leon Radzinowicz, *A History of English Criminal Law* (1948), I, 194–96.

Head: *Jackson's Recantation*

1. Head was able to speed up the writing of *Jackson's Recantation* by frequent self-plagiarisms. With the first three paragraphs, here, cf. *The English Rogue*, chs. lxv, lix, lxv— in this order.

2. This saying of Seneca (*Epistles*, Loeb, lxi) was also a favorite of Meriton Latroon.

3. *becullendred:* full of holes.

4. *nick the nicker:* cheat the card-cheat.

5. Jackson's pranks that follow are amplified versions of Meriton Latroon's (cf. *The English Rogue*, ch. xlvii).

6. "in lasting memory of the affair."

7. *scoutmasters of the road:* padders, highwaymen.

8. Head was fond of this image of the River Nile dogs (see *The English Rogue*, ch. xlvii), which he could have found easily in Phaedrus' fable of "The Dog and the Crocodile" or Pliny the Elder's *Natural History* VIII, lxi.

9. The paragraph is borrowed from *The English Rogue*, ch. lviii.

NOTE

10. One of the most often repeated proverbs in picaresque literature (e.g., Cervantes' *Don Quixote* I, xxx) and criminal fiction (e.g., *The Counterfeit Lady Unveiled*, p. 89).

11. The "directions" were culled originally from John Clavel's *A Recantation of an Ill-Led Life* (1628), but immediately from the author's own book, *The English Rogue*, chs. lx–lxiv.

12. The procedure was that if a person were robbed between sunrise and sunset on a day other than the Sabbath, he raised a "hue and cry," that is, a posse made up of men living nearby. Should the hue and cry fail to recover the victim's money, he was entitled to receive half the amount from the county in which the robbery took place. With the trick described here, cf. William Morrell's in *The Complete Memoirs*, p. 354.

13. *cypress hood:* a black crepe mask.

14. The name "Swiftnicks" was given to more than one troublesome highwayman. "Swift Nix alias Clerk" appeared, with others, in a proclamation for Nov. 17, 1669, offering £20 reward for his arrest and conviction. Head's "Samuel Swiftnicks" was identified by Anthony Wood as "an Irishman and a great robber on the highways near London." Captain Alexander Smith first told the story of a certain Mr. Nicks's being honored by Charles II with the name "Swiftnicks" for an incredibly fast ride from London to York. Then Daniel Defoe, brilliantly retelling the story in his *Tour* (1724), added that the famous ride took place "in the year 1676 or thereabouts." The exploit has also been assigned to John (or William) Nevison and even to Dick Turpin.

Don Tomazo

1. John Clavel's *A Recantation of an Ill-Led Life* (1628).

2. The important English translation of Mateo Alemán's *Guzmán de Alfarache* (1599) is James Mabbe's *The Rogue* (1623).

NOTE

3. *Lazarillo de Tormes* (1554) was translated into English by David Rowland as *The Pleasant History of Lazarillo de Tormes* (1586). Editions were published also in 1596, 1624, and 1639.

4. Late in October, 1679, Dangerfield began his "discoveries" of a sham Protestant uprising—"the Meal Tub Plot."

5. "The jar will long keep the fragrance of what it was once steeped in when new"—Horace's *Epistles* (Loeb) I, ii, 69–70.

6. The capture of Gaius Marius (157–86 B.C.) in the marshes of Minturnae is vividly told in Sir Thomas North's translation of *Plutarch's Lives* (Temple, 1899), IV, 337–39.

7. "What a great to-do. Is the fellow mad?"

8. *cinque and quatre:* cinquanter, a man of fifty.

9. A bodle is a Scotch copper coin, three of which "make a halfpenny English." The name may be a corruption of "Bothwell," the name of a mintmaster.

10. *healed up:* covered up.

11. *peel-garlic:* pilgarlic, a wretched creature.

12. A nickname, probably "Tom-noddy"—a simpleton or foolish person.

13. Iskenderun, formerly Alexandretta, southern Turkey.

14. Thomas Sutton began his large fortune in Durham by leasing lands rich in coal. At the time of his death in 1611, he was reputed to be the wealthiest commoner in England. See Thomas Fuller's sketch of this rise to success (*The History of the Worthies of England*, 1662). Hugh Audley started out in 1605 with £200 and, through hard dealings as a moneylender, accumulated £400,000 by 1662, the year he died. His "life" was told in *The Way to be Rich, According to the Practice of the Great Audley* (1662).

15. For instance, in *Lazarillo de Tormes*, ch. ii, the Spanish picaro is driven by hunger to steal the holy bread of the

priest, his second master. When the priest installs a mouse-trap, Lazarillo is able to spice his fare with the cheese parings used for bait.

16. *St. Martin's ware:* counterfeit goods.

17. *fullums:* loaded dice, a high fulham marked 4, 5, or 6; a low fulham, under 4.

18. Quintus Curius, one of Catiline's conspirators, told the plot to his mistress Fulvia, who passed it on to Cicero.

19. *Hogen Mogens:* Dutchmen.

20. "Wrong cannot be done to a person who is willing."

21. Actually "the statutes of the kingdom" provided capital punishment for the counterfeiting of both foreign and domestic coin (Radzinowicz, I, 653). The only difference—and this may explain Don Tomazo's remark about the statutes—was that the capital penalty held for the counterfeiting of foreign coin which was "suffered to be current within this realm" (18 Eliz. c, 1).

22. *coyt:* quoit (?). "Give a man luck and cast him into the sea" (proverb).

23. *tale of a roasted horse:* a nonsensical story.

24. "The pitcher that goes too often to the well leaves behind either the handle or the spout." See *Jackson's Recantation,* note 10.

25. "There is knavery in all trades, but most in tailors."

26. Dangerfield wrote the *Particular Narrative of the Late Popish Designs* (1679) and *A True Narrative of the Popish Plot* (1680). On the other side, Colonel Roderick Mansell produced *An Exact and True Narrative* (1680).

Settle: *The Complete Memoirs of . . . Will. Morrell*

1. Daniel v, 26–27.

NOTE

2. Sir William Davenant's *Gondibert* (1651), II, v.

3. *cole:* money.

4. *"Hans-en-Kelder":* the expected child.

5. *a spill of yellow boys:* a gift of guineas.

6. "Old maids lead apes in Hell" (proverb).

7. The forcible abduction of an heiress was a capital offense "without benefit of clergy" (Radzinowicz, I, 436–42). Later in *The Complete Memoirs,* the servant Tom is reported under arrest for stealing an heiress.

8. *bum:* bumbailiff, a sheriff's assistant.

9. A real Humphrey Wickham served as justice of the peace in Oxfordshire from 1684 to 1696.

10. *dog-rogue:* a mischievous child (?).

11. See note 6.

12. *St. Hugh's bones:* shoemaker's tools.

13. *Devil's books:* playing cards.

14. *rhino:* money.

15. For this common trick of highwaymen, see *Jackson's Recantation,* note 12.